INVESTIGATIONS 3
IN NUMBER, DATA, AND SPACE®

D1404085

GRADE 2 UNIT 1

COINS, NUMBER STRINGS, AND STORY PROBLEMS
Addition, Subtraction, and the Number System 1

PEARSON

TERC

Glenview, Illinois • Boston, Massachusetts • Chandler, Arizona • New York, New York

Photographs

Photo locators denoted as follows: Top (T), Center (C), Bottom (B), Left (L), Right (R), Background (Bkgd)

All photographs ©Pearson Education.

Elaborations text ©Illustrative Mathematics.

The Investigations curriculum was developed by TERC, Cambridge, MA.

This material is based on work supported by the National Science Foundation ("NSF") under Grant No. ESI-0095450. Any opinions, findings, and conclusions or recommendations expressed in this material are those of the author(s) and do not necessarily reflect the views of the National Science Foundation.

PEARSON

ISBN-13: 978-0-328-85906-1

ISBN-10:   0-328-85906-0

DEVELOPERS

Investigations Curriculum Center
Education Research Collaborative at TERC

Cambridge, MA
investigations.terc.edu

T E R C

COLLABORATING TEACHERS

This group of dedicated teachers carried out extensive field testing in their classrooms, met regularly to discuss issues of teaching and learning mathematics, provided feedback to staff, welcomed staff into their classrooms to document students' work, and contributed both suggestions and written material that has been incorporated into the 2nd and 3rd editions of the curriculum.

Bethany Altchek	Susan Gillis	Deborah O'Brien
Linda Amaral	Steve Goldman*	Jolene O'Brien*
Lindsay Barton*	Diane Griggs*	Timothy O'Connor
Kimberly Beauregard	Danielle Harrington	Anne Marie O'Reilly
Barbara Bernard	Elaine Herzog	Mark Paige
Nancy Buell	Francine Hiller	Margaret Riddle
Carolyn Callender*	Kirsten Lee Howard	Karen Schweitzer
Katie Carr*	Liliana Klass	Elisabeth Seyferth
Rose Christiansen	Leslie Kramer	Susan Smith
Chris Colbath-Hess	Melissa Lee Andrichak	Debra Sorvillo
Lisette Colon	Kelley Lee Sadowski	Shoshanah Starr
Kim Cook	Gizelle Lev*	Stacy Sweeney*
Frances Cooper	Jennifer Levitan	Janice Szymaszek
Mary Elizabeth Cranton*	Mary Lou LoVecchio	Karen Tobin
Justin Cravens*	Kristen McEnaney	JoAnn Trauschke
Kathleen Drew	Maura McGrail	Ana Vaisenstein
Kathleen Earley*	Kathe Millett	Ashley Warlick*
Cailin Eaton*	Katrina Mills*	Yvonne Watson
Rebeka Eston Salemi	Florence Molyneaux	Jerilyn Willig*
Kerri Favreau*	Amy Monkiewicz	Lucy Wittenberg*
Thomas Fisher	Elizabeth Monopoli	Michelle Woods
Michael Flynn	Carol Murray	Mary Wright
Jen Gehling*	Robyn Musser	
Holly Ghazey	Christine Norrman	

*Collaborating teachers for *Investigations 3*

Investigations 3 is built on the work of many authors who contributed to the first, second, and third editions of the curriculum. We acknowledge the critical contributions of these authors in developing the content and pedagogy of *Investigations*.

AUTHORS

Joan Akers

Virginia Bastable

Michael T. Battista

Katie Hickey

Douglas H. Clements

Keith Cochran

Darrell Earnest

Karen Economopoulos

Arusha Hollister

Nancy Horowitz

Marlene Kliman

Erin Leidl

Jan Mokros

Megan Murray

Ricardo Nemirovsky

Young Oh

Beth W. Perry

Andee Rubin

Susan Jo Russell

Deborah Schifter

Kathy Sillman

Cornelia Tierney

Lucy Wittenberg

CONTRIBUTING AUTHORS

Mary Berle-Carman

Denise Baumann

Nancy Belkov

Lorraine Brooks*

Christopher Clancy*

Rebecca B. Corwin

Jennifer DiBrienza

Rebeka Eston

Claryce Evans

Hollee Freeman

Anne Goodrow

Paula Hooper

Cliff Konold

Chris Mainhart

Sue McMillen

Katrina Mills

Jerrie Moffet

Stephen Monk

Tracy Noble

Mary Beth O'Connor

Kim O'Neil

Mark Ogonowski

Julie Sarama

Amy Shulman Weinberg

Margie Singer

Katie Stokinger*

Judy Storeygard

Annie Sussman

Amy Taber*

Denise Treacy

Elizabeth Van Cleef

Virginia Woolley

Carol Wright

Tracey Wright

*Administrative Staff for *Investigations 3*

REVIEWERS

George Avrunin
Professor
Department of Mathematics and Statistics
University of Massachusetts Amherst

Ben Ford
Professor
Department of Mathematics and Statistics
Sonoma State University

Scott J. Hendrickson
Associate Teaching Professor
Mathematics Education
Brigham Young University

DeAnn Huinker
Professor, Mathematics Education
Director, Center for Mathematics and Science
Education Research
University of Wisconsin-Milwaukee

Reva Kasman
Associate Professor
Mathematics
Salem State University

Elham Kazemi
Professor
Mathematics Education
University of Washington

Harriet Pollatsek
Professor Emerita
Mathematics
Mount Holyoke College

Edward Silver
Professor of Education & Mathematics
University of Michigan

Virginia C. Stimpson
Mathematics Educator
University of Washington

Lucy West
President and Founder
Metamorphosis Teaching Learning
Communities

CONTENTS

UNIT 1 COINS, NUMBER STRINGS, AND STORY PROBLEMS

INTRODUCTION AND OVERVIEW

INVESTIGATION 1
INTRODUCING MATH TOOLS AND CLASSROOM ROUTINES

INVESTIGATION 2
DOES ORDER MATTER?

INVESTIGATION 3
COMPARING QUANTITIES AND COUNTING BY GROUPS

INVESTIGATION 4
SOLVING ADDITION AND SUBTRACTION STORY PROBLEMS

PROFESSIONAL DEVELOPMENT

Content Focus

Each session has one Classroom Routine that is done outside of math time.

A full description of these Classroom Routine activities is available in Review and Practice in This Unit.

CLASSROOM ROUTINES

Today's Number
CCSS 2.OA.B.2, 2.NBT.A.2, 2.NBT.B.5, 2.MD.B.6

Quick Images
CCSS 2.OA.B.2, 2.NBT.B.9, Supports 2.MD.C.8

What Time Is It?
CCSS Supports 2.MD.C.7

Fact Fluency
CCSS 2.OA.B.2

INVESTIGATIONS

INVESTIGATION 1

Introducing Math Tools and Classroom Routines

Students encounter math tools they will use all year. They are also introduced to three of the year-long Classroom Routines that support work and provide review and practice in number, data, and geometry.

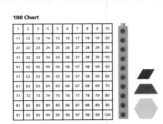

CCSS
2.OA.B.2, 2.NBT.A.2, 2.NBT.A.3, 2.MD.B.6, 2.MD.C.8, 2.G.A.1, Supports 2.NBT.A.1a, Supports 2.MD.C.7

INVESTIGATION 2

Does Order Matter?

Much of this investigation involves adding and subtracting within 20 and using known facts to solve problems. Students consider whether order matters when adding two or more numbers. They are introduced to Fact Cards, a tool used throughout the year that supports the development of fluency within 20.

$$2 + 6$$
$$6 + 2$$
Clue: _____

CCSS
2.OA.A.1, 2.OA.B.2, 2.NBT.A.2, 2.NBT.B.9, 2.MD.B.6, Supports 2.MD.C.8

INVESTIGATION 3

Comparing Quantities and Counting by Groups

Students compare two quantities as they solve Enough for the Class? problems. They begin working with coin equivalencies. They count cubes by groups of 2, 5, and 10. They look at the patterns that result from organizing quantities into 10s and record the number of 10s and leftovers.

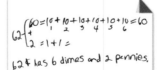

CCSS
2.OA.A.1, 2.OA.B.2, 2.NBT.A.2, 2.NBT.B.5, 2.NBT.B.6, 2.NBT.B.9, 2.MD.B.6, 2.MD.C.8

INVESTIGATION 4

Solving Addition and Subtraction Story Problems

Students solve addition and subtraction story problems with unknown totals and results. They share strategies for solving problems and ways to record their strategies.

$$10+10=20$$
$$6+7=13$$
$$20+13=33 \text{ cans}$$

CCSS
2.OA.A.1, 2.NBT.B.9, 2.MD.B.6

Session Structure

DAY	SESSION	CLASSROOM ROUTINES	ACTIVITY			DISCUSSION	MATH WORKSHOP		ASSESSMENT	SESSION FOLLOW-UP
1	1.1 Today's Number		●	●	●	●				●
2	1.2 Counting Cubes and Pattern Blocks	●	●			●	●			●
3	1.3 Quick Images	●	●	●			●			●
4	1.4 The 100 Chart	●	●	●		●	●			●
5	1.5 How Many Pennies?	●	●			● ●	●			●
6	1.6 Telling Time	●	●			●	●			●
7	2.1 Revisiting Today's Number	●	●	●	●	●				●
8	2.2 Five-in-a-Row with Four Cards	●	●	●		●				●
9	2.3 Does Order Matter?	●	●			●	●			●
10	2.4 How Many Pockets?	●	●				●		●	●
11	2.5 Addition Facts	●	●	●		●				●
12	2.6 Five-in-a-Row: Subtraction with Three Cubes	●	●	●		●				●
13	2.7 Quick Images: Ten Frames	●	●				●			●
14	2.8 Number Strings	●				●	●		●	●
15	3.1 Introducing Enough for the Class? Problems	●	●	●	●	●				●
16	3.2 Subtraction Facts	●	●	●	●					●
17	3.3 Collect 50¢	●	●			●	●			●
18	3.4 Comparing Two Numbers	●				●	●			●
19	3.5 Groups of 2, 5, and 10	●	●	●		●				●
20	3.6 Tens and Ones	●	●				●		●	●
21	3.7 Enough for the Class?	●				●	●		●	●
22	4.1 Introducing Story Problems	●	●	●	●	●				●
23	4.2 Strategies for Solving a Subtraction Story Problem	●	●	●	●	●				●
24	4.3 Strategies for Solving an Addition Story Problem	●	●	●	●	●				●
25	4.4 Strategies for Subtracting	●	●	●	●	●				●
26	4.5 Solving Story Problems	●							●	●

Unit Focus

Coins, Number Strings, and Story Problems is the first of eight units in the Grade 2 sequence and the first of five units in the Grade 2 Number and Operations strand of *Investigations*. This strand develops students' ideas about counting and quantity, place value and the structure of the base-10 number system, the meaning of operations with whole numbers, the development of computational fluency, and generalizations about numbers and operations.

This unit focuses on adding and subtracting single-digit numbers in any order, focusing particularly on adding numbers in any order; shifting from counting by 1s to counting by groups, particularly groups of tens and ones, which lays the foundation for students' work with place value and the base-10 number system; and developing and refining strategies for solving a variety of addition and subtraction problems. As the first unit in Grade 2, it also introduces the mathematical tools, processes, and ways of working that will be the foundation of math class. As part of this work, students are introduced to several year-long classroom routines that offer regular practice with composing and decomposing numbers, developing visual images of quantities, addition and subtraction facts, telling time, and counting, collecting, and analyzing data.

CONNECTIONS: LOOKING BACK

This unit builds on all of the Kindergarten and Grade 1 number units, which focused in large part on counting, composing and decomposing numbers, fluency with single-digit computation within 10, and on representing and solving a variety of types of addition and subtraction problems.

It also builds on the foundational work in those grades with place value. Specifically that ten ones make one ten; that the teens numbers are composed of one ten and some number of ones; that multiples of 10 can be made with groups of ten; and that the 2 digits of a 2-digit number represent amounts of tens and ones.

This unit focuses on the following four main math ideas:

1 Understanding and extending the counting sequence

Early in this unit, students count sets of objects, write the number sequence, and explore and compare two representations of the numbers: the number line and the 100 chart. Because counting by 1s—knowing the sequence, counting each object once and only once, having a system for keeping track, and knowing the last number said represents the total number of objects—is the basis of much of the number work in the primary grades, these activities provide an opportunity to assess students' counting abilities.

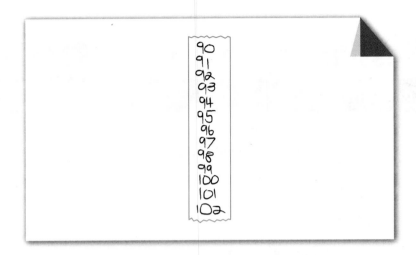

Most Grade 2 students are in the process of making a critical shift, from thinking and working primarily in 1s, to thinking and working with *groups* of 1s. To help them make this shift, students have many opportunities to develop strategies for grouping and for counting by groups. This work is initially grounded in contexts that encourage counting by groups of 2, 5, or 10—counting a set in more than one way, representing quantities with tally marks, counting ears or fingers, and using coin equivalencies to make trades and count money. It culminates in activities focused specifically on groups of 10 and on the tens-and-ones structure of our number system (e.g., 58 is made up of 5 tens and 8 ones).

MATH FOCUS POINTS IN SESSIONS

○ Using the number line to reason about, and keep track of information about, the magnitude and relationship of numbers

○ Counting sets of up to 100 objects

○ Counting a quantity in more than one way

○ Counting, writing, and reading numbers to 100 and beyond

○ Identifying and using patterns in the number sequence to count, read, and write numbers to 100 and beyond

○ Developing an understanding of the structure of the 100 chart

○ Identifying and recognizing coins and the dollar bill and their values

○ Combining coins to a total of 50¢

○ Identifying and using coin equivalencies

○ Counting by groups of 2, 5, and 10

MATH FOCUS POINTS IN CLASSROOM ROUTINES

○ Identifying coins and their values

○ Counting by 5s and 10s

○ Identifying patterns in the multiples of 2, 5, and 10

2 Fluency within 20

To develop efficient computation strategies, students need to become fluent with the addition facts up to and including 10 + 10 and the subtraction counterparts. Students encounter these problems in a variety of contexts (i.e., Classroom Routines, activities, games) and explicitly practice them with sets of Fact Cards.

The work with the Fact Cards helps students see and think about sets of related problems. For example, can you find the cards that involve adding (or subtracting) 1? What can you say about all of those cards? What do you know about those problems? In this unit, students review and consolidate the facts within 10, as well as a few others, sorting them into envelopes of *Facts I Know* and *Facts I Am Still Working On*. These facts include the following sets: Plus 1, Plus 2, Make 10, Doubles, Minus 1, Minus 2, 10 Minus, the subtraction problems related to the Doubles (also known as Minus Half), and a handful that do not fit into any of these categories.

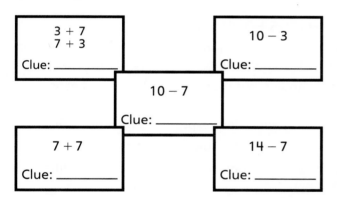

These activities provide an opportunity to think about important properties of addition and subtraction. One is whether order matters. There are a variety of contexts which encourage students to make generalizations about order in addition (e.g., *Today's Number, Five-in-a-Row,* and practice with the Fact Cards), and number strings expand the generalization to more than two addends. Because students sometimes think that generalizations that are true about addition are automatically true of subtraction, they also begin to investigate order in subtraction. See **Mathematical Practices in This Unit** for more about students' work with order. Other generalizations related to the operations that commonly come up as students add single-digit numbers are described in **Teacher Note 1: Algebra Connections in This Unit**.

$$6 + 3 + 4 = 13$$
$$3 + 6 + 4 = 13$$
$$4 + 3 + 6 = 13$$

MATH FOCUS POINTS IN SESSIONS

○ Developing and analyzing visual images for quantities up to 10

○ Developing fluency with addition and subtraction within 20

○ Naming and comparing strategies for adding and subtracting two single-digit numbers

○ Considering whether order matters in addition

○ Using known facts to add two or more numbers

○ Considering whether reordering three addends results in the same total

○ Considering a generalization about reordering addends for all numbers

○ Considering whether reordering the numbers in a subtraction problem results in the same difference

MATH FOCUS POINTS IN CLASSROOM ROUTINES

○ Developing and analyzing visual images for quantities up to 10

○ Finding the two-addend combinations that equal 10

○ Considering a generalization about reordering addends for all numbers

○ Using known facts to add two or more numbers

3 Understanding, representing, and solving problems involving addition and subtraction

Much of this unit focuses on problems involving addition and subtraction. Students play games that involve finding the sum or difference of dice rolls or cards. They use addition and subtraction to describe images of groups of coins or Ten Frame Cards, to generate expressions or equations that equal a given number, and to find the total number of pockets.

Throughout Grade 2 and specifically in this first unit, students focus on making sense of different types of addition and subtraction story problems and developing strategies to solve them. For example, as students work on Enough for the Class? problems, they are thinking about a comparison situation. As they solve the story problems in Investigation 4, they are working with addition situations that involve combining or finding the total of two groups and subtracting situations in which one quantity is removed from another.

Throughout their work, the focus is on helping students:

- make sense of the problem
- think about what they know and what they are trying to find out
- solve the problem in a way that makes sense to them
- show their work so that someone can see how they solved it
- think about how standard notation can represent the problem, and their thinking

As Grade 2 students solve addition and subtraction problems, their strategies will fall into one of several categories. A few students may start the year *counting all*, showing all of the individual parts of the problem. Some students *count on or count back* from one number. Others *add or subtract one number in parts*, choosing parts based on something they "just know" (e.g., $32 - 7 = 32 - 2 - 5$). Some *add by place* (e.g., $17 + 16 = 10 + 10 + 13$), while others *make an easier problem* (e.g., $19 + 16 = 20 + 15 = 35$). Some Grade 2 students *add up* for subtraction problems, using the relationship between addition and subtraction to think about subtracting as finding a missing addend (e.g., "I think of $30 - 19$ as 19 plus what makes 30 and I count up."). This range of strategies provides useful examples that form the basis of many whole-class discussions that focus on describing and comparing strategies and thinking about how they represent a problem. Refining strategies for addition and subtraction is a focus throughout the year. The work in this unit is the beginning of a yearlong process of developing an understanding of the operations of addition and subtraction, and developing accurate and efficient strategies for solving addition and subtraction problems.

$$10 + 10 = 20$$
$$6 + 7 = 13$$
$$20 + 13 = 33 \text{ cans}$$

$$16 + 17 = \boxed{33}$$
$$16 + 10 = 26$$
$$26 + 7 = 33 \text{ cans}$$

MATH FOCUS POINTS IN SESSIONS

- Using standard notation ($>$, $<$) to express the relationship between two quantities
- Using standard notation ($+$, $-$, $=$) to record expressions or equations
- Generating equivalent expressions for a number
- Sharing strategies for solving addition problems
- Solving a comparison story problem with the difference unknown
- Using numbers, pictures, words and/or notation to represent a solution to a problem
- Visualizing, representing, and solving put together/take apart story problems with the total unknown, and add to and take from story problems with the result unknown
- Using standard notation ($+$, $-$, $=$) to represent addition and subtraction situations
- Using numbers, symbols, pictures, and/or words to represent a solution to a problem
- Sharing strategies for solving put together/take apart story problems with the total unknown, and add to and take from story problems with the result unknown

MATH FOCUS POINTS IN CLASSROOM ROUTINES

- Generating equivalent expressions for a number
- Using standard notation ($+$, $-$, $=$) to record expressions or equations

4 Understanding place value

Fluency with the combinations that make 10 and with ways to apply them (e.g., $7 + 6 = 7 + 3 + 3$) are foundational to building an understanding of the structure of the base-10 number system and place value. Also critical is understanding that 10 ones is equivalent to one ten, and using that knowledge to count by groups of 10. Students' work with place value in this unit begins by reviewing and consolidating these ideas. Counting by groups, specifically groups of 10, provides a context for thinking about the place-value system for writing 2-digit numbers. By looking carefully at what happens when an amount is decomposed into groups of 10 and a group of leftovers, students come to recognize that number in the tens place of a 2-digit number specifies the number of tens; the ones place, the number of ones. Students use this knowledge to solve problems about tens and ones, for example:

○ If Sally has 3 towers of 10 (or dimes) and 7 single cubes (or cents), how many cubes (cents) does she have?

○ Jake has 43 cubes (or cents). How many towers of 10 (or dimes) can he make? How many leftovers (pennies) will he have?

This understanding, along with students' understanding of the operations of addition and subtraction, becomes the basis for developing accurate and efficient computation strategies in subsequent units and grades.

MATH FOCUS POINTS IN SESSIONS

○ Recognizing that the first digit of a 2-digit number designates the number of groups of 10 and the second digit designates the number of ones

○ Solving problems about 10s and 1s

The following content is also included in this unit:

MATH FOCUS POINTS IN SESSIONS

○ Developing vocabulary to name and describe 2-D shapes

○ Finding combinations of shapes that fill a region

○ Examining equivalencies among the pattern-block shapes, and the relationship between the size and the number of blocks used to fill a region

○ Naming, notating, and telling time to the hour using analog and digital formats

○ Collecting, counting, representing, and comparing data

MATH FOCUS POINTS IN CLASSROOM ROUTINES

○ Naming, notating, and telling time to the hour using analog and digital formats

○ Determining what time it will be when given start and elapsed times that are multiples of 60 minutes

○ Naming, notating, and telling time to the half hour using analog and digital formats

The Mathematical Practices, Classroom Routines, Homework, and Daily Practice pages are also a critical part of the mathematics of this unit. See the **Mathematical Practices in This Unit** and **Review and Practice in This Unit** for more information.

CONNECTIONS: LOOKING FORWARD

Students apply their growing knowledge of numbers, quantities, and the operations of addition and subtraction in all of the units in the Grade 2 sequence. In Unit 3, the next number unit, students encounter a base-10 context—a store that sells stickers singly, in strips of 10, or in sheets of 100—and use it to examine the composition of 2- and 3-digit numbers and to represent and solve addition and subtraction problems. They continue to work with the operations of addition and subtraction as they play games that involve getting to 100 (or a dollar), and as they solve put together/take apart story problems with one or both addends unknown, and story problems that involve an unknown change or an unknown start. They extend the counting sequence to 500, thinking about how to count, read, write, and compare numbers to 500. Fluency with addition and subtraction facts within 20 is part of the work of every unit in Grade 2.

The eight Mathematical Practices are a critical part of students' mathematics learning. Mathematical Practice Notes are included throughout the unit to indicate opportunities for engaging students in these practices. Each unit focuses specifically on two Mathematical Practices.

In this unit, the highlighted practices are MP1, Make sense of problems and persevere in solving them, and MP8, Look for and express regularity in repeated reasoning. This essay describes each of these practices and provides examples from the unit of how to engage Grade 2 students in them.

🔍 MP1 Make sense of problems and persevere in solving them.

Mathematically proficient students at the elementary grades explain to themselves the meaning of a problem, look for entry points to begin work on the problem, and plan and choose a solution pathway. For example, young students might use concrete objects or pictures to show the actions of a problem, such as counting out and joining two sets to solve an addition problem. If students are not at first making sense of a problem or seeing a way to begin, they ask questions that will help them get started. As they work, they continually ask themselves, "Does this make sense?" When they find that their solution pathway does not make sense, they look for another pathway that does. They may consider simpler forms of the original problem . . . Once they have a solution, they look back at the problem to determine if the solution is reasonable and accurate. They often check their answers to problems using a different method or approach.

Mathematically proficient students consider different representations of the problem and different solution pathways, both their own and those of other students, in order to identify and analyze correspondences among approaches. They can explain correspondences among physical models, pictures or diagrams, equations, verbal descriptions, tables, and graphs.

(Illustrative Mathematics, *Standards for Mathematical Practice: Commentary and Elaborations for K–5*)

Because MP1, Make sense of problems and persevere in solving them, is central to all of students' mathematics work throughout the school year, it is a highlighted practice for this first mathematics unit. These first weeks of school are an important time to establish what you expect of students when they encounter a new problem. Through your questions and the examples you provide, you can set the expectation that your students make sense of and reason through the tasks you give them.

Story problems are essential mechanisms for helping students make sense of mathematics. Through the use of familiar contexts, students learn to attach meaning to mathematical symbols. For example, addition is used in stories that involve joining amounts; subtraction, in stories about separating. Throughout their elementary years, students will learn about many mathematical ideas through story problems.

Especially because of the central role story problems will have for years to come, it is essential that students learn to approach story problems with the expectation of making sense. For example, in the following scenario, students are developing the habit of reading through the story and picturing in their mind what is happening. Even before they begin solving the problem, the context gives them clues about the solution.

Teacher:	I am going to tell you a story. I want you to close your eyes and imagine the story in your mind. Here's the story. *Kira has 16 baseball cards. She gave 7 of them away. How many baseball cards does Kira have left?* Open your eyes now and tell your partner what you see, but don't solve the problem yet.

After students have had a chance to talk to their partners, the teacher asks for a volunteer to retell the story.

Nadia:	Kira had baseball cards and gave some away.
Teacher:	How many cards did Kira have at the beginning?
Leo:	Kira had 16 cards.
Katrina:	She gave away 7.
Teacher:	What is the question? What do we want to figure out?

Alberto:	How many she had left.
Anita:	What she had after she gave some away.
Juanita:	What she had after she gave away 7.
Teacher:	Will the answer be more than 16 or less than 16?
Juanita:	It has to be less because she started with 16 and gave away 7.

Note that the teacher asks students to close their eyes and imagine the story in their mind as she reads it aloud. Everyone in the class has a chance to picture Kira with her baseball cards and Kira giving some of them away. Students learn that this is a key step in working on a problem. Before working on the solution, they must first picture what is happening in the story. Later, when they read the problem on their own, they will go through the same process: First imagine what is happening in the problem, then work on solving it.

But there is another important step between picturing the problem and working to solve it. That is, identifying some sense of what the solution will be. In this scenario, the teacher asks, "Will the answer be more than 16 or less than 16?" Students who can picture Kira giving away some of her 16 cards realize that Kira will end up with less than 16.

With an understanding that the answer is less than 16, while students work, they can check what they are doing against that expectation. If they realize that their strategy will give them a number greater than 16, they will see that their pathway doesn't make sense and will look for another one.

Throughout the unit, students must first make sense of the task they are being asked to do. In Enough for the Class? problems, students begin their work on multidigit addition and subtraction, which will be a major concentration throughout the year. By using the same problem structure but with different numbers, students have an extended opportunity to make sense of what the problems are asking and develop strategies for solving them. As students share their strategies, classmates have the opportunity to follow the approaches of others.

Watch to make sure every student has a way to enter into each task and observe students' strategies. The Ongoing Assessments suggest what you might look for as students engage in the tasks. This is your opportunity to get to know your students as mathematical thinkers.

The following chart shows where Mathematical Practice Notes specifically address MP1 and when that mathematical practice is assessed.

MP1 Make sense of problems and persevere in solving them.

SESSION	MPN	ASSESSMENT CHECKLIST
1.1	●	
1.2	●	
1.4	●	
2.1	●	
3.1	●	
3.2	●	
3.3		●
3.4	●	●
3.5	●	
3.6	●	●
3.7	●	●
4.1	●	
4.2	●	

📖 MP8 Look for and express regularity in repeated reasoning.

Mathematically proficient students at the elementary grades look for regularities as they solve multiple related problems, then identify and describe these regularities. For example, students . . . might notice that when tossing two-color counters to find combinations of a given number, they always get what they call "opposites," an idea that will later be formalized as the Commutative Property of Addition—when tossing 6 counters, they get 2 red, 4 yellow and 4 red, 2 yellow; and when tossing 4 counters, they get 1 red, 3 yellow and 3 red, 1 yellow. Mathematically proficient students formulate conjectures about what they notice. For example, they notice that whenever they toss counters, for each combination that comes up, its "opposite" can also come up. As students practice articulating their observations, they learn to communicate with greater precision (MP6). As they explain why these generalizations must be true, they construct, critique, and compare arguments (MP3).

(Illustrative Mathematics, *Standards for Mathematical Practice: Commentary and Elaborations for K–5*)

As young children begin to learn about numbers and operations, they begin to see regularities in our number system and to think about what stays the same among things that are changing. For example, many young students notice that when adding two numbers, they can change the order of the addends and the sum will remain the same: $4 + 5 = 9$ and $5 + 4 = 9$; $12 + 3 = 15$ and $3 + 12 = 15$. The habit of looking for and articulating such regularities is critical to students' understanding of mathematics. Equally important is analysis of why and when this works.

In the following vignette, students have explained that, when adding two numbers, "you can switch them around" and get the same total. Now they have noticed that to add $8 + 4 + 2$, you can add the 4 and 2, and then add 8; or you can add 8 and 2, and then add the 4; or you can add the 8 and 4, and then add 2. No matter what order the students choose, the three numbers add up to 14. After students have had time to investigate individually and in pairs what happens with other numbers, the teacher calls them together for discussion.

Teacher: We saw that when we added $8 + 4 + 2$, we could change the order of the addends and still get a total of 14. Is there something special about these numbers? Or does that work for any numbers? No matter what numbers I give you, can you add them up in any order and always get the same total?

Melissa: [holding up three cube towers] You can start with any one. When you add them together, you'll always get the same answer. You're not taking any cubes out of the box and you're not putting any back. It stays the same amount of cubes.

Teacher: Is that always true?

Jeffrey: It's *always* true. It doesn't matter how big the towers are. If you're not adding any more cubes and you're not taking any away, it will stay the same.

Esteban: And it doesn't matter how many towers you have. You can add four numbers or five. It can be in any order and it will stay the same.

Katrina: Yeah. You can add 200 numbers, and it will stay the same.

As the students in this vignette consider whether they will *always* get the same total, no matter what order the numbers are added, they do not rely only on the particular examples they have tested. Based on their understanding of what addition does, and relying on the image of cube towers, they can say with confidence that any number of addends can be added in any order and the total will remain constant.

Students will apply this idea throughout the unit as they work on number strings. Later, when they begin to apply numerical reasoning to 2-digit addition calculations, this idea will arise again. For example, when adding $35 + 24$, many students will break the numbers apart into tens and ones—$30 + 5 + 20 + 4$—and rearrange the four parts—first adding the tens to get 50 and the ones to get 9—to produce the total, 59.

Throughout this unit, there are several additional regularities students may notice. For example:

○ When 1 is added to an addend, the sum increases by 1.

○ When 1 is subtracted from an addend, the sum decreases by 1.

○ When 1 is added to one addend and 1 is subtracted from another addend, the sum remains the same.

○ Any subtraction problem can be solved by finding a missing addend.

When you notice such regularities implicit in student work, pose questions to bring them to students' attention. When students offer such observations, give time for classmates to hear and consider the ideas. Note that not all students will come to these concepts at the same time. They will arise repeatedly over the year.

These concepts will become mathematical structures students apply as they learn to calculate (MP7). In Unit 1, students may apply the structures to remember addition and subtraction facts. (See **Teacher Note 1**: Algebra Connections in This Unit.) Later, the same structures will be applied in strategies for multidigit calculations.

The following chart shows where Mathematical Practice Notes specifically address MP8 and when that mathematical practice is assessed.

EQ	MP8 Look for and express regularity in repeated reasoning.	
SESSION	MPN	☑ ASSESSMENT CHECKLIST
1.3	●	
1.4	●	
1.5	●	
2.1	●	
2.2	●	
2.3	●	●
2.4		●
2.6	●	
2.7		●
2.8	●	●
3.2	●	
3.5	●	
4.2	●	

SESSION	BENCHMARK 1	BENCHMARK 2	BENCHMARK 3	BENCHMARK 4	MP1	MP8	PORTFOLIO
INVESTIGATION 1							
1.1							
1.2							•
1.3							
1.4							•
1.5							
1.6							
INVESTIGATION 2							
2.1							
2.2							
2.3						•	•
2.4	•					•	•
2.5							
2.6							
2.7						•	
2.8		•				•	•
INVESTIGATION 3							
3.1							•
3.2							
3.3					•		
3.4					•		
3.5							
3.6	•				•		•
3.7			•		•		•
INVESTIGATION 4							
4.1							
4.2							•
4.3							
4.4							
4.5				•			•

Assessing the Benchmarks

Opportunities for assessment are carefully woven throughout the unit. These opportunities, which include written assessments and observations of students at work, provide an in-depth portrait of each student's understandings of and proficiencies with key mathematical concepts.

Observing students as they engage in activities and conversation about their ideas is a primary means of assessing students' learning. Such formative assessment opportunities are built into every session, particularly in the **Ongoing Assessment: Observing Students at Work** feature, which offers questions to consider as students work.

Assessments are tied to Unit Benchmarks that set clear expectations for what students should know and be able to do. These assessments include:

○ **Embedded Assessments** Students solve problems and show or explain their solution strategies. These assessments are accompanied by Teacher Notes that provide examples of student work.

○ **Quizzes** Quizzes are short assessments that also serve to monitor students' progress.

○ **Assessment Checklists** Assessment Checklists focus on particular Benchmarks and/or Mathematical Practices. These checklists are used to record notes about what students understand as you observe them at work.

All assessments are available as print and digital resources.

Benchmarks

Benchmark 1: Recognize and identify coins and their values.

Quiz 1 (Resource Masters, A2) in Session 2.4

Quiz 2 (Resource Masters, A5–A6) in Session 3.6

Benchmark 2: Use known combinations to add several numbers in any order.

Number Strings* (Resource Masters, A3) in Session 2.8

Benchmark 3: Solve a comparison story problem with the difference unknown.

Enough for the Class?* * (Resource Masters, A7) in Session 3.7

Benchmark 4: Solve put together/take apart story problems with the total unknown, and add to and take from story problems with the result unknown.

Solving Story Problems* * (Resource Masters, A8–A10) in Session 4.5

*Throughout *Investigations*, students are asked to show their work. As they describe their strategies, they are often asked to consider/explain why they work. See the cited sessions (and related Assessment Teacher Notes) for details.

**When students solve problems about combining, comparing, or removing, some use the number line to represent the problem, solve the problem, and/or show their work. See the cited sessions (and related Assessment Teacher Notes) for details.

Mathematical Practices

Assessment Checklist: MP1, Make sense of problems and persevere in solving them (Resource Masters, A4) in Session 3.3 and again in Sessions 3.4, 3.6, and 3.7.

This is the first of two formal opportunities to assess this math practice. The second opportunity to assess MP1 is in Unit 8.

Assessment Checklist: MP8, Look for and express regularity in repeated reasoning (Resource Masters, A1) in Session 2.3 and again in Sessions 2.4, 2.7, and 2.8

This is the first of two formal opportunities to assess this math practice. The second opportunity to assess MP8 is in Unit 8.

Portfolio Opportunities

In addition to all written assessments and quizzes, the following student work is appropriate for a portfolio:

Sample of Ways to Fill (*Student Activity Book,* pp. 5–10) in Session 1.2

Counting Strips (*Student Activity Book,* p. 24) in Session 1.4

Problems about Three Groups (*Student Activity Book,* pp. 31–32) in Session 2.3

Selection of Number Strings (*Student Activity Book,* pp. 33–38) in Session 2.3

Enough for the Class? (*Student Activity Book,* p. 50) in Session 3.1

Problems about 10s and 1s (*Student Activity Book,* pp. 61–64) in Session 3.6

How Many Cards, Cans, and Pennies? (*Student Activity Book,* pp. 71–72) in Session 4.2

Today's Number: 18 (*Student Activity Book,* p. 83) in Session 4.5

	SESSION	CR: Today's Number	CR: Quick Images	CR: What Time Is It?	CR: Fact Fluency	DAILY PRACTICE	HOMEWORK	GAMES	MATH WORDS AND IDEAS
INVESTIGATION 1	1.1					•			•
	1.2	•				•	•		•
	1.3	•				•			•
	1.4		•			•			•
	1.5		•			•		•	•
	1.6	•				•		•	•
INVESTIGATION 2	2.1			•		•			•
	2.2	•				•	•	•	•
	2.3		•			•		•	•
	2.4	•				•		•	
	2.5			•		•	•		•
	2.6	•				•		•	•
	2.7			•		•		•	
	2.8		•			•		•	
INVESTIGATION 3	3.1			•		•			•
	3.2		•			•			•
	3.3	•				•	•	•	
	3.4	•				•		•	•
	3.5	•				•			•
	3.6		•			•	•	•	
	3.7	•				•		•	
INVESTIGATION 4	4.1			•		•			•
	4.2		•			•	•		•
	4.3			•		•			
	4.4				•	•	•		
	4.5	•				•			

Review and Practice

Review and practice play an integral role in helping students develop proficiency with mathematical skills and concepts. Students have frequent opportunities to review and practice mathematical ideas over the course of a unit and grade.

Daily opportunities for review and practice are found in the following activities or features:

○ **Classroom Routines (CR)**, to be done in ten minutes outside of math class, are introduced in a unit and repeated throughout the grade. Specific directions for the day's activity are included in each session.

○ The **Session Follow-Up** includes a **Daily Practice** page for every session and **Homework** approximately 2 times per week. The Daily Practice pages provide both reinforcement of the content in the unit and ongoing review of previously covered topics. The Homework pages are most often an extension of the work done in class.

○ **Games** are a central part of the *Investigations* curriculum. They provide engaging opportunities for students to develop concepts and to practice skills.

○ **Math Words and Ideas** provide illustrations of important words and ideas that students encounter in math class. Students can also review words and ideas that they encountered in previous units or grades.

All of these activities and features are available as print and digital resources.

Classroom Routines

For the full description and variations of the Classroom Routines activities, see *Implementing Investigations in Grade 2*.

Today's Number

Students generate equivalent expressions for a number using addition and/or subtraction. Variations include using only two addends or using three addends to make *Today's Number*. In another variation, students practice counting by numbers other than 1 as they are "counting around the class" by 5s or 10s.

MATH FOCUS POINTS

○ Generating equivalent expressions for a number

○ Using standard notation (+, −, =) to record expressions or equations

○ Finding the two-addend combinations that equal 10

○ Counting by 5s and 10s

○ Identifying patterns in the multiples of 5 and 10

Quick Images

Students view arrangements of coins, discuss how many of each they see, how many altogether, and how they know. In another variation they view multiple Ten Frames and focus on using combinations that make 10 to determine the total number of dots.

MATH FOCUS POINTS

○ Identifying and recognizing coins and their values

○ Developing and analyzing visual images for quantities up to 10

○ Using known facts to add two or more numbers

What Time Is It?

Students practice telling and notating time to the hour and half hour and determine what time it will be in 60-minute intervals.

MATH FOCUS POINTS

○ Naming, notating, and telling time to the hour and half hour using analog and digital formats

○ Determining what time it will be when given start and elapsed times that are multiples of 60 minutes

Fact Fluency

Students review and practice the facts in their "Facts I Am Still Working On" envelope.

MATH FOCUS POINT

○ Developing fluency with addition and subtraction within 20

Session Follow-Up

Practice Practice opportunities in this unit provide review of counting and quantity, place value and the structure of the base-10 number system, adding and subtracting within 20, telling time, and counting money.

Homework Homework in this unit provides practice with finding combinations of different numbers, writing expressions, combining amounts, and counting money.

Games

In this unit, students play the following games:

○ *Do We Have 100?* introduced in Session 1.5

○ *Five-in-a-Row with Four Cards* introduced in Session 2.2

○ *How Many Pockets?* introduced in Session 2.4

○ *Five-in-a-Row: Subtraction with Three Cubes* introduced in Session 2.6

○ *Collect 50¢* introduced in Session 3.3

The games in this unit help students with number sense, solving addition and subtraction problems, counting on as a strategy to add, adding 2-digit numbers to 100, recognizing the value of coins, and counting.

Math Words and Ideas

Students and families may wish to review math words and ideas related to this unit.

Supporting the Range of Learners

See *Implementing Investigations in Grade 2* for more information.

The *Investigations* program is designed to engage and support the range of learners. Throughout the unit, you will find session-specific suggestions for Intervention and Extension in the **Differentiation: Supporting the Range of Learners** feature.

Each Intervention or Extension is labeled with a specific strategy to support students with the content of the session. These strategies include:

- Adapt the Learning Situation
- Adapt the Problem
- Adapt a Material
- Clarify the Problem
- Vary the Problem
- Scaffold a Solution
- Extend Thinking
- Suggest a Tool

At the end of each investigation, you will find three different **Expanded Differentiation Activities** to address the needs of the range of learners.

- **Intervention** activities are designed to support the students who are having difficulty with a particular concept.
- **Practice** activities provide additional opportunities for students to practice important ideas and concepts.
- **Extension** activities support and engage students who are ready for additional challenges.

Supporting English Language Learners (ELL)

See *Implementing Investigations in Grade 2* for more information.

In each of the Expanded Differentiation Activities and in some sessions, you will find embedded ELL support, again labeled with a specific strategy. These strategies include:

- Model Thinking Aloud
- Partner Talk
- Provide Vocabulary Support
- Provide Sentence Stems
- Repeat and Clarify
- Provide a Sequence
- Provide Opportunities for Practice
- Allow Varied Responses

SESSION	INTERVENTION	PRACTICE	EXTENSION	ELL SUPPORT
INVESTIGATION 1				
1.1	● ●		●	
1.2	■ ● ●			■ ●
1.3	●	■	■ ● ●	■ ■ ●
1.4	● ●		●	●
1.5	● ● ●		●	●
1.6			● ●	●
INVESTIGATION 2				
2.1	●		●	●
2.2	● ●			●
2.3	● ● ● ● ■	■	● ● ● ■	■ ■ ■ ●
2.4			●	
2.5				●
2.6	●			●
2.7	●		● ●	●
2.8			● ●	
INVESTIGATION 3				
3.1	● ● ■		● ■	■ ■ ●
3.2	●		●	●
3.3	● ● ●	■	●	■ ●
3.4	● ●		●	
3.5	●		●	●
3.6	●		●	●
3.7				●
INVESTIGATION 4				
4.1	● ●		●	●
4.2	● ●		●	●
4.3	●		●	●
4.4	● ● ■		■ ●	■ ■
4.5		■		● ■

● **Session-level support**
■ **Expanded Differentiation Activity**

Previewing Unit Content for English Language Learners

Counting and Number Names As students count, read, and write numbers sequentially from 1 to 100 and beyond, English Language Learners may need additional practice to learn the English number names. Work with these students to practice counting 1 through 10, then 1 through 20, and so on, until students can recite the counting sequence from 1 through 100. Encourage students to refer to classroom tools such as the calendar, the number line, and the 100 chart as they practice counting.

Vocabulary Recognizing and understanding addition-related words (*add, combine, double,* and *plus*) and subtraction-related words (*count back, remove, minus,* and *subtract*) is an important foundation to the work students will do in Grade 2. Many of the games and activities in this unit offer students opportunities to use and practice these words in context. Initially, English Language Learners may benefit from working on these activities in a small group with you so that you can model and encourage their use of the words as they engage in the work. Also, help students understand the meanings of the phrases *greater than* and *less than* as they work with addition and subtraction and compare numbers. Model these concepts for students by using cubes to represent the relationship between two quantities. Model the use of the sentence stem, "*This tower is bigger. It has more cubes. [8] is greater than [6]. This tower is smaller. It has fewer cubes. [6] is less than [8].*" After providing an example, encourage students to build their own example and explain it to the group using the sentence stem.

Math Word Wall/Chart Make a Math Word Wall/Chart for math vocabulary words and ideas and add to the chart as new math words and ideas are introduced throughout the unit. Use the *Math Words and Ideas* digital resource for additional support.

Classroom Routines Preview and/or review the Classroom Routines in a small group setting with English Language Learners. For example, in Session 1.3, students are introduced to money and coins: pennies, nickels, dimes, quarters, and dollars, which are then used in the *Quick Images* and *Today's Number* routines. Because English Language Learners may be unfamiliar with the U.S. monetary system, the names and value of the money presented may be new to them. Prior to Session 1.3, preview money with these students, first focusing on the names of coins and the dollar bill and then the values of each coin. Have students look at and describe the coins. Focus on the value of each coin by pairing verbal cues such as: **One penny equals 1 cent and one nickel equals 5 cents.** Show this equivalency with the coins and ask students to do the same. Repeat for the dime, quarter, and dollar bill.

Expanded Differentiation Activities

These activities, which take between 15 and 30 minutes, can be done in small groups, pairs, or with individuals. It may be appropriate for some students to complete more than one of the activities within an investigation or unit.

INVESTIGATION 1 Introducing Math Tools and Classroom Routines

Intervention: **Strategies for Counting**
Use anytime after Session 1.2.

Practice: **Cube Buildings**
Use anytime after Session 1.3.

Extension: **Cube Building Riddles**
Use anytime after Session 1.3.

INVESTIGATION 2 Does Order Matter?

Intervention: **Does Order Matter?**
Use anytime after Session 2.3.

Practice: **More Than 2 Addends**
Use anytime after Session 2.3.

Extension: **More Than 3 Addends and Larger Numbers**
Use anytime after Session 2.3.

INVESTIGATION 3 Comparing Quantities and Counting by Groups

Intervention: **Will Each Person Get One?**
Use anytime after Session 3.1.

Practice: **Enough or Not Enough?**
Use anytime after Session 3.3.

Extension: **Two or More Bones**
Use anytime after Session 3.1.

INVESTIGATION 4 Solving Addition and Subtraction Story Problems

Intervention: **Visualizing Story Problems**
Use anytime after Session 4.4.

Practice: **Solving Story Problems**
Use anytime after Session 4.5.

Extension: **Story Problems with Multiple Parts**
Use anytime after Session 4.4.

INVESTIGATION 1

INTRODUCING MATH TOOLS AND CLASSROOM ROUTINES

Main Math Ideas

○ Understanding and extending the counting sequence

○ Fluency within 20

Introducing Math Tools and Classroom Routines

	SESSION 1.1	SESSION 1.2
	TODAY'S NUMBER Students play *Guess My Number* on the number line to determine that *Today's Number* is 10. *Today's Number*, one of the yearlong Classroom Routines in Grade 2, involves generating equivalent expressions for a given number. In this first instance, students find different ways to arrange 10 cubes and use addition expressions to describe them. Discussion focuses on ways to make 10.	**COUNTING CUBES AND PATTERN BLOCKS** Math Workshop is introduced. Students work on two activities that focus on counting and becoming familiar with the characteristics of connecting cubes and pattern blocks.
Professional Development	**TEACHER NOTE 2** **DIALOGUE BOX 1** **Part 2: Using *Investigations*** in *Implementing Investigations in Grade 2*: The Investigations Classroom **Part 4: Classroom Routines** in *Implementing Investigations in Grade 2*: Today's Number	**TEACHER NOTE 3**
Materials to View Ahead of Time	**TEACHER PRESENTATION:** 🎦 **Activity** Introducing *Today's Number* with 10 Cubes 🎦 DIFFERENTIATION: ENGLISH LANGUAGE LEARNERS See **Differentiation in This Unit** for session content to preview with students.	**TEACHER PRESENTATIONS:** 🎦 **Classroom Routine** *Today's Number: 9* 🎦 **Activity** Introducing Ways to Fill
Materials to Gather	**Large clothespins or clips** (2) **Scrap paper** 🔧 **Connecting cubes** (10 of one color per student) **Folders or large envelopes** (optional)	🔧 **Connecting cubes** (50 per student) **Number line** 🔧 **Pattern blocks** (1 set per 6–8 students)
Materials to Prepare	**Number line** Post 0–120 of the number line at student eye level. 📄 **T1, Grid Paper** Make copies. (optional; for the Intervention)	📄 **S1, Ways to Fill: Shape A** Make 1 copy for display. (optional)
Common Core State Standards	**Session:** 2.OA.B.2, 2.MD.B.6 **Daily Practice:** 2.OA.B.2	**Classroom Routines:** 2.OA.B.2, 2.MD.B.6 **Session:** 2.NBT.A.2, 2.MD.B.6, 2.G.A.1 **Daily Practice:** 2.OA.B.2

SESSION 1.3	SESSION 1.4
QUICK IMAGES Students are introduced to money, another math tool they will use throughout the year. Exploring a set of money and recording what they notice is added to Math Workshop. Class ends with an introduction to *Quick Images*, another of the yearlong Classroom Routines that focuses on developing and analyzing visual images of quantities and shapes.	**THE 100 CHART** The 100 chart is introduced, and students compare it to the number line. Activities that ask students to write and use the counting sequence are added to Math Workshop. Class discussion focuses on what students have noticed about money.

	SESSION 1.3	SESSION 1.4
Professional Development	**TEACHER NOTE 4** **Part 4: Classroom Routines** in *Implementing Investigations in Grade 2*: Quick Images	**TEACHER NOTE 2**
Materials to View Ahead of Time	**TEACHER PRESENTATIONS:** **Classroom Routine** *Today's Number: 11* **Activity** *Quick Images: Coins* DIFFERENTIATION: ENGLISH LANGUAGE LEARNERS See **Differentiation in This Unit** for session content to preview with students.	**TEACHER PRESENTATIONS:** **Classroom Routine** *Quick Images: Coins* **Activity** Introducing the 100 Chart and Missing Numbers
Materials to Gather	**Set of real money: penny, nickel, dime, quarter, and dollar** (1 of each) **Real pennies** (1 per student) **Sets of money: penny, nickel, dime, quarter, dollar** (1 of each per student) **Materials for Ways to Fill** (from Session 1.2) **Materials for Building Cube Things** (from Session 1.2)	Enlarged copies of T2 (from Session 1.3; optional) **Tape** (as needed) **Materials for Exploring Money** (from Session 1.3) **Materials for Ways to Fill** (from Session 1.2) **Materials for Building Cube Things** (from Session 1.2) **Chart: "Money"** (from Session 1.3)
Materials to Prepare	**T2, Money** Make copies. (5 copies of each coin, enlarged for display; optional) **S1–S6, Ways to Fill: Shapes A–F** Make copies. (as needed) **Chart: "Money"** Title a piece of paper "Money" along the long side and divide it into five columns: "Penny," "Nickel," "Dime," "Quarter," and "Dollar." Paste the appropriate images (one heads, one tails) from T2 in each column.	**Pocket 100 chart** Post a pocket 100 chart with removable numbers at student eye level. **S7, Missing Numbers** Make 1 copy for display. **Counting strips** Cut adding machine tape into strips about 2 feet long. (3–4 per student) **S1–6, Ways to Fill: Shape A–F** Make copies. (as needed; optional; for the Extension)

	SESSION 1.3	SESSION 1.4
Common Core State Standards	**Classroom Routines:** 2.OA.B.2, 2.MD.B.6 **Session:** 2.OA.B.2, 2.NBT.A.2, 2.G.A.1, Supports 2.MD.C.8 **Daily Practice:** 2.OA.B.2	**Classroom Routines:** 2.OA.B.2, Supports 2.MD.C.8 **Session:** 2.NBT.A.2, 2.NBT.A.3, 2.MD.B.6, 2.MD.C.8, 2.G.A.1, Supports 2.NBT.A.1a **Daily Practice:** 2.NBT.A.3

Introducing Math Tools and Classroom Routines

	SESSION 1.5	SESSION 1.6
	HOW MANY PENNIES? The session begins with a discussion about the dollar bill and coin values. *Do We Have 100?*, a counting and accumulation game, is added to Math Workshop. Class ends with a discussion about what students have been learning about the pattern blocks as they do Ways to Fill.	**TELLING TIME** The class discusses strategies for accurate counting. Math Workshop continues. Classroom Routines *What Time Is It?* is introduced.
Professional Development	**TEACHER NOTE 3**	**TEACHER NOTE 5** **DIALOGUE BOX 2** **Part 4: Classroom Routines** in *Implementing Investigations in Grade 2*: What Time Is It?
Materials to View Ahead of Time	**TEACHER PRESENTATIONS:** 🖳 **Classroom Routine** *Quick Images: Coins* 🎲 **Activity** Introducing *Do We Have 100?* 🖳 **Discussion** Ways to Fill	**TEACHER PRESENTATIONS:** 🖳 **Classroom Routine** *Today's Number: 12* 🖳 **Activity** Introducing the Time Routine
Materials to Gather	Enlarged copies of T2 (from Session 1.3; optional) 🔧 **Pennies** (100 or so per pair) **Chart: "Money"** (completed; from Session 1.4) **Materials for Missing Numbers** (from Session 1.4) **Materials for Counting Strips** (from Session 1.4) **Materials for Ways to Fill** (from Sessions 1.2–1.4)	🔧 **Connecting cubes** (50) 🔧 **Demonstration analog clock** (optional) **Digital clock** set to 2:00 (optional) 🔧 **Student clocks** (1 per pair) **Materials for *Do We Have 100?*** (from Session 1.5) **Materials for Missing Numbers** (from Session 1.4) **Materials for Counting Strips** (from Session 1.4)
Materials to Prepare	📄 **C1, Coin Cards** Make 2 copies and cut apart to make a deck. (for display, optional; 1 deck per pair) 📄 **T3, How Many Pennies?** Make copies. (1 per student) 📄 **G1, *Do We Have 100?* Directions** Make copies. 📄 **T4, Blank Ten Frames** Make copies. (optional; for the Intervention) 📄 **S8–S11, Missing Numbers: 101–200 Charts 1–4** Make copies. (optional; for the Extension) **Chart: "How Many Pennies?"** Title a piece of chart paper "How Many Pennies?" and divide it into four columns. Label the columns "Name," "What does it look like?," "How much is it worth?," and "How many pennies?" Paste the images from T2 in the second column. See page 55.	**Chart: "How We Count"** Title a piece of chart paper "How We Count." **Partial counting strips** Create 1 or 2 partial counting strips showing common errors such as the transition to 3-digit numbers or writing the number that comes after 109. 🔧📄 **T5, 100 Chart** Make copies. (optional; for the Extension) 📄 **G2, *Guess My Number* Directions** Make copies. (optional, for the Extension) 📄 **T6, Clocks** Make 1 copy and cut apart. **Charts: "Analog Clock"** and **"Digital Clock"** Label two pieces of chart paper "Analog Clock" and "Digital Clock" and attach the appropriate clock face from T6.
Common Core State Standards	**Classroom Routines:** 2.OA.B.2, Supports 2.MD.C.8 **Session:** 2.NBT.A.2, 2.NBT.A.3, 2.G.A.1, Supports 2.MD.C.8; **Daily Practice:** Supports 2.MD.C.8	**Classroom Routines:** 2.OA.B.2, 2.MD.B.6 **Session:** 2.NBT.A.2, 2.NBT.A.3, Supports 2.MD.C.7 **Daily Practice:** 2.NBT.A.2, 2.NBT.A.3

Today's Number

MATH FOCUS POINTS

- Using the number line to reason about, and keep track of information about, the magnitude and relationship of numbers
- Using standard notation ($>$, $<$) to express the relationship between two quantities
- Using standard notation ($+$, $=$) to record expressions or equations
- Generating equivalent expressions for a number
- Establishing use of tools, routines, and expectations for math class

VOCABULARY

- number line
- greater than
- less than
- plus
- equals
- add

TODAY'S PLAN	MATERIALS
⏱ 10 Class **1** ACTIVITY ***Guess My Number* on the Number Line**	Number line* Large clothespins or clips (2) Scrap paper
⏱ 10 Class **2** ACTIVITY **Introducing *Today's Number* with 10 Cubes**	Teacher Presentation (or use 10 connecting cubes of one color)
⏱ 35 👤 Individuals **3** ACTIVITY ***Today's Number* with 10 Cubes**	📖 *Student Activity Book*, p. 1 📄 T1*(optional; for the Intervention) 🔧 Connecting cubes (10 of one color per student)
⏱ 15 Class **4** DISCUSSION ***Today's Number* with 10 Cubes**	📖 *Student Activity Book*, p. 1 (completed; from Activity 3) Students' final cube arrangements (from Activity 3)
SESSION FOLLOW-UP: REVIEW AND PRACTICE **Daily Practice**	📖 *Student Activity Book*, pp. 2–4 Folders or large envelopes (optional)

* See *Materials to Prepare* in the Investigation 1 Planner.

Common Core State Standards	Session: 2.OA.B.2, 2.MD.B.6	Daily Practice: 2.OA.B.2

1 ACTIVITY

Guess My Number on the Number Line

Begin by orienting students to the math classroom.

Every day we have school, we will have math. We're going to be thinking a lot about numbers and shapes, about how to use math to measure things and to gather information about questions we have, and about how to solve a wide range of problems.

We have lots of tools in our classroom that we'll use as we do math together.

Point out some of the tools, where they are located, and how they will work. **PD1**

Then, call students' attention to the posted number line. Ask whether they are familiar with this tool and how they have used it in the past. **MWI1** **MPN** **PD2**

The number line is a tool we will be using in math this year. It can help you count and solve problems. It can also help you figure out how to write a number or the order of the numbers. What do you notice about our number line? **MN**

❝ STUDENTS MIGHT SAY ❞

"The numbers are in a line. They start at zero and go to 120."

"The spaces are even."

"The numbers show how to count: 1, 2, 3. It keeps counting up and up."

Once students have shared some observations, ask them to locate a few numbers on the number line. Then, use the number line to play a round of *Guess My Number*.

We're going to play a game called *Guess My Number*. **PD3** **I'm thinking of a number that is between 0 and 25. I am going to write the secret number on a scrap of paper, so I don't forget it.** Secretly, write "10" on a piece of paper.

We know that my number is between 0 and 25. Another way to say that is, my number is greater than 0 and less than 25. Use > and < to record this information.

Review the symbols for greater than and less than, and encourage students to share strategies for remembering what they mean. **MWI2**

PROFESSIONAL DEVELOPMENT

PD1 **Part 2: Using *Investigations* in** *Implementing Investigations in Grade 2*: The Investigations Classroom

PD2 TEACHER NOTE 2: The Number Line and the 100 Chart: Two Models of Our Number System

PD3 DIALOGUE BOX 1: Guess My Number

MATH WORDS AND IDEAS

MWI1 Number Line

MWI2 Math Symbols: Comparing

MATH PRACTICE NOTE

MPN **MP5 Use appropriate tools strategically.** In order to be able to use mathematical tools strategically, students must become familiar with the tools and recognize their different features. The number line is a particularly concise and powerful tool which students will use for years to come.

MATH NOTE

MN **The Number Line** As students locate numbers on the number line and use it to count and keep track of numbers, they begin to see it as a tool that represents whole numbers as equally spaced points corresponding to the numbers 0, 1, 2, etc. With varied experiences over the course of the year, students begin to see it as a way to represent or solve problems or to show a solution, and they no longer need every number labeled.

Let's mark 0 and 25 on the number line, to help us remember what we know.

Ask a volunteer to place one clip on 0 and another on 25. Summarize what is known, gesturing to the right of the clip on 0, as you talk about greater than, and to the left of the clip on 25, as you talk about less than.

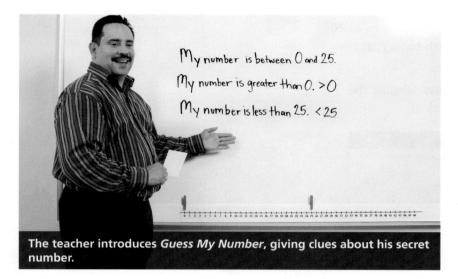

The teacher introduces *Guess My Number*, giving clues about his secret number.

Now, your job is to ask questions that will help you guess my number. The challenge is to do it in the fewest, or smallest, number of guesses. After you guess, I will give you more information about my number.

Take guesses from one student at a time. Respond to each with a new clue. For example, if a student guesses [7], tell students "My number is [greater than] [7]," and add this to the list of clues.

What do we know now? How should we move the clips?

Move the left clip from 0 to [7], showing that your number is located between [7] and 25.

Continue until students guess the number, revealing the piece of paper reading "10."

2 ACTIVITY

Introducing *Today's Number* with 10 Cubes

Explain that there are a few activities that students will do every few days, all year long, and they are going to learn one of them now. **TN**

TEACHING NOTE

TN **Classroom Routines** Classroom Routines are an ongoing part of the K–2 *Investigations* curriculum. They provide regular practice with important ideas such as counting, number combinations, computation, data, and time. *Today's Number* occurs approximately once every 3 days and includes variations that reflect the math concepts and ideas that students are working on over the course of the year.

Today's Number is an activity that we'll be doing all year. It always involves one special number. You just guessed what *Today's Number* is: it's 10. I can write 10 in different ways. I can use a number (write "10"), I can write the word (write "ten"). I can also draw pictures (draw a cube train with 10). **PD** **MPN**

Explain that students are going to think about different combinations of 10 by arranging a set of connecting cubes, another of the math tools that they will be using all year. **TN1** **TN2**

For example, I made something that looks like a set of stairs. Display the Teacher Presentation (or use 10 connecting cubes of one color).

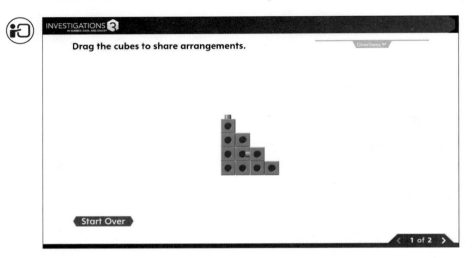

Does my staircase use 10 cubes? How do you know?

 STUDENTS MIGHT SAY ""

"Count them. 1, 2, 3, . . ., 10. There are 10."

 "1 + 2 is 3. 3 + 3 is 6. And 6 + 4 is 10. Yes!"

If I were going to use numbers to describe my arrangement, I might say it's 1 (point to each "stair") plus 2 plus 3 plus 4. And we agree that that equals 10.

Model how to record the arrangement and write that equation, as students will on *Student Activity Book* page 1.

PROFESSIONAL DEVELOPMENT

PD **Part 4: Classroom Routines** in *Implementing Investigations in Grade 2*: Today's Number

MATH PRACTICE NOTE

MPN **MP4 Model with mathematics.** The numeral *10*, the word *ten*, and a picture of 10 cubes are all ways to model the quantity 10.

TEACHING NOTES

TN1 **Math Manipulatives** This unit introduces math tools like connecting cubes and pattern blocks (in Session 1.2) that students used extensively in Kindergarten and Grade 1. If students are unfamiliar with these materials and their attributes, find time for students to freely explore them (e.g., as they arrive in the morning, during free time or indoor recess, at the end of the day).

TN2 **New Materials** When introducing any new material, it is important to establish clear ground rules. You will want to discuss where connecting cubes are stored and how they will be used and cared for.

I'm going to draw squares for the cubes. Then I'm going to write "1" for this step, because it has one cube. Then I added two cubes, so I'm going to write "+ 2". What would I write next? Why do you think so?

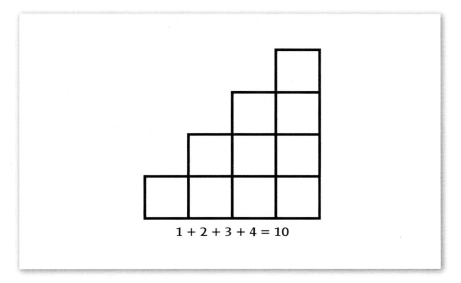

$$1 + 2 + 3 + 4 = 10$$

Explain that students should make one arrangement with 10 cubes and then record it before making another. Just like you did, they should use addition notation to describe their image. *Student Activity Book* page 1 has room for four arrangements.

---

3 ACTIVITY

Today's Number with 10 Cubes

Students use connecting cubes of one color to make arrangements of 10 and record them on *Student Activity Book* page 1. They use addition notation to describe their work.

ONGOING ASSESSMENT Observing Students at Work

Students generate different combinations of 10 and use addition notation to record their work.

○ **How do students make arrangements?** Do they work randomly or do they have a plan (e.g., "I'm going to make a house.")?

○ **How do students explain how they know their arrangement has 10?** Do they count the cubes by 1s? Explain how the groups combine to make 10? Reason that they started with 10, and they didn't take any more cubes or remove any cubes? **MN**

○ **How do students record?** Can they draw the arrangements on paper? Can they use addition notation to describe them?

Circulate as students work, asking how they know their arrangement has 10, asking them to describe it to you, and supporting them in finding ways to record. **MPN**

MATH NOTE

MN **Explaining an Answer** It is important to regularly ask students to explain the thinking behind an answer, whether it is correct or incorrect. You might ask, for example, "How were you thinking about that problem?"

MATH PRACTICE NOTE

MPN **MP1 Make sense of problems and persevere in solving them.** Inviting students to express their mathematical ideas is a step toward helping them understand that mathematics is about making sense. When students feel challenged, praise them for their hard work and persistence. See the essay **Mathematical Practices in This Unit** for more about MP1.

When it is time to transition, ask students to bring the last completed cube arrangement they have and their copy of *Student Activity Book* page 1 to the discussion. **TN**

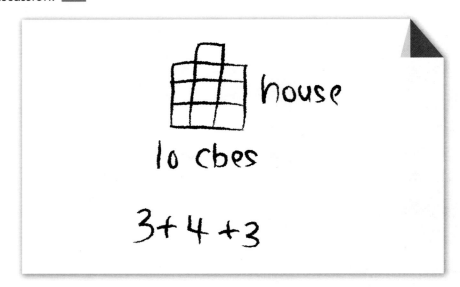

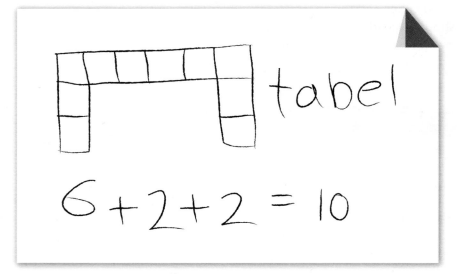

RESOURCE MASTERS, T1

TEACHING AIDS

NAME   DATE

Grid Paper

| T1 | © Pearson Education 2

 DIFFERENTIATION Supporting the Range of Learners

INTERVENTION **Suggest a Tool** Talk with students who have difficulty recording an arrangement of cubes about strategies for doing so. For example, they might place the arrangement right next to their paper and draw one square at a time. Others might trace each cube, though disconnecting the cubes may present other challenges. Recording on grid paper (T1) is another option.

INTERVENTION **Scaffold a Solution** Some students have difficulty using addition notation to describe an arrangement. Ask these students to describe their arrangement to you, and help them see how numbers and symbols could be used. For example, "I see that you made a table. There are two legs and a top. How many cubes did you use to make this leg of the table?" Help students label their first arrangement, taking dictation as needed. Then, encourage them to make another arrangement and to use the first to help them think about how to label the second.

TEACHING NOTE

TN **Transitions and Cleanup** At the end of this time, ask students to check the floor for cubes and return all extra cubes to their containers (or push them to the middle of the table). Many teachers have found that giving a warning a few minutes before the end of a work period helps students be aware that a transition is about to occur. Often you will want students to stop working and to focus their attention on a discussion. Because materials may be out on tables, some students may be distracted and continue playing with them during the discussion. It is important to set clear limits during these first sessions. Establishing such routines is emphasized throughout this first unit.

Extend Thinking Students who make and record four arrangements can compare work with a partner. Did they use the same addition expression to describe any arrangements? Are those arrangements the same or different? They can also try to build each other's arrangements based on what their partner recorded. **MPN**

---

4 DISCUSSION

Today's Number with 10 Cubes

MATH FOCUS POINTS FOR DISCUSSION

○ Generating equivalent expressions for a number

○ Using standard notation (+, =) to record expressions or equations

Gather students to discuss their work on *Today's Number* with 10 Cubes. They should bring their copy of *Student Activity Book* page 1 and the last cube arrangement they made.

We decided that my staircase showed one way to make something with 10 cubes. Who has a different way they would like to share with us?

[Malcolm] made this. Look carefully. Did [Malcolm] use 10 cubes? How do you know? How would you describe [Malcolm]'s arrangement?

Sketch the student's arrangement. Below it, use equations to record the various ways students describe it. **TN**

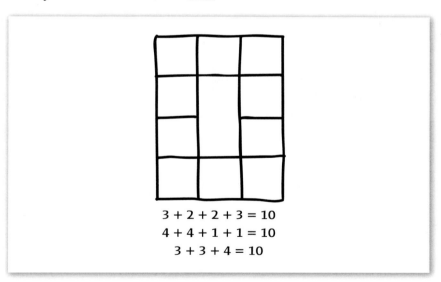

$$3 + 2 + 2 + 3 = 10$$
$$4 + 4 + 1 + 1 = 10$$
$$3 + 3 + 4 = 10$$

MATH PRACTICE NOTE

MPN **MP7 Look for and make use of structure.** When different arrangements are represented by the same arithmetic expression, they share the same mathematical structure.

TEACHING NOTE

TN **"That's Not Right!"** Some students may be bothered when their classmates describe their arrangement differently than they did. For example, this arrangement could be described as: $4 + 2 + 4$, $4 + 4 + 1 + 1$, $3 + 2 + 2 + 3$, etc. Encourage students to consider how each expression maps onto the cube arrangement, emphasizing that there are different ways to see a shape.

Look at your cubes and your recording sheet. Who made something that looked like [Malcolm]'s? Who made something different? **MPN**

This question encourages students to look carefully at what has been shared so far and at their own work. It acknowledges the work of many students without each individually sharing.

Continue looking at different arrangements as time allows.

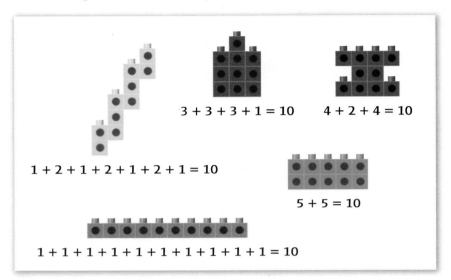

$3 + 3 + 3 + 1 = 10$

$4 + 2 + 4 = 10$

$1 + 2 + 1 + 2 + 1 + 2 + 1 = 10$

$5 + 5 = 10$

$1 + 1 + 1 + 1 + 1 + 1 + 1 + 1 + 1 + 1 = 10$

STUDENT ACTIVITY BOOK, P. 2

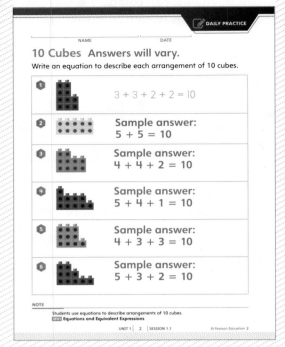

DAILY PRACTICE

NAME   DATE

10 Cubes Answers will vary.
Write an equation to describe each arrangement of 10 cubes.

1    $3 + 3 + 2 + 2 = 10$

2   Sample answer:
     $5 + 5 = 10$

3   Sample answer:
     $4 + 4 + 2 = 10$

4   Sample answer:
     $5 + 4 + 1 = 10$

5   Sample answer:
     $4 + 3 + 3 = 10$

6   Sample answer:
     $5 + 3 + 2 = 10$

NOTE
Students use equations to describe arrangements of 10 cubes.
MPN Equations and Equivalent Expressions

UNIT 1 | 2 | SESSION 1.1   © Pearson Education 2

SESSION FOLLOW-UP: REVIEW AND PRACTICE

Daily Practice

DAILY PRACTICE For reinforcement of this unit's content, students complete *Student Activity Book* page 2.

FAMILY LETTER Send home *Student Activity Book* pages 3–4. You might also send a large envelope or folder for storing math information and materials that will come home in the future.

MATH PRACTICE NOTE

MPN **MP3 Construct viable arguments and critique the reasoning of others.** To critique does not mean to criticize. It means to determine if others' reasoning makes sense, and if not, to find where the reasoning fails. Asking students to look at their classmates' work and compare it to their own is a step toward critiquing the reasoning of others.

Counting Cubes and Pattern Blocks

MATH FOCUS POINTS

- Counting sets of up to 50 objects
- Finding combinations of shapes that fill a region
- Developing vocabulary to name and describe 2-D shapes
- Establishing use of tools, routines, and expectations for math class

VOCABULARY

- hexagon
- trapezoid
- rhombus
- square
- triangle

	TODAY'S PLAN	MATERIALS
10 Class	**CLASSROOM ROUTINES: REVIEW AND PRACTICE** ***Today's Number: 9***	Teacher Presentation (or use cubes and a number line)
15 Class	**1 ACTIVITY** **Introducing Building Cube Things and Ways to Fill**	Teacher Presentation (or use S1* and pattern blocks) Connecting cubes (50) Number line
40	**2 MATH WORKSHOP** **Counting Cubes and Pattern Blocks** 2A Building Cube Things 2B Ways to Fill	**2A** Connecting cubes (50 per student) **2B** *Student Activity Book*, pp. 5–10 Pattern blocks (1 set per 6–8 students)
5 Class	**3 DISCUSSION** **Establishing a Mathematics Community**	
	SESSION FOLLOW-UP: REVIEW AND PRACTICE **Daily Practice and Homework**	*Student Activity Book*, pp. 11–14

* See *Materials to Prepare* in the Investigation 1 Planner.

Common Core State Standards	Classroom Routines: 2.OA.B.2, 2.MD.B.6 Session: 2.NBT.A.2, 2.MD.B.6, 2.G.A.1	Daily Practice: 2.OA.B.2

CLASSROOM ROUTINES: REVIEW AND PRACTICE

Today's Number: 9

MATH FOCUS POINTS

○ Generating equivalent expressions for a number

○ Using standard notation (+, −, =) to record expressions or equations

Display the Teacher Presentation (or use cubes and a number line).

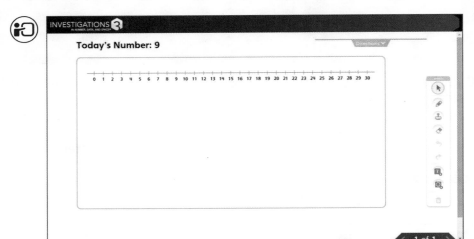

Explain that Today's Number is 9, and ask students to help you find it on the number line and write the number word (i.e., nine). As a class, students generate expressions that equal 9. Students can use cubes, as they did in Session 1.1, or work mentally. Students will likely suggest subtraction expressions. Model them with cubes, as needed. Record the expressions, encouraging students to explain how they know they equal 9.

---

1 ACTIVITY

Introducing Building Cube Things and Ways to Fill

In math this year, there will be times when a few different activities are available and you can choose which you'd like to do. This time is called Math Workshop, and we're going to have our first one today. **TN**

I'm going to introduce two new activities, and then you can decide which one you would like to work on first. The first is called Building Cube Things, and it's similar to what you worked on in the previous session, except you're going to use 50 cubes.

Show students a bin of loose cubes, and explain that the first thing they'll do is count out 50 cubes. **MPN**

Count out 50 cubes into (unconnected) rows of 10. Ask a volunteer to point to the numbers on the number line as the class counts aloud with you. Note how comfortable students seem with the sequence of numbers to 50.

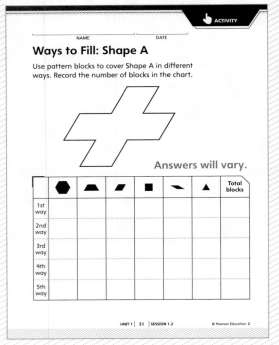

TEACHING NOTE

TN **Math Workshop** Math Workshop is a format that recurs throughout the *Investigations* curriculum. In it, students choose among several mathematically related activities, available over the course of several days. During this first Math Workshop, it is important that you establish routines and expectations that support this structure. See *Implementing Investigations in Grade 2*: Math Workshop.

MATH PRACTICE NOTE

MPN **MP2 Reason abstractly and quantitatively.** In order to develop an understanding of numbers and their structures, students must connect numerals and number names with the quantities they represent. For this reason, students count quantities of objects.

If you choose Building Cube Things, the first thing you do is count out 50 cubes. Try to arrange them so that they are easy to count, because once you have 50, your partner is going to check your count. And you will check your partner's set.

Ask students how they would double-check your cubes. Some suggest counting from 1; others say, "We know because we just counted them!" and still others use the groups of 10 (e.g., "Look, here's 10, 20, 30, 40, 50.") If no one comments on the groups of 10, demonstrate counting the cubes by 10s yourself.

Once you agree that you have 50, build something with your cubes. It could be an animal, a toy, or something else. You may not need exactly 50 cubes to build your cube thing. It's OK to use a few more or a few less. But when you are finished, you should know exactly how many cubes you used. **TN**

Explain that when they are finished, partners should share their cube things with each other and show how they know exactly how many cubes they used.

The other activity is called Ways to Fill. It uses another one of our math tools—pattern blocks—that most of you used in Kindergarten and first grade.

Display a collection of pattern blocks and ask what students know about them, which will likely include their names and the types of things they can make with them. **MN1**

Display the Teacher Presentation (or use Ways to Fill: Shape A (S1), and pattern blocks) to introduce the activity.

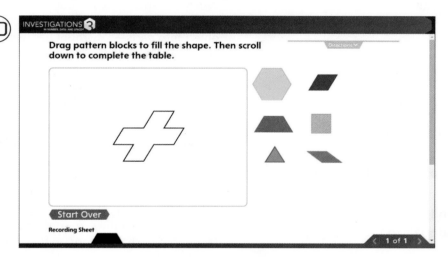

You will use pattern blocks to fill in the outline and record the shapes you used in the table.

Ask students to help you use pattern blocks to fill in the outline of Shape A and to use the first row of the table to show the number of each shape and the total number used. Use this as an opportunity to review the names of the pattern block shapes.

How many hexagons did we use to fill Shape A? That's the name of the yellow shape with six sides. How many trapezoids [blue rhombuses, squares, tan rhombuses, triangles] did we use? **MWI**

Once the first row is filled in, ask about other ways to fill the outline.

Do you think there is another way we could use pattern blocks to fill Shape A? A way that uses different blocks or a different number of blocks? **MN2**

Ask a volunteer to demonstrate a different way to fill Shape A, and again ask students to help you record the results.

TEACHING NOTE

TN **Exactly 50, About 50** Asking students to count and organize exactly 50 provides an opportunity to observe students' counting skills and their comfort with groups. The flexibility in the total number used to build a Cube Thing allows students to make something that matches their vision, but it also usefully complicates the matter of finding the final total, providing opportunities for students to use reasoning (e.g., "Each leg has 10, that's 40, and I used 15 in the body, so I used 55.") and to develop strategies for keeping track.

MATH NOTES

MN1 **Pattern Blocks** The set of pattern block shapes includes a regular hexagon (six sides of equal length and six equal angles) and a regular triangle (three sides of equal length and three equal angles), an isosceles trapezoid (the non-parallel sides have equal length), and three different rhombuses (quadrilaterals with four equal sides), one of which is a square.

MN2 **What Counts as Different?** Expect students to disagree about what is a *different* way to make a shape. For example, some students suggest using all blue rhombuses to fill Shape A, and then find "different" solutions by replacing each of those rhombuses with two green triangles, one at a time. Some think of any solution that uses 4 blue rhombuses and 2 green triangles as the same. Others think that different arrangements of those shapes within the outline are different. Encourage students to explain their thinking. Acknowledge that both arguments make sense; but in this case, you are focusing on the number of each kind of block. So if a combination uses the same number of the same blocks, they are the same, whatever their orientation.

MATH WORDS AND IDEAS

MWI Pattern Block Shapes

Explain that the first sheet challenges them to find five different ways to fill Shape A, and they will do the same with Shapes B–F.

Let students know that this activity, along with Building Cube Things, will be available for several days, so students will have plenty of time to work on both activities. **MPN1**

Counting Cubes and Pattern Blocks

 40

Before students begin work, review the rules for using materials and any additional expectations related to Math Workshop (e.g., working productively and cooperatively, keeping noise at an acceptable level).

Today, and for parts of the next few days, everyone will have a chance to do the activities we just learned—Building Cube Things and Ways to Fill.

Explain where the materials for both activities will be located and how many students can be working on each at one time. Explain that during Math Workshop, students can select the same activity more than once, but they need to work on and complete each activity at least once while it is available. **TN**

Then, help students make their choices and begin work. Remind them that you will let students know when they have 5 minutes left to work and when it is time to clean up.

ONGOING ASSESSMENT Observing Students at Work

Students make choices about and engage with two different activities. **MPN2**

○ **Do students stick with the same activity for a period of time, or do they move from place to place?** Are they focused on the activity at hand?

○ **Do they work alone or in pairs?** Do they talk to others about what they are doing? Can they share the materials successfully?

○ **Are students using materials responsibly?** Can they find what they need and get started? Do they clean up and return materials to the appropriate place?

In Ways to Fill, students use pattern blocks to fill a region in different ways.

MATH PRACTICE NOTES

MPN1 **MP7 Look for and make use of structure.** Both activities engage students with the structure of geometric objects. When students check the number of cubes in their cube thing, they decompose the object into parts—"My robot has two arms, two legs, a body, and a head"—and count the number of cubes in each part. In Ways to Fill, shapes are decomposed into the pieces of the pattern blocks.

MPN2 **MP1 Make sense of problems and persevere in solving them.** In Math Workshop, where students have autonomy to decide what to work on, they learn to engage in mathematical tasks with purpose. Students develop strategies for what to do when they are confused or the task becomes challenging. Do they ask a question? Do they try something else?

TEACHING NOTE

TN **Math Workshop Logistics** The number of students that can work on each activity will depend on the supply of materials and the space available in particular areas of the room. Plan how to communicate this information (e.g., the number of chairs at a table or a display). Students can often get to two activities in a session. They can select the same activity more than once and, in fact, should be encouraged to do so. However, they will also need to visit each choice at some time while it is available.

Note any issues you observe, so that you can be sure to raise them in the discussion at the end of this session.

Note any issues you observe, so that you can be sure to raise them in the discussion at the end of this session.

2 A Building Cube Things

Students count out 50 cubes and organize them so they are easy to count. Partners check each other's counts. Then, students make a Cube Thing with about 50 cubes. Partners share their constructions and explain how they know the exact number of cubes used.

ONGOING ASSESSMENT Observing Students at Work

Students count and organize a set of 50 connecting cubes, use about that many to build an object, and keep track of how many they've used.

○ **How accurate are students in their counting?** Do they know the sequence to 50? Do they count each cube once and only once? Do they count by 1s or groups? Do they double-check? **PD**

○ **How do students organize their set of 50 cubes to show their partner that they have 50?** Do they use groups? Of what size? Can they explain their organization and how it is helpful? **TN**

○ **How do they keep track of the total number of cubes as they work?** Do they count the cubes from 1 once they have finished? Do they keep track of the changing number as they work? Do they count the number in various parts and combine those numbers? How do they count or keep track of cubes that are hidden from view?

Students count out 50 connecting cubes and use them to build a Cube Thing.

PROFESSIONAL DEVELOPMENT

PD TEACHER NOTE 3: Counting by Groups

TEACHING NOTE

TN **Counting by Groups** Observe as students organize their cubes so that their partner can quickly and easily see that they have 50. This will give you an initial sense of whether and how students are using groups to count a set of objects. Investigation 3 will focus on counting by groups and, in particular, on the importance and usefulness of groups of 10.

DIFFERENTIATION Supporting the Range of Learners

INTERVENTION **Scaffold a Solution** Meet with students who have difficulty successfully counting 50 to discern whether the issue is knowing the counting sequence, having a strategy for counting each cube once and only once, or keeping track of what has/has not been counted. You might use *Math Words and Ideas*, Counting, to model, discuss, and practice strategies for accurate counting. Try to find the greatest number of cubes that students are able to count accurately. Then help them expand that set so it has 50 cubes with which they can build. `TN` `MWI1` `MWI2`

> For a more comprehensive intervention activity to be done outside of class, see *Strategies for Counting* at the end of this investigation.

ENGLISH LANGUAGE LEARNERS **Provide Vocabulary Support** Help students learn the English number names. Emphasize the repeating pattern of the ones digit as students count each decade: . . . *twenty-one, twenty-two, twenty-three,* . . . *thirty-one, thirty-two, thirty-three,* and so on. Reinforce the connection between the name of each multiple of 10 and the name of the corresponding ones digit (e.g., *twenty* and *two, thirty* and *three, forty* and *four, sixty* and *six,* and so on). Connect the English number names to the number names in students' first languages, when possible, to promote understanding and retention.

---

2 B   **Ways to Fill**

Students find as many as five ways to use pattern blocks to fill the six different shape outlines on *Student Activity Book* pages 5–10. They record the number of each type of block and the total number of blocks used for each way they find.

ONGOING ASSESSMENT Observing Students at Work

Students find different ways to fill a region with pattern blocks and record their work.

○ **Are students able to fill the outlines without spaces or overlaps?**

○ **How do students name and describe the pattern block shapes?** Do they use their geometric names? Color? Number of sides?

○ **Are students seeing and using relationships among the pattern block shapes?** For example, do they see that they can replace one yellow hexagon with six green triangles? Or that two red trapezoids equal one yellow hexagon?

○ **Do students see that some shapes (e.g., the orange square and tan rhombus) do not fit in the outlines, no matter how they are arranged?**

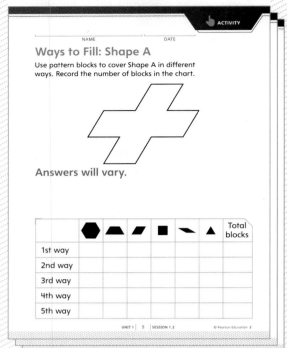

Ways to Fill: Shape A

Use pattern blocks to cover Shape A in different ways. Record the number of blocks in the chart.

Answers will vary.

	⬢	◗	◢	◼	◣	▲	Total blocks
1st way							
2nd way							
3rd way							
4th way							
5th way							

UNIT 1   5   SESSION 1.2   © Pearson Education 2

TEACHING NOTE

`TN` **Counting by Ones** Being able to count a set of objects by 1s is a foundational skill that underlies many of the big ideas in elementary mathematics. In this first investigation, identify any students who are not fluently counting sets of up to 50. Focus observations on the following skills that fluent counting requires: Do they know the names and sequence of the numbers? Do they count each object once and only once? Do they have a system for keeping track of what's been counted and what remains to be counted? Do they know that the last number they say represents the total number of objects? Students who are not secure with these skills will benefit from immediate and focused support.

MATH WORDS AND IDEAS

`MWI1` Why Do We Count?

`MWI2` Ways to Count

DIFFERENTIATION Supporting the Range of Learners

INTERVENTION Scaffold a Solution Some students find it challenging to fill an outline in different ways. For example, some students only see Shape A as being made up of blue rhombuses. Place a different pattern block than they have used on their Shape A outline, and challenge them to finish it. "What if I put this [green triangle] here. Do you think you could finish the rest of the puzzle?"

3 DISCUSSION

Establishing a Mathematics Community

MATH FOCUS POINT FOR DISCUSSION

○ Establishing use of tools, routines, and expectations for math class

Most discussions in Grade 2 focus on the mathematics that students are working on. Use this discussion as an opportunity to establish and develop the mathematical community. To that end, talk with students about how Math Workshop is (or is not) working. You might discuss the following issues:

○ using and sharing materials

○ caring for and storing materials

○ noise level

○ working together

○ working purposefully

SESSION FOLLOW-UP: REVIEW AND PRACTICE

Daily Practice and Homework

 DAILY PRACTICE For reinforcement of this unit's content, students complete *Student Activity Book* page 11.

 HOMEWORK On *Student Activity Book* page 12, students arrange 10 objects in two different ways. They record the arrangements and use an equation to describe each.

 FAMILY LETTER Send home *Student Activity Book* pages 13–14.

STUDENT ACTIVITY BOOK, P. 11

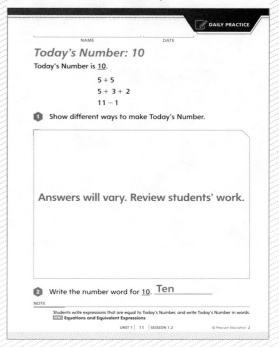

STUDENT ACTIVITY BOOK, P. 12

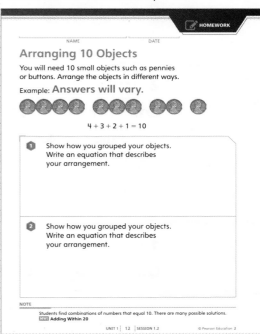

4" />

1.3

Quick Images

MATH FOCUS POINTS

- Identifying and recognizing coins and their values
- Counting sets of up to 50 objects
- Finding combinations of shapes that fill a region
- Developing and analyzing visual images for quantities up to 10

VOCABULARY

- money
- cents
- penny
- nickel
- dime
- quarter
- dollar
- doubles

TODAY'S PLAN	MATERIALS

 (10) **CLASSROOM ROUTINES: REVIEW AND PRACTICE**
Today's Number: 11

Teacher Presentation (or use cubes and a number line)

(15) **1** ACTIVITY
Exploring Money

T2*

Chart: "Money"*

Set of real money: penny, nickel, dime, quarter, and dollar (1 of each)

Real pennies (1 per student)

 (30) **2** MATH WORKSHOP
Counting and Exploring Coins

2A Exploring Money

2B Ways to Fill

2C Building Cube Things

2A *Student Activity Book*, pp. 15–16

Sets of money: penny, nickel, dime, quarter, dollar (1 of each per student)

2B S1–S6* (as needed)

Materials from Session 1.2

2C Materials from Session 1.2

 (15) **3** ACTIVITY
Quick Images: Coins

Teacher Presentation (or use enlarged copies of coins made from T2)

SESSION FOLLOW-UP: REVIEW AND PRACTICE
Daily Practice

Student Activity Book, p. 17

* See *Materials to Prepare* in the Investigation 1 Planner.

Common Core State Standards	Classroom Routines: 2.OA.B.2, 2.MD.B.6 Session: 2.OA.B.2, 2.NBT.A.2, 2.G.A.1, Supports 2.MD.C.8	Daily Practice: 2.OA.B.2

Today's Number: 11

MATH FOCUS POINTS

○ Generating equivalent expressions for a number

○ Using standard notation $(+, -, =)$ to record expressions or equations

Display the Teacher Presentation (or use cubes and a number line).

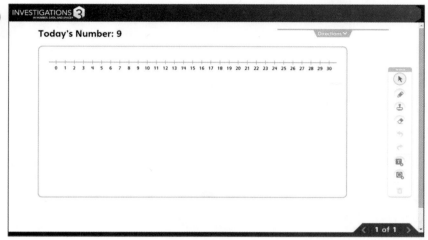

Explain that Today's Number is 11, and ask students to help you find it on the number line and write the number word (i.e., eleven). As a class, students generate addition and/or subtraction expressions that equal 11.

Record the expressions, encouraging students to explain how they know they equal 11.

1 ACTIVITY

Exploring Money

Display a penny, a nickel, a dime, a quarter, and a dollar.

This year we are going to be doing a lot of work with money. We'll figure out how many cents different coins and bills are worth, learn about different combinations of coins, and use money as we solve addition and subtraction problems. Over the next few days, you are going to look very closely at a set of coins and dollar bills and write about what you know and what you notice. Then we'll make a list of what we know about (point to each) pennies, nickels, dimes, quarters, and dollars. **PD** **MWI**

Give each student a real penny.

Let's look at the penny together. Look closely at your penny. . . . Now turn to someone sitting near you and talk about what you notice about it. Then we will talk together as a whole class. **TN**

PROFESSIONAL DEVELOPMENT

PD TEACHER NOTE 4: Money as a Mathematical Tool

MATH WORDS AND IDEAS

MWI Money

TEACHING NOTE

TN **Talking with a Partner** Asking students to talk with a partner, before discussing as a whole group, allows everyone to share their thinking with at least one other person. Additionally, it offers students an opportunity to "practice" their ideas before sharing in front of the group. While this may not be a part of every discussion, consider building in such opportunities occasionally.

After a few minutes, display the "Money" chart and record students' observations about the penny.

Money

Penny	Nickel	Dime	Quarter	Dollar
• It has a man on it. • It's a different color from the other ones. • It's one cent. • It has words on it.				

Explain that during Math Workshop students will be looking carefully at all of the kinds of money on the "Money" chart, and they will record their observations on *Student Activity Book* pages 15–16. Review the name of each kind of money, connecting it to the real examples. `TN`

2 MATH WORKSHOP

Counting and Exploring Coins

(30)

Briefly review each of the activities and remind students about routines and expectations for Math Workshop. Encourage students who, based on your observations in Session 1.2, need practice counting objects to revisit Building Cube Things.

2 A Exploring Money

Students look closely at a penny, a nickel, a dime, a quarter, and a dollar, and record their observations about each on *Student Activity Book* pages 15–16.

STUDENT ACTIVITY BOOK, P. 15

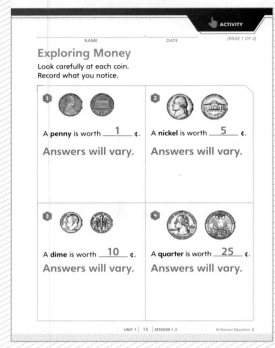

STUDENT ACTIVITY BOOK, P. 16

TEACHING NOTE

`TN` **My Quarter Doesn't Look Like That!** Depending on the money students are using (i.e., commercial manipulatives vs. real money), the images on the coins they are exploring may be different than the images on the *Student Activity Book* page. Discuss this with students, and encourage them to record that as something they noticed. They can describe what they notice about the coin that is pictured and/or the real coin.

Students explore another mathematical tool: coins and dollar bills.

○ **What do students notice?** Do they comment on size/thickness? The color/material? What's pictured and/or written? Do they know/can they figure out the value of each?

○ **Can students recognize and identify the coins?** Can they respond to both types of questions: "Can you show me the quarter?" vs. "What's the name of this coin?"

○ **Do students know any equivalencies?** For example, do they know that a dime is worth 10 pennies or 2 nickels?

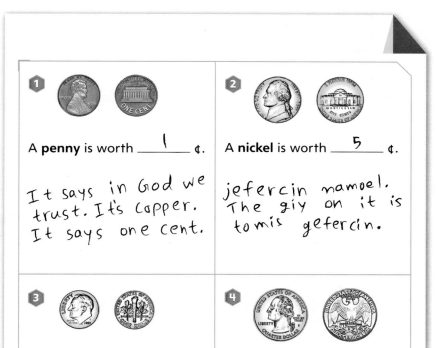

1 A **penny** is worth ___1___ ¢.

It says in God we trust. It's copper. It says one cent.

2 A **nickel** is worth ___5___ ¢.

jefercin mamoel. The giy on it is tomis gefercin.

3 A **dime** is worth ___10___ ¢.

The giys name is rosavel.

4 A **quarter** is worth ___25___ ¢.

It has diforit stof on the back.

5

A **dollar bill** is worth ___100___ ¢.

It's paper. The giy is Giorg washntin It's green. It has a lot of stof on the back.

DIFFERENTIATION Supporting the Range of Learners

INTERVENTION **Scaffold a Solution** Some students may have difficulty matching real coins to the images on *Student Activity Book* pages 15–16 because some—quarters, for example—have a variety of images on the back, including ones that may not match the image shown. Help them match the coins, focusing on the front image and the size of the coin instead.

ENGLISH LANGUAGE LEARNERS **Provide Opportunities for Practice** Review the new vocabulary with students. Pair students, have them look at and hold each coin and dollar, and review the value of each piece. Then have partners practice identifying coins and their values by asking each other specific questions. For example, one student might ask another, "Can I have 1 penny?" or "Can I have 2 dimes?" Model an example for students before they begin. Then observe students as they work in pairs, helping them name and identify the coins correctly. Encourage students to ask each other questions about the value of the coins.

2 B **Ways to Fill**

For complete details about this activity, see Session 1.2.

 DIFFERENTIATION Supporting the Range of Learners

EXTENSION **Vary the Problem** Students who complete *Student Activity Book* pages 5–10 can be challenged to choose a shape from one of the pages and find all of the possible ways to cover that shape with different numbers of pattern blocks. They should count only solutions that fill a row in the table in a new way (e.g., different arrangements of the same blocks do not count as different solutions). For example, Shape A can be covered with 4, 5, 6, 7, 8, 9, or 10 pattern blocks. They might want multiple blank copies of that shape (S1–S6), to keep track of their work.

2 C **Building Cube Things**

For complete details about this activity, see Session 1.2.

 DIFFERENTIATION Supporting the Range of Learners

> For a more comprehensive practice activity to be done outside of class, see *Cube Buildings* at the end of this investigation.

EXTENSION **Extend the Problem** Some students may be interested in writing riddles for the number of different colored cubes they used in their building. For example, a clue might be "I used 14 blue cubes. The number of red cubes is 10 more than the number of blue cubes." They write a clue for each color and then exchange riddles with a partner. After solving the riddle, they double-check the cubes in each other's Cube Building.

> For a more comprehensive extension activity to be done outside of class, see *Cube Building Riddles* at the end of this investigation.

RESOURCE MASTERS, S1–S6

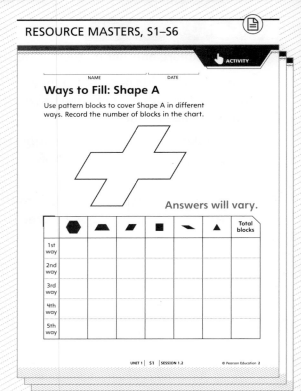

RESOURCE MASTERS, T2

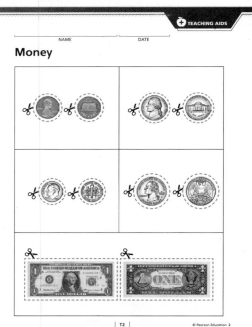

Quick Images: Coins

MATH FOCUS POINT FOR DISCUSSION

○ Identifying coins and their values

Explain to students that they are going to learn another of the Classroom Routines that they will encounter every few days, all year long. In *Quick Images*, students look at an arrangement or set of objects for a few seconds and then describe what they saw. PD MPN

I'm going to show you an image for 3 seconds. Then I'll hide it, and you think about it. You'll get another chance to see it, and then we'll talk about what you saw and how you remembered the image. TN1

Display the Teacher Presentation (or use enlarged copies of the coins from T2) to display a group of 3 pennies and a group of 3 nickels. TN2

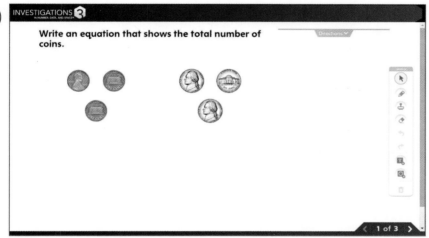

Use the following process:

○ Briefly show the image.

○ Students think about what they saw.

○ Show the image again, briefly.

○ Students revise their thinking.

○ With the image showing, volunteers share which and how many coins they saw, how they were arranged, and how they remembered.

Focus the discussion on the number of pennies (3), the number of nickels (3), and the total number of coins (6), and how students remembered the image. Ask questions that require students to both identify (e.g., What's the name of this coin?) and recognize (e.g., Which coin is the penny?) the coins. End by asking students to help you write an equation that shows the total number of coins. TN3

Next, present an image that shows 4 nickels and 4 dimes.

If time remains, present an image that shows 5 dimes and 5 quarters.

End the session by asking students what they noticed about the three problems, using the opportunity to introduce the idea of "doubles."

MATH PRACTICE NOTE

MPN **MP7 Look for and make use of structure.** *Quick Images* happens throughout the year, promoting students' noticing of mathematical structures. In this unit, *Quick Images* helps students focus on the structure of numbers: 6 is composed of 3 and 3; 8 is composed of 4 and 4. In Investigation 3, *Quick Images* focuses on relationships between problems like $7 + 3$, $7 + 4$, and $7 + 5$, and how knowing that $7 + 3 = 10$ can help with finding the total of $7 + 4$ and of $7 + 5$.

TEACHING NOTES

TN1 **Options for *Quick Images*** This session assumes that the images are projected using a digital device. (Using a document camera to project images of real coins is another option.) Otherwise, cover enlarged copies of images of coins, such as the ones on T2, with a piece of paper.

TN2 **Timing** You may need to adjust the amount of time you flash the image. If you show it for too long, students will not need to build a mental image; if you show it too briefly, they will not have time to form a mental image.

TN3 **How Many Coins?** The first few *Quick Images* with coins focus on identifying and recognizing coins and seeing and finding the total of equal groups (e.g., 3 and 3). Later, once students are fluent with coin values and begin to think about equivalencies, they will also figure out how many cents the set of coins is worth.

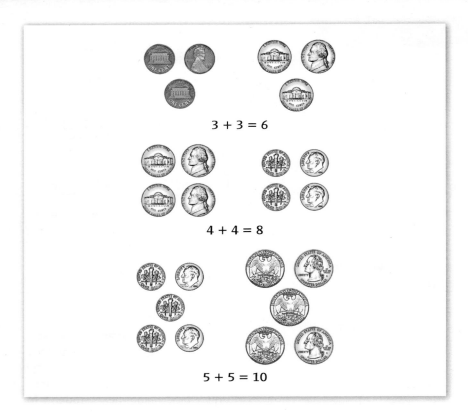

3 + 3 = 6

4 + 4 = 8

5 + 5 = 10

STUDENT ACTIVITY BOOK, P. 17

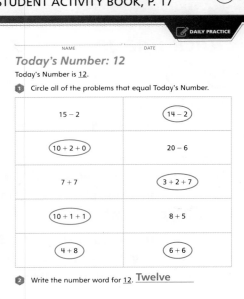

DAILY PRACTICE

NAME   DATE

Today's Number: 12

Today's Number is 12.

1 Circle all of the problems that equal Today's Number.

15 − 2	(14 − 2)
(10 + 2 + 0)	20 − 6
7 + 7	(3 + 2 + 7)
(10 + 1 + 1)	8 + 5
(4 + 8)	(6 + 6)

2 Write the number word for 12. Twelve

NOTE

Students determine which expressions are equal to Today's Number, and write Today's Number in words.
MPN Equations and Equivalent Expressions

UNIT 1 | 17 | SESSION 1.3   © Pearson Education 2

" STUDENTS MIGHT SAY "

"It was 3 and 3, then 4 and 4, then 5 and 5."

"Those are the doubles! You have a number and you add that number."

"That's what I hope to roll when I play games at home!"

You're right, some people call these problems the doubles. Doubling means that you add a number to itself. Or, you add the same number twice. Lots of you know your doubles from first grade and from playing games with dice. We're going to be thinking and talking this year about how knowing things like the doubles can help with math problems you *don't* know the answer to. MPN

SESSION FOLLOW-UP: REVIEW AND PRACTICE

Daily Practice

 DAILY PRACTICE For reinforcement of this unit's content, students complete *Student Activity Book* page 17.

MATH PRACTICE NOTE

MPN 🔍 **MP8 Look for and express regularity in repeated reasoning.** Looking for patterns is a mathematical habit to be encouraged. It is a step toward recognizing mathematical structures.

The 100 Chart

MATH FOCUS POINTS

○ Developing an understanding of the structure of the 100 chart
○ Counting, writing, and reading numbers to 100 and beyond
○ Identifying and recognizing coins and their values
○ Finding combinations of shapes that fill a region
○ Counting sets of up to 50 objects

VOCABULARY

○ 100 chart

	TODAY'S PLAN	MATERIALS
10 / Class	**CLASSROOM ROUTINES: REVIEW AND PRACTICE** *Quick Images: Coins*	Teacher Presentation (or use enlarged copies of coins from T2)
15 / Class	**1 ACTIVITY** **Introducing the 100 Chart and Missing Numbers**	Teacher Presentation (or use a pocket 100 chart*) S7*
5 / Class	**2 ACTIVITY** **Introducing Counting Strips**	A counting strip (from Math Workshop 3B)

30	**3 MATH WORKSHOP**
	 Counting and Coins
	
	 3A Missing Numbers
	 3B Counting Strips
	 3C Exploring Money
	 3D Ways to Fill
	 3E Building Cube Things
		3A *Student Activity Book*, pp. 18–23
		 3B Counting strips* (3–4 per student)
		      Tape (as needed)
		 3C Materials from Session 1.3
		 3D S1–S6* (optional; for the Extension)
		      Materials from Session 1.2
		 3E Materials from Session 1.2

10 / Class	**4 DISCUSSION** **Money**	*Student Activity Book* pp. 15–16 (completed; from Math Workshop 3C) Chart: "Money" (from Session 1.3)
	SESSION FOLLOW-UP: REVIEW AND PRACTICE **Daily Practice**	*Student Activity Book*, p. 24

* See *Materials to Prepare* in the Investigation 1 Planner.

Common Core State Standards	**Classroom Routines:** 2.OA.B.2, Supports 2.MD.C.8 **Session:** 2.NBT.A.2, 2.NBT.A.3, 2.MD.B.6, 2.MD.C.8, 2.G.A.1, Supports 2.NBT.A.1a	**Daily Practice:** 2.NBT.A.3

CLASSROOM ROUTINES: REVIEW AND PRACTICE

Quick Images: Coins

(10)

MATH FOCUS POINTS

○ Developing and analyzing visual images for quantities up to 10

○ Identifying and recognizing coins and their values

Display the Teacher Presentation (or use enlarged copies of the coins from T2) to display a group of 3 nickels and a group of 3 quarters.

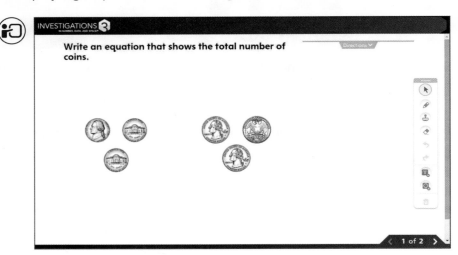

Follow the process introduced in Session 1.3. **TN**

Focus the discussion on the number of nickels, the number of quarters, and the total number of coins, and how students remembered the image. Ask questions that require students to both identify (e.g., What's the name of this coin?) and recognize (e.g., Which coin is the nickel?) the coins. End by asking students to help you write an equation that shows the total number of coins.

Repeat with an image that shows 2 pennies, 2 nickels, and 2 dimes.

TEACHING NOTE

TN *Quick Images* **Routine**

○ Briefly show the image.

○ Students think about what they saw.

○ Show the image again, briefly.

○ Students revise their thinking.

○ With the image showing, volunteers share which and how many coins they saw, how they were arranged, and how they remembered.

1 ACTIVITY

Introducing the 100 Chart and Missing Numbers

Display the Teacher Presentation (or use a pocket 100 chart).

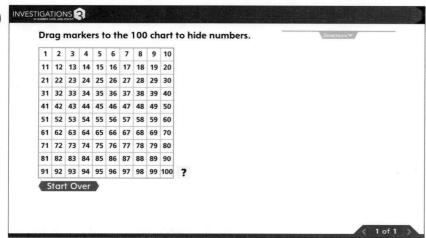

Ask students whether they are familiar with this tool and how they have used it before.

The 100 chart is another tool we will be using in math this year. Like the number line, it can help us count and solve problems or determine how to write a number or figure out the order of the numbers. **What do you notice about the 100 chart?** MWI1 MWI2

❝❝ STUDENTS MIGHT SAY ❞❞

"These are the numbers you say when you count. There are 10 of them in a row."

"One row has all the 20s—except the number at the end. And the next row has all the 30s. And it keeps going."

"If you look at the numbers going up and down, first they all end in a 1. Then they all end in a 2. Then a 3, all the way up."

"I agree with [Lonzell]. There are 10 numbers in a row. *And* there are 10 rows. It looks like a square."

MATH WORDS AND IDEAS

MWI1   100 Chart

MWI2   Number Line

Once students have shared a few observations, ask them to locate a few numbers on the 100 chart.

What if we compare the 100 chart to the number line? How are they the same? How are they different?

Ask students to find a few more numbers, this time on both the 100 chart and the number line, to help students think about how the representations are the same and different.

❝❝ STUDENTS MIGHT SAY ❞❞

 "On the number line 51 looks so far from 1. But on the 100 chart it doesn't."

 "It's easier to see that 20 is 10 away from 30 on the number line. On the 100 chart it looks like it's just 1 away."

After discussing students' comments, count from one number to the other on both representations to reinforce that the sequence of numbers are the same, despite the arrangement.

Finally, ask students to cover or close their eyes while you remove (or turn over) several numbers on the 100 chart. Ask students what numbers are missing and how they know (e.g., counting from 1, counting from the first number in a row, thinking about columns, or using the numbers before/after or above/below).

Students use different strategies to determine what numbers are missing on the 100 chart.

Explain that students will be doing a similar activity on paper during Math Workshop. Display the Teacher Presentation (or use S7) to briefly introduce that activity, explaining that first students solve a few problems and write those answers in the appropriate squares on the 100 chart. Then, they fill in the rest of the missing numbers.

MATH NOTE

MN **Comparing Math Tools** The number line and the 100 chart are two different organizations of the counting numbers from 1 to 100. While the number line is a continuous representation (and in later grades will also be used to represent numbers between whole numbers), the 100 chart is discrete and organized into rows of 10. See **Teacher Note 2:** The Number Line and the 100 Chart: Two Models of Our Number System.

2 ACTIVITY

Introducing Counting Strips

Ask students how high they think they can count, and record the numbers they say. Explain that in this activity, they are going to have an opportunity to count and write numbers as high as they can.

Tape a piece of adding machine tape vertically to the board and write several numbers one underneath the other, starting with zero. **MN**

0
1
2
3
4
5
6
7
8
9
10
11

When you make your counting strip, start with zero and write the numbers, one under the other. Make sure that you write each number large enough so that it is easy to read. If you need more paper, you can tape strips of paper together. MPN1

What if you get to 49 and you can't remember what number comes next? What can you do? Where in our classroom can you look? MPN2 MWI

Remind students that looking at the patterns in the numbers they have already written can also help them write more numbers. **MPN3**

3 MATH WORKSHOP

Counting and Coins

Briefly review each of the activities and remind students about routines and expectations for Math Workshop. Explain that today will be the last day for Exploring Money and Building Cube Things. Students should finish Exploring Money by the end of Math Workshop as the discussion at the end of the session will focus on it. **TN**

MATH NOTE

MN **Vertical Counting Strips** Writing numbers vertically, rather than horizontally, highlights the patterns that exist in the number sequence.

MATH PRACTICE NOTES

MPN1 **MP6 Attend to precision.** In creating their counting strips, students must attend to a variety of factors, including following the counting sequence and writing numerals legibly.

MPN2 **MP1 Make sense of problems and persevere in solving them.** Students learn that when they don't know something, they can find tools in the classroom or employ other strategies to help them move forward.

MPN3 **MP8 Look for and express regularity in repeated reasoning.** Noticing patterns in the numbers of their counting strip, students become aware of the structure of numbers. Ask students to describe the patterns they see and to explain how they used those patterns to continue counting.

MATH WORDS AND IDEAS

MWI Numbers 0 to 120

TEACHING NOTE

TN **How Long Should Activities Be Available?** Having an activity available for 2–3 days seems to be the right amount of time for Grade 2 students. However, there will be times that your students may benefit from more (or less) time with an activity. You, as the teacher who knows your students best, must make such choices about how to implement this curriculum in your classroom. See *Implementing Investigations in Grade 2*: The Teacher-Student-Curriculum Partnership.

---

3 A   Missing Numbers

Students solve equations and fill in 100 charts with missing numbers on *Student Activity Book* pages 18–23. **MPN**

ONGOING ASSESSMENT   Observing Students at Work

Using patterns in the number sequence, students fill in the answers to addition and subtraction problems, as well as the remaining blanks on a 100 chart.

○ **How do students solve the equations?** Do they "just know" the answers, or do they pause to solve them?

○ **How do students figure out what numbers are missing?** Do they count from 1? From some other number? Do they use the numbers before and after the missing number? Do they use the structure of the 100 chart to help them? (e.g., "I know it's in the 20s because this row goes from 21 to 30," or "I know it ends in 3 because every number in this column ends in 3.") Do they have more than one strategy?

○ **Do students recognize numbers, and are they fluent with the number sequence to 100?**

○ **How accurate and legible are students' written numbers?**

 DIFFERENTIATION   Supporting the Range of Learners

INTERVENTION Adapt the Learning Situation Meet in a small group with students who are challenged by Missing Numbers, to look more closely at the structure of the 100 chart and the patterns on it. Remove a few cards from the top half of the 100 chart, and think together about how to figure out what number is missing.

ENGLISH LANGUAGE LEARNERS Provide Opportunities for Practice Point to a 2-digit number on the 100 chart and ask students to read the number aloud. Ask about the number of tens and the number of ones in the number. Repeat the process for other 2-digit numbers.

3 B   Counting Strips

Students start with zero and write the counting numbers vertically.

STUDENT ACTIVITY BOOK, P. 19

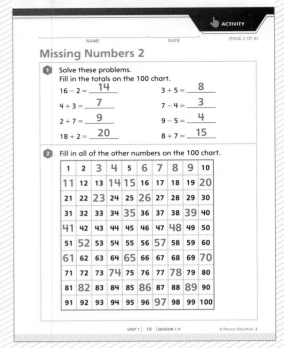

STUDENT ACTIVITY BOOK, P. 20

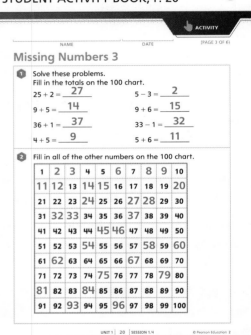

MATH PRACTICE NOTE

MPN **MP7 Look for and make use of structure.** As students begin to solve problems using the 100 chart, the observations they make here will connect to their understanding of the structure of numbers.

ONGOING ASSESSMENT Observing Students at Work

Students practice reading and writing numbers and using patterns in the sequence of numbers to think about what comes next.

- ○ **Are students fluent with the rote counting sequence?** As they read numbers aloud, do they say the right names for numbers?

- ○ **Are students able to make the transition between decades [39, 40, . . ., 49, 50]?** Can students continue counting beyond 100? Do they write these numbers correctly?

- ○ **Do students recognize and use any patterns in the counting sequence?**

- ○ **How accurate and legible are students' written numbers?**

 DIFFERENTIATION Supporting the Range of Learners

INTERVENTION Scaffold a Solution Encourage students who have difficulty finding the name of the next number to read the numbers they have written so far. Sometimes saying the sequence aloud can trigger the name of the next number. If this does not help, ask them how they can use one of the resources in the classroom (e.g., the number line or the 100 chart) to figure out what the next number is.

---

3 C | **Exploring Money**

For complete details about this activity, see Session 1.3.

---

3 D | **Ways to Fill**

For complete details about this activity, see Session 1.2.

 DIFFERENTIATION Supporting the Range of Learners

EXTENSION Adapt the Problem Students ready for more challenge can revisit the outlines on S1–S6 to investigate if each can be filled using only 1 pattern block shape; 2 different shapes; 3 different shapes; etc.

---

3 E | **Building Cube Things**

For complete details about this activity, see Session 1.2.

STUDENT ACTIVITY BOOK, P. 21

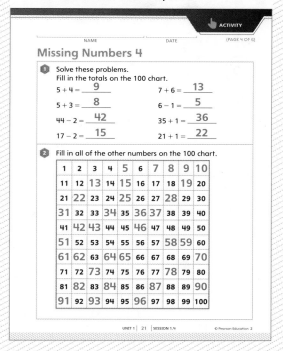

STUDENT ACTIVITY BOOK, P. 22

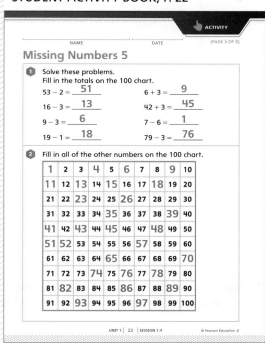

Money

MATH FOCUS POINT FOR DISCUSSION

○ Identifying coins and their values

Display the "Money" chart and collect students' observations about the nickel, dime, quarter, and dollar.

Money

Penny	Nickel	Dime	Quarter	Dollar
• It has a man on it. • It's a different color from the other ones. • It's one cent. • It has words on it. • It has numbers on it. • It is small and a circle.	• It is bigger than a penny. • It has a building on the back. • It costs five cents. • It is shiny. • It has a man on it. • You can buy little things with it.	• It is metal. • It has bumps on the side. • It has words on it. • It has a plant on the back. • It is worth 10 cents. • It has numbers on it.	• It's 25 cents. • It's the biggest one. • It has bumps on the side like the dime.	• It is paper. • It is a rectangle. • It has a man on one side. • There's a pyramid and an eagle on the back. • It has words on it. • It's green.

Daily Practice

 DAILY PRACTICE For reinforcement of this unit's content, students complete *Student Activity Book* page 24.

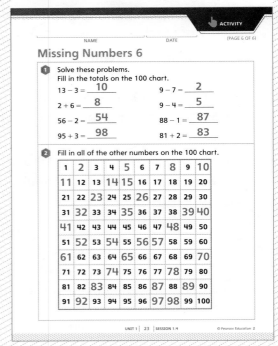

STUDENT ACTIVITY BOOK, P. 24

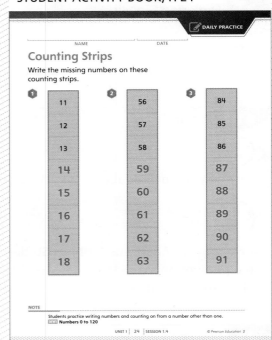

How Many Pennies?

MATH FOCUS POINTS

- Identifying and recognizing coins and the dollar bill and their values
- Counting sets of up to 100 objects
- Counting, writing, and reading numbers to 100 and beyond
- Finding combinations of shapes that fill a region
- Examining equivalencies among the pattern block shapes and the relationship between the size and the number of blocks used to fill a region

VOCABULARY

- cents
- cents sign
- dollar sign

	TODAY'S PLAN	MATERIALS
10 Class	**CLASSROOM ROUTINES: REVIEW AND PRACTICE** *Quick Images: Coins*	 Teacher Presentation (or use enlarged copies of coins from T2)
10 Class	**1 DISCUSSION** **How Many Pennies? How Many Cents?**	T2 (enlarged copies from Session 1.3; optional) Chart: "How Many Pennies?"* Chart: "Money" (completed; from Session 1.4)
10 Class	**2 ACTIVITY** **Introducing *Do We Have 100?***	*Do We Have 100?* (or use C1* and pennies) One set of game materials (from Math Workshop 3A)
30	**3 MATH WORKSHOP** **Counting and Coins** 3A *Do We Have 100?* 3B Missing Numbers 3C Counting Strips 3D Ways to Fill	3A G1* T3* T4* (optional; for the Intervention) Coin Cards (1 deck per pair) Pennies (100 or so per pair) 3B S8–S11* (optional; for the Extension) Materials from Session 1.4 3C Materials from Session 1.4 3D Materials from Sessions 1.2–1.4
10 Class	**4 DISCUSSION** **Ways to Fill**	Teacher Presentation (or use S2 and pattern blocks) *Student Activity Book*, p. 6 (completed; from Math Workshop 3D)
	SESSION FOLLOW-UP: REVIEW AND PRACTICE **Daily Practice**	*Student Activity Book*, p. 25

* See *Materials to Prepare* in the Investigation 1 Planner.

Common Core State Standards	**Classroom Routines:** 2.OA.B.2, Supports 2.MD.C.8 **Session:** 2.NBT.A.2, 2.NBT.A.3, 2.G.A.1, Supports 2.MD.C.8	**Daily Practice:** Supports 2.MD.C.8

CLASSROOM ROUTINES: REVIEW AND PRACTICE

Quick Images: Coins

MATH FOCUS POINTS

○ Developing and analyzing visual images for quantities up to 10

○ Identifying and recognizing coins and their values

Display the Teacher Presentation (or use enlarged copies of the coins from T2) to show a penny, a nickel, and a dime.

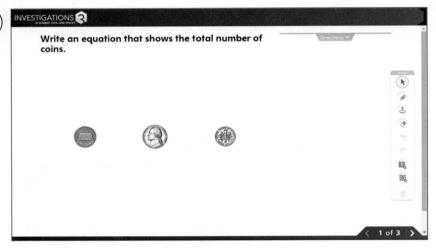

Follow the usual process. **TN**

Ask questions that require students to both identify (e.g., What's the name of this coin?) and recognize (e.g., Which coin is the penny?) the coins.

Next, present an image that shows a nickel, a dime, and a quarter.

Finally, present an image that shows one of each coin.

1 DISCUSSION

How Many Pennies? How Many Cents?

MATH FOCUS POINT FOR DISCUSSION

○ Identifying the name and values of coins and the dollar bill, in cents

We've looked really carefully at different kinds of money over the last couple of days. Today we're going to make a chart that shows the number of pennies each coin and the dollar bill is worth. This chart will be another math tool that you can use when we play games and do activities that involve money. MPN

Display the "How Many Pennies?" chart. Orient students to it and ask them to help you fill it in. Discuss the term *cents* if it is not mentioned, and refer students back to the posted "Money" chart completed in Session 1.4.

[Chen] said that 5 cents means the same thing as 5 pennies and we write it with this symbol (write ¢), called the cents sign. What does that mean about a nickel? . . . Is a nickel the same as 5 pennies? If you go to a store and a piece of gum costs 5 cents, what coins could you pay with?

Discuss the value of each coin and record the information on the chart.

Ask students what they know about the dollar and discuss different ways to talk about a dollar.

Just as each coin is worth a certain number of pennies or cents, we can describe a dollar in similar ways. A dollar is 100 cents or the same as 100 pennies. That's a lot of pennies! I'm just going to write 100 pennies, because it would take me a very long time to draw 100 pennies.

But people also have another symbol that means dollar; it's called a dollar sign. Does anyone know what that symbol looks like?

Talk about students' suggestions and record the different ways to represent a dollar on the chart.

How Many Pennies?			
Name	What does it look like?	How much is it worth?	How many pennies?
Penny	🪙 🪙	1 cent or 1¢	⓵¢
Nickel	🪙 🪙	5 cents or 5¢	1¢ 1¢ 1¢ 1¢ 1¢
Dime	🪙 🪙	10 cents or 10¢	1¢ 1¢ 1¢ 1¢ 1¢ 1¢ 1¢ 1¢ 1¢ 1¢
Quarter	🪙 🪙	25 cents or 25¢	1¢ 1¢ 1¢ 1¢ 1¢ 1¢ 1¢ 1¢ 1¢ 1¢ 1¢ 1¢ 1¢ 1¢ 1¢ 1¢ 1¢ 1¢ 1¢ 1¢ 1¢ 1¢ 1¢ 1¢ 1¢
Dollar	💵 💵	100 cents or 100¢ or one dollar or $1 or $1.00	100 pennies

End by asking students for any challenges or surprises they encountered in looking carefully at the money. (If the following ideas don't come up, ask questions about them.)

 STUDENTS MIGHT SAY ,,

 "The nickel and the quarter are tricky. They look a lot alike."

 "The dime is the smallest, but it's 10!"

 "Yeah, I was surprised that a nickel's bigger than a dime but worth less."

 "I wonder why the penny is the only one that's not silver?"

Encourage students who had similar thoughts to raise their hands and to share strategies for, say, remembering the difference between a nickel and a quarter. Know that many students know a good deal about money names, values, and equivalencies, but some need time to work on these concepts.

---

2 ACTIVITY

Introducing *Do We Have 100?*

Display the Game Presentation (or use Coin Cards (C1) and pennies) to introduce *Do We Have 100?*

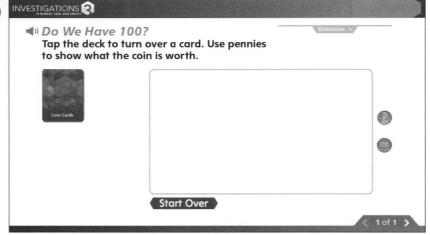

RESOURCE MASTERS, C1

CARDS

NAME   DATE

Coin Cards

C1   © Pearson Education 2

Explain that pairs work together to get 100 pennies. They take turns flipping over Coin Cards and counting the correct number of pennies. Ask a volunteer to be your partner in a sample game.

In this game, partners take turns flipping over a Coin Card. They identify the coin on the card, and then take however many pennies that coin is worth.

Turn over the top card.

What coin is on our card? (nickel) How many pennies should I take? (5)

Remind students that the "How Many Pennies?" chart is available as a reference. **MWI1**

Count out the set of pennies, and then ask your partner to flip over the next card.

[Esteban], what coin is on your card? (quarter) How many pennies should you take to make a quarter? (25)

Have [Esteban] take 25 pennies.

I took 5 pennies, and [Esteban] took 25 pennies. Now we have a lot of pennies! We need to figure out a way to organize our pennies so that they are easy to count and so that we can keep track of how many pennies we have so that we know when we get 100. What are some ways we could keep track of the pennies we've collected?

STUDENTS MIGHT SAY

"Push them together and count them."

"I'd keep them separate. You know that's 25 and then count 5 more."

"Make groups of 10. Those are easy to count."

[Henry] suggested making groups of 10. I could also use groups of 5 pennies or make a pile for each card, like [Tia] said. **MWI2**

Explain that partners need to agree on how to organize their pennies and that, for this game, you and your partner will use piles of 10. Use this as an opportunity to model making and counting by groups of 10 and to have students count along with you.

Play a few more rounds, until students understand the game. Reiterate that the game is over when pairs have accumulated 100 pennies.

RESOURCE MASTERS, T3

RESOURCE MASTERS, G1

MATH WORDS AND IDEAS

MWI1 Money

MWI2 Counting by Groups

3 MATH WORKSHOP

Counting and Coins

 30

Briefly review each of the activities and remind students about routines and expectations for Math Workshop. Explain that today will be the last day for Ways to Fill.

---

3 A *Do We Have 100?*

Pairs take turns flipping over a Coin Card, identifying the coin, and counting the appropriate number of pennies until they reach 100. They need a deck of Coin Cards, approximately 100 pennies, and a copy of How Many Pennies? (T3). The directions are available on G1.

ONGOING ASSESSMENT Observing Students at Work

○ **How do students know how many pennies they need?** Do they recognize the coin on the card? Do they know how many pennies are equivalent to that coin? If they don't, can they use the "How Many Pennies?" chart appropriately?

○ **How accurate are students in their counting?** Do they know the sequence? Do they count each penny once and only once? Do they count by 1s or groups? **PD**

○ **How do students keep track of how many pennies they have?** Do they count them all from 1 after each addition? Do they use groups? Of what size? How do they find the total of the groups of coins?

 DIFFERENTIATION Supporting the Range of Learners

INTERVENTION **Scaffold a Solution** Play in a small group with students who are still developing fluency with the coins and their values. Work together, thinking about how to use How Many Pennies? (T3) or *Math Words and Ideas*, Money, as a resource while playing this game.

INTERVENTION **Adapt the Problem** Students who struggle to count a set of pennies accurately or who have to recount the total after each turn, beginning with 1, need immediate attention focused on counting skills. These students may benefit from playing *Do We have 50?* and using Ten Frames (T4) to organize groups of 10. **MN**

INTERVENTION **Suggest a Tool** Some students count amounts accurately by 1s, but may not have a reliable way of organizing and keeping track of a growing group. Suggest that they put their pennies in groups of 10. (They could use a Ten Frame (T4), making a group of 10 pennies once the Ten Frame is full.) Help students think about how to figure out how many pennies they have so far, modeling counting by 10s and practicing it together. (Some may be better able to make sense of counting by 10s if all of the pennies are placed on multiple Ten Frames.)

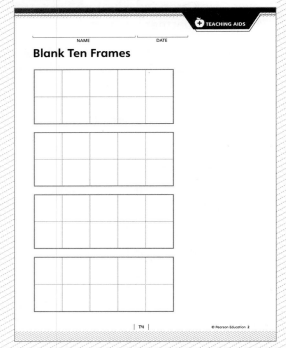

TEACHING AIDS

NAME   DATE

Blank Ten Frames

T4   © Pearson Education 2

PROFESSIONAL DEVELOPMENT

PD TEACHER NOTE 3: Counting by Groups

MATH NOTE

MN **Ten Frames** The Ten Frame is a 2×5 array of squares, which is filled left to right, top row first. This tool can help students organize a quantity to be counted and also supports counting on. The Primary Number Cards also use a Ten Frame arrangement to represent the numbers to 10. Together these tools help students build mental images of numbers that are based on their relationship to 5 and 10. For example a student might see the image below as "5 and 3 more; that's 8" while another sees "10, but with 2 empty squares, so it's 8."

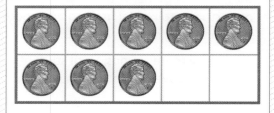

Similarly, two (or more) Ten Frames offer a model of a 2-digit number being composed of one (or more) ten(s) plus some number of ones.

ENGLISH LANGUAGE LEARNERS **Provide Vocabulary Support** Before pairs play *Do We Have 100?*, meet with students in a small-group setting to review the game directions and the coins and their values. Review the terms *cents sign* and *dollar sign*. Explain that *worth* means "equal to." Provide a sentence stem for students to complete as they play the game: *My ___ [coin name] is worth ___ pennies.*

---

3 B **Missing Numbers**

For complete details about this activity, see Session 1.4.

 DIFFERENTIATION Supporting the Range of Learners

EXTENSION **Adapt the Problem** Students who have accurately completed the 100 charts on *Student Activity Book* pages 18–23 can work on Missing Numbers: 101–200 (S8–S11).

---

3 C **Counting Strips**

For complete details about this activity, see Session 1.4. **MWI**

---

3 D **Ways to Fill**

For complete details about this activity, see Sessions 1.2.–1.4.

---

4 DISCUSSION

Ways to Fill

MATH FOCUS POINT FOR DISCUSSION

○ Finding combinations of shapes that fill a region

Gather students to discuss different ways to fill Shape B. They should have access to pattern blocks and their completed copies of *Student Activity Book* page 6.

RESOURCE MASTERS, S8

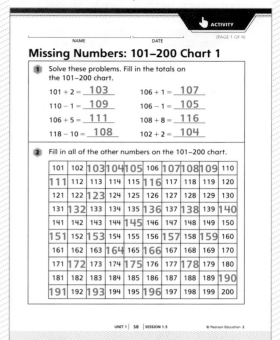

ACTIVITY (PAGE 1 OF 4)

NAME   DATE

Missing Numbers: 101–200 Chart 1

1 Solve these problems. Fill in the totals on the 101–200 chart.

$101 + 2 = $ __103__ $106 + 1 = $ __107__
$110 - 1 = $ __109__ $106 - 1 = $ __105__
$106 + 5 = $ __111__ $108 + 8 = $ __116__
$118 - 10 = $ __108__ $102 + 2 = $ __104__

2 Fill in all of the other numbers on the 101–200 chart.

101	102	103	104	105	106	107	108	109	110
111	112	113	114	115	116	117	118	119	120
121	122	123	124	125	126	127	128	129	130
131	132	133	134	135	136	137	138	139	140
141	142	143	144	145	146	147	148	149	150
151	152	153	154	155	156	157	158	159	160
161	162	163	164	165	166	167	168	169	170
171	172	173	174	175	176	177	178	179	180
181	182	183	184	185	186	187	188	189	190
191	192	193	194	195	196	197	198	199	200

UNIT 1 | S8 | SESSION 1.5   © Pearson Education 2

RESOURCE MASTERS, S9

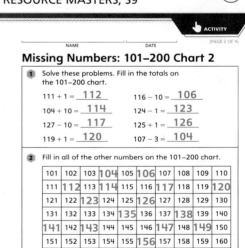

ACTIVITY (PAGE 2 OF 4)

NAME   DATE

Missing Numbers: 101–200 Chart 2

1 Solve these problems. Fill in the totals on the 101–200 chart.

$111 + 1 = $ __112__ $116 - 10 = $ __106__
$104 + 10 = $ __114__ $124 - 1 = $ __123__
$127 - 10 = $ __117__ $125 + 1 = $ __126__
$119 + 1 = $ __120__ $107 - 3 = $ __104__

2 Fill in all of the other numbers on the 101–200 chart.

101	102	103	104	105	106	107	108	109	110
111	112	113	114	115	116	117	118	119	120
121	122	123	124	125	126	127	128	129	130
131	132	133	134	135	136	137	138	139	140
141	142	143	144	145	146	147	148	149	150
151	152	153	154	155	156	157	158	159	160
161	162	163	164	165	166	167	168	169	170
171	172	173	174	175	176	177	178	179	180
181	182	183	184	185	186	187	188	189	190
191	192	193	194	195	196	197	198	199	200

UNIT 1 | S9 | SESSION 1.5   © Pearson Education 2

MATH WORDS AND IDEAS

MWI Numbers 0 to 120

Display the Teacher Presentation (or use S2 and pattern blocks) to collect data about which pattern blocks students used to fill in Shape B.

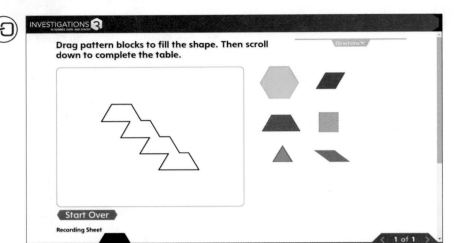

Did anyone use only one kind of pattern block to fill Shape B?

STUDENTS MIGHT SAY

 "I used all red trapezoids."

 "Instead of trapezoids I used triangles."

 "I used the blue rhombuses *and* triangles."

Ask students to help you record the data for solutions that used only one block.

[Amaya] used only trapezoids, and [Nadia] used only triangles. Why are these the two shapes that work? **MPN**

STUDENTS MIGHT SAY

 "I took three triangles and made a trapezoid, so it's the same. See like this [covers one trapezoid with three triangles]. You can tell because they're exactly stacked."

 "If you can do it with trapezoids, you can do it with triangles. Because you can always replace one trapezoid with three triangles."

RESOURCE MASTERS, S10

ACTIVITY
(PAGE 3 OF 4)

NAME _____ DATE _____

Missing Numbers: 101–200 Chart 3

1 Solve these problems. Fill in the totals on the 101–200 chart.

136 − 10 = __126__   105 + 10 = __115__
122 + 2 = __124__   128 − 5 = __123__
102 + 4 = __106__   132 − 10 = __122__
140 − 1 = __139__   101 + 10 = __111__

2 Fill in all of the other numbers on the 101–200 chart.

101	102	103	104	105	106	107	108	109	110
111	112	113	114	115	116	117	118	119	120
121	122	123	124	125	126	127	128	129	130
131	132	133	134	135	136	137	138	139	140
141	142	143	144	145	146	147	148	149	150
151	152	153	154	155	156	157	158	159	160
161	162	163	164	165	166	167	168	169	170
171	172	173	174	175	176	177	178	179	180
181	182	183	184	185	186	187	188	189	190
191	192	193	194	195	196	197	198	199	200

UNIT 1 | S10 | SESSION 1.5   © Pearson Education 2

RESOURCE MASTERS, S11

ACTIVITY
(PAGE 4 OF 4)

NAME _____ DATE _____

Missing Numbers: 101–200 Chart 4

1 Solve these problems. Fill in the totals on the 101–200 chart.

126 − 3 = __123__   117 + 2 = __119__
172 + 4 = __176__   159 − 3 = __156__
161 − 10 = __151__   144 + 3 = __147__
192 + 7 = __199__   197 − 6 = __191__

2 Fill in all of the other numbers on the 101–200 chart.

101	102	103	104	105	106	107	108	109	110
111	112	113	114	115	116	117	118	119	120
121	122	123	124	125	126	127	128	129	130
131	132	133	134	135	136	137	138	139	140
141	142	143	144	145	146	147	148	149	150
151	152	153	154	155	156	157	158	159	160
161	162	163	164	165	166	167	168	169	170
171	172	173	174	175	176	177	178	179	180
181	182	183	184	185	186	187	188	189	190
191	192	193	194	195	196	197	198	199	200

UNIT 1 | S11 | SESSION 1.5   © Pearson Education 2

MATH PRACTICE NOTE

MPN **MP3 Construct viable arguments and critique the reasoning of others.** Students offer mathematical arguments to explain why it's true that if a shape can be filled with trapezoids, it can also be filled with triangles.

Once students are convinced that both ways work, ask what they notice about the number of each block it took to fill Shape B. Many notice that it takes more triangles to cover the shape than it does trapezoids. Some may explain that larger shapes take up more room and so you need fewer blocks, and vice versa. Encourage students to try to articulate such generalizations. **MPN**

Then, discuss and record some of the other ways students found to fill Shape B.

[Travis], you said you used triangles and rhombuses. Can you show us?

While you were working, I heard lots of interesting strategies about how to come up with different ways to fill the shape. Can anyone look at [Travis]'s solution and think of a way to turn it into a different solution?

 STUDENTS MIGHT SAY

 "Change just the top one to be one whole trapezoid."

 "Or the second one!"

 "You could change it to 3 triangles instead and leave the rest!"

Such discussions will highlight how fluent students are with the pattern blocks and the equivalencies among them.

SESSION FOLLOW-UP: REVIEW AND PRACTICE

Daily Practice

✏️ **DAILY PRACTICE** For reinforcement of this unit's contents, students complete *Student Activity Book* page 25.

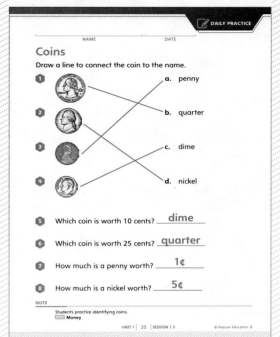

DAILY PRACTICE

NAME   DATE

Coins

Draw a line to connect the coin to the name.

1   a. penny
2   b. quarter
3   c. dime
4   d. nickel

5   Which coin is worth 10 cents? __dime__
6   Which coin is worth 25 cents? __quarter__
7   How much is a penny worth? __1¢__
8   How much is a nickel worth? __5¢__

NOTE
Students practice identifying coins.
MPN Money

UNIT 1 | 25 | SESSION 1.5   © Pearson Education 2

MATH PRACTICE NOTE

MPN 🔍 **MP8 Look for and express regularity in repeated reasoning.** When students notice a pattern—for example, it takes fewer large pieces than small pieces to cover a shape—encourage them to state the generalization. Once mathematicians state such a claim, their next questions are, Is this always true? and How do you know?

Telling Time

MATH FOCUS POINTS

- o Counting sets of up to 100 objects
- o Identifying and using patterns in the number sequence to count, read, and write numbers to 100 and beyond
- o Identifying and recognizing coins and their values
- o Naming, notating, and telling time to the hour using analog and digital formats

VOCABULARY

- o analog clock
- o small hand
- o hour
- o digital clock
- o hour hand
- o big hand
- o o'clock
- o minute hand

TODAY'S PLAN	MATERIALS
⏱ 10 · 🧑‍🏫 Class **CLASSROOM ROUTINES: REVIEW AND PRACTICE** ***Today's Number: 12***	📲 Teacher Presentation (or use cubes and a number line)
⏱ 15 · 🧑‍🏫 Class · 👥 Pairs **1 DISCUSSION** **Strategies for Counting Accurately**	Chart: "How We Count"* Connecting cubes (50) Partial counting strips*

⏱ 30
2 MATH WORKSHOP
Counting and Coins
  2A *Do We Have 100?*
  2B Missing Numbers
  2C Counting Strips
	2A Materials from Session 1.5
	📄 **2B** G2* (optional; for the Extension)
	🔧📄 T5* (optional; for the Extension)
	  Materials from Session 1.4
	2C Materials from Session 1.4

⏱ 15 · 🧑‍🏫 Class · 👥 Pairs **3 ACTIVITY** **Introducing the Time Routine**	📲 Teacher Presentation (or use a demonstration analog clock and a digital clock) 📄 T6* 🔧 Student clocks (1 per pair) Charts: "Analog Clock" and "Digital Clock"*
SESSION FOLLOW-UP: REVIEW AND PRACTICE **Daily Practice**	📖 *Student Activity Book*, p. 26

* See *Materials to Prepare* in the Investigation 1 Planner.

Common Core State Standards	**Classroom Routines:** 2.OA.B.2, 2.MD.B.6 **Session:** 2.NBT.A.2, 2.NBT.A.3, Supports 2.MD.C.7	**Daily Practice:** 2.NBT.A.2, 2.NBT.A.3

CLASSROOM ROUTINES: REVIEW AND PRACTICE

Today's Number: 12

MATH FOCUS POINTS

○ Generating equivalent expressions for a number

○ Using standard notation (+, −, =) to record expressions or equations

Display the Teacher Presentation (or use cubes and a number line).

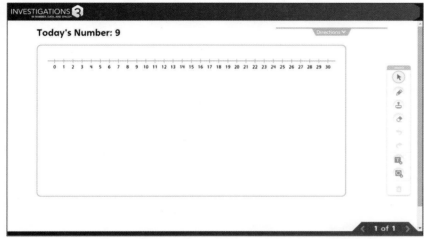

Explain that Today's Number is 12, and ask students to help you find it on the number line and write the number word (i.e., twelve). As a class, students generate addition and/or subtraction expressions that equal 12. Record the expressions, encouraging students to explain how they know they equal 12.

---

1 DISCUSSION

Strategies for Counting Accurately

MATH FOCUS POINTS FOR DISCUSSION

○ Developing strategies for accurately counting sets of up to 100 objects

○ Identifying and using patterns in the number sequence to count, read, and write numbers to 100 and beyond

Introduce this discussion by asking students why it is important to count carefully. Also ask about times when accurate counting is especially important.

Over the last week, you've been counting pattern blocks, connecting cubes, and pennies. I'm going to count out 50 cubes. As I do, watch carefully. When I am finished, I want you to describe the things I am doing as I count.

Count out 50 connecting cubes, one at a time, as the class observes. Touch each cube as you say the number and move the counted cube into a separate group. Model double-checking your work by recounting the pile of cubes.

Talk for a minute with someone next to you about what you noticed as I was counting the cubes. . . . What did people notice about the way I counted the cubes?

Record students' comments to post as a reference. MPN

HOW WE COUNT

Say one number for each connecting cube.

Keep track of what you have counted by touching and moving each cube.

You can also count by putting the objects into groups or rows.

The last number you say tells you the number of cubes in the group.

Double-check when you are finished.

Another way you've been counting is by writing the numbers on your counting strips.

Post a partial counting strip that shows a common second grade error such as the transition to 3-digit numbers or writing the number that comes after 109. PD MN

90	90	95	100
91	91	96	101
92	92	97	102
93	93	98	103
94	94	99	104
95	95	100	105
96	96	101	106
97	97	102	107
98	98	103	108
99	99	104	109
100	100	105	1010
1001	200	106	
1002	300	107	
1003	400	108	
1004	500	109	
1005		200	

MATH PRACTICE NOTE

MPN **MP6 Attend to precision.** Students identify strategies that help them attend to precision as they count.

PROFESSIONAL DEVELOPMENT

PD DIALOGUE BOX 2: What Comes After 109?

MATH NOTE

MN **Writing Numbers in the 100s** Much of students' experience with numbers in the 100s has been with counting orally. Learning to write numbers in the 100s and greater takes time. As students become more familiar with how numbers are composed, they will become fluent with the written numbers above 100 and beyond.

Ask students whether they can figure out what part of your counting strip is incorrect. Discuss what is wrong, how they know, and how they could fix it. Focus the discussion on why someone might have made the errors. MPN

Leave your strip posted. Encourage students to look at their work during Math Workshop to see whether they would like to make any changes based on the discussion.

2 MATH WORKSHOP

Counting and Coins

 30

Briefly review each of the activities and remind students about routines and expectations for Math Workshop. Explain that today will be the last day for each of these activities.

2 A *Do We Have 100?*

For complete details about this game, see Session 1.5. TN

 DIFFERENTIATION Supporting the Range of Learners

EXTENSION Adapt the Problem Students who are easily able to identify coins and count out the correct number of pennies can be challenged to flip over two cards at once.

ENGLISH LANGUAGE LEARNERS Repeat and Clarify Observe students as they count the pennies, and then describe their process to them. For example, you might say: **When you counted the pennies, you touched each penny. Then you moved the penny to the side.**

2 B Missing Numbers

For complete details about this activity, see Session 1.4.

 DIFFERENTIATION Supporting the Range of Learners

EXTENSION Extend Thinking Pairs play *Guess My Number* on the 100 chart (T5). Players take turns writing a secret number on a scrap of paper and asking questions to determine the secret number. The directions are available on G2.

2 C Counting Strips

For complete details about this activity, see Session 1.4.

RESOURCE MASTERS, T5

⊕ TEACHING AIDS

NAME _____ DATE _____

100 Chart

1	2	3	4	5	6	7	8	9	10
11	12	13	14	15	16	17	18	19	20
21	22	23	24	25	26	27	28	29	30
31	32	33	34	35	36	37	38	39	40
41	42	43	44	45	46	47	48	49	50
51	52	53	54	55	56	57	58	59	60
61	62	63	64	65	66	67	68	69	70
71	72	73	74	75	76	77	78	79	80
81	82	83	84	85	86	87	88	89	90
91	92	93	94	95	96	97	98	99	100

| T5 | © Pearson Education 2

MATH PRACTICE NOTE

MPN **MP3 Construct viable arguments and critique the reasoning of others.** As students identify errors in the counting strips and consider why someone might have made those errors, they are critiquing others' reasoning. When they refer to the patterns they have noticed to explain which number is incorrect, they are using the structure of numbers to make their argument.

TEACHING NOTE

TN **The Importance of Games** Games engage students in many ways, but it is only through the repeated experience of playing a game that students begin to grasp some of the important ideas and skills embodied in the game. Games also offer repeated practice with skills such as developing fluency in using the addition combinations.

3 ACTIVITY

Introducing the Time Routine

What Time Is It? is another of the yearlong Grade 2 Classroom Routines. This brief introduction reviews types of clocks and telling time to the hour.
PD1 **PD2** **TN1**

Display the Teacher Presentation (or use a demonstration analog clock and a digital clock). **MWI**

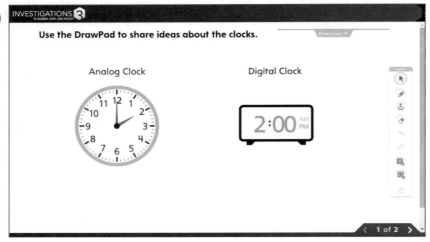

> One of the things we'll be working on this year is telling time. Let's start by looking at two different types of clocks.

Introduce the names of the clocks if no one mentions them. Explain that each tells you the hour and the minutes.

> **What do you notice about the analog clock? The digital clock? What is the same about these clocks? What is different?**

Record students' observations on the prepared "Digital Clock" and "Analog Clock" charts.

Next, distribute an analog student clock to each pair and give partners a minute or so to explore them. **TN2**

> Let's take a closer look at an analog clock. Let's list the different parts.

The class compares an analog clock to a digital clock and discusses the parts of an analog clock.

PROFESSIONAL DEVELOPMENT

PD **Part 4: Classroom Routines** in *Implementing Investigations in Grade 2: What Time Is It?*

PD **TEACHER NOTE 5:** Understanding and Learning to Tell Time

TEACHING NOTES

TN1 **Telling Time** Grade 1 students ended the year telling time to the half hour. Grade 2 students begin the year reviewing telling time to the hour and half hour and end the year telling time to the nearest 5 minutes. Telling time to the minute is a Grade 3 benchmark.

TN2 **Storing Clocks** Since students will be using these clocks throughout the year, think about how to provide easy access to them. Students might keep them in their desks or cubbies or, if you do Classroom Routines in a meeting area, you can store them there.

MATH WORDS AND IDEAS

MWI Clocks

Ask how the parts of the analog clock help you know what time it is.

STUDENTS MIGHT SAY

"The numbers on the clock tell you what hour it is, and the little lines tell you how many minutes."

"The little hand tells the hour, and the big hand tells the minutes."

For the next few days, we are going to focus on telling time to the hour. The big hand of the clock will be on the 12. That hand is called the minute hand. The small hand of the clock will tell what hour it is. That hand is called the hour hand.

Set the demonstration clock to show 4:00. Point out the position of the hands and review the way people refer to what time it is.

When you read this clock you say, "It's 4 o'clock." Some people call this an "on the hour time" or an "o'clock time." When you read the clock you say, "It's 2 o'clock" or "It's 5 o'clock." Let's see whether everyone can set their clocks so that they read 3 o'clock.

Remind students that the small hand points to the hour. Ask a pair who has set the clock correctly to show the setting on the demonstration clock.

Ask a volunteer to record 3 o'clock in digital format. Review how the two ways of showing 3:00 are related.

Repeat with 5 o'clock and 9 o'clock.

SESSION FOLLOW-UP: REVIEW AND PRACTICE

Daily Practice

 DAILY PRACTICE For reinforcement of this unit's content, students complete *Student Activity Book* page 26.

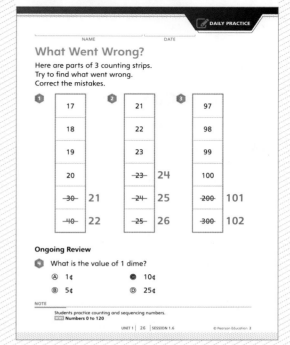

DAILY PRACTICE

NAME _____ DATE _____

What Went Wrong?
Here are parts of 3 counting strips.
Try to find what went wrong.
Correct the mistakes.

①	②	③
17	21	97
18	22	98
19	23	99
20	~~23~~ 24	100
~~30~~ 21	~~24~~ 25	~~200~~ 101
~~40~~ 22	~~25~~ 26	~~300~~ 102

Ongoing Review

④ What is the value of 1 dime?

Ⓐ 1¢   ● 10¢

Ⓑ 5¢   Ⓓ 25¢

NOTE
Students practice counting and sequencing numbers.
Numbers 0 to 120

UNIT 1 | 26 | SESSION 1.6   © Pearson Education 2

Strategies for Counting

MATH FOCUS POINT

○ Counting sets of up to 60 objects

MATERIALS: connecting cubes (60 per student); 5 index cards labeled with the numbers 25, 32, 40, 51, 60 (1 set per pair); class number line; T4 (2 copies per pair)

Extend the Building Cube Things activity (Session 1.2) by having students use Blank Ten Frames (T4) to organize and then count several sets of cubes. It is important to identify the baseline amount that students can count accurately and build from there.

Distribute a copy of T4 and at least 60 cubes to each student and a set of numbered index cards to each pair of students.

Ask students to find the card with the number 25. **Let's find 25 on our class number line.** Ask a volunteer to mark 25 on the class number line. If students have difficulty, have them begin at 1 and count up to 25.

Today you and a partner are going to count out several sets of cubes. You will organize your cubes on these Ten Frames. Place one cube in each square of a Ten Frame, and count out 25 cubes for your partner. When you think you have 25, your partner will double-check your work.

Once students have finished assembling their set of 25 cubes and double-checking their partner's set, ask them to share strategies for counting 25 cubes.

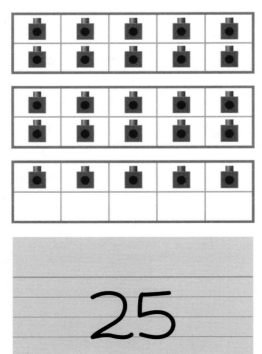

"I counted every cube."

"I could see that there are 10 cubes in every full Ten Frame, so I counted 10, 20. Then I counted the other extra cubes—21, 22, 23, 24, 25."

Discuss how the Ten Frame is a helpful tool for organizing and keeping track while counting a set of objects. Because the Ten Frame organizes cubes into groups of 5 and 10, it may help students to see these subsets and use them to count.

Repeat with a new number card, adjusting the amount for each student depending on his or her accuracy. Students use the Ten Frames to count out a set with that many cubes and then switch sets with their partner.

After pairs have counted at least three sets, they can choose one set of their cubes to build a Cube Thing.

DIFFERENTIATION

ENGLISH LANGUAGE LEARNERS **Repeat and Clarify** Help students understand what it means to "double-check" another student's work by providing an example for students, using the term *double-check*. **After you and your partner count out the 25 cubes, trade piles of cubes and count them again. This is a way to *double-check* that you each have 25. If you *double-check* each other's work, you can make sure your answers are correct.**

ADDITIONAL RESOURCES

Math Words and Ideas Why Do We Count?; Ways to Count

Cube Buildings

MATH FOCUS POINT

○ Counting sets of up to 60 objects

MATERIALS: connecting cubes, S12

RESOURCE MASTERS, S12

ACTIVITY

NAME   DATE

Cube Buildings

Make Cube Buildings using the following number of cubes.

1. 10 red cubes
   10 brown cubes
   15 green cubes
   20 yellow cubes

   How many cubes will you use in all? __55__

2. 20 white cubes
   30 orange cubes
   15 black cubes
   5 blue cubes

   How many cubes will you use in all? __70__

3. Decide how many cubes you will use for your
   Cube Building. Answers will vary.

   _____ red cubes

   _____ blue cubes

   _____ green cubes

   _____ yellow cubes

   How many cubes will you use
   in all? _____

UNIT 1 | S12 | INVESTIGATION 1   © Pearson Education 2

This activity gives students additional practice counting larger sets of objects using a specified number of objects.

Today you will build a Cube Building using a list that tells how many of each color cube to use.

Distribute a copy of Cube Buildings (S12) to each student. Display the list for the first Cube Building.

> **10 red cubes**
>
> **10 brown cubes**
>
> **15 green cubes**
>
> **20 yellow cubes**

First count out the number of cubes for each color. Then, determine how many cubes you will use in all. How many cubes will you use in all for the first Cube Building? Have students share strategies for counting the total number of cubes.

" **STUDENTS MIGHT SAY** "

"I know that 10 and 10 is 20, so there are 20 reds and browns. Then I would count 21, 22, 23, 24, . . . until all of the cubes were counted."

"I would start with the 20 yellows and then count the reds and then the browns. When I count I would keep them in their color piles and move each pile after I counted it."

Each student should count out the specified number of cubes and determine the total number of cubes. Then have them make a Cube Building.

After students have created their Cube Buildings, have them find a partner and discuss the following questions. **How are your Cube Buildings the same? How are they different?** Students should realize that both Cube Buildings have the same number of cubes (of each color and total) even if their designs are different.

Then have partners take turns explaining how they know their Cube Buildings have the correct number of cubes.

DIFFERENTIATION

ENGLISH LANGUAGE LEARNERS Provide Vocabulary Support
Some students may be unfamiliar with color names in English. Help them create a color code before beginning this activity by drawing and labeling a red, brown, green, yellow, white, orange, black, and blue cube.

ADDITIONAL RESOURCES

Math Words and Ideas Why Do We Count?; Ways to Count

Cube Building Riddles

MATH FOCUS POINT

○ Counting sets of up to 60 objects

MATERIALS: connecting cubes, S13–S14

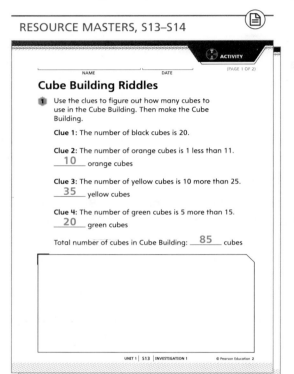

RESOURCE MASTERS, S13–S14

Write the following clues on the board.

Clues

1. **The number of red cubes is 10.**

2. **The number of green cubes is 5 more than the number of red cubes.**

3. **The number of brown cubes is 1 more than 14.**

4. **The number of white cubes is 10 more than the number of red cubes plus green cubes.**

Just as we used number clues to play *Guess My Number*, we can also use number clues to determine the number of cubes you will need to make a Cube Building.

Present each clue and discuss strategies for finding the correct number of cubes for each color. **Clue 1 tells us that there are 10 red cubes. Clue 2 says, "The number of green**

cubes is 5 more than the number of red cubes." How many green cubes will there be? (15) How do you know?

Clue 3 tells us that the number of brown cubes is 1 more than 14. How many brown cubes will there be? (15) How do you know? Clue 4 says, "The number of white cubes is 10 more than the number of red cubes plus green cubes." How many white cubes will there be? (35) How do you know?

〝 STUDENTS MIGHT SAY 〟

"I know that red and green together is 25, and 10 more is the number of white cubes. 25 plus 10 would be 35. There are 35 white cubes."

"I knew that 10 plus 15 was 25 too. And 35 is 10 more than 25. You can see that on the 100 chart. You need 35 white cubes."

After each clue has been discussed, record the number of each color cube on the board.

Then, discuss strategies for determining the total number of cubes.

Distribute copies of Cube Building Riddles (S13–S14).

After you figure out each clue, take that number of cubes. Then figure out the total number of cubes in your Cube Building. Record your strategy on your Cube Building Riddles page.

DIFFERENTIATION

ENGLISH LANGUAGE LEARNERS Repeat and Clarify Reread the clues with students, breaking them down into just the necessary information. For example: Clue 1: Red cubes = 10. Clue 2: Green cubes = 10 red cubes + 5 = 15. Continue until you have recorded all four clues and helped students figure out the number of colored cubes for each clue. Do this again for a second problem, helping students break down the clues, but this time have students record the clues.

ADDITIONAL RESOURCES

Math Words and Ideas Ways to Count; 100 Chart ⓂⓌⒾ

INVESTIGATION 2

DOES ORDER MATTER?

Main Math Ideas

○ Fluency within 20

○ Understanding, representing, and solving problems involving addition and subtraction

Does Order Matter?

	SESSION 2.1	SESSION 2.2
	REVISITING TODAY'S NUMBER Students play *Guess My Number* on the number line to determine Today's Number. They generate and discuss equivalent expressions for the number 7.	**FIVE-IN-A-ROW WITH FOUR CARDS** Students learn, play, and discuss *Five-in-a-Row with Four Cards.* Players turn over four Primary Number Cards and can cover the sum of any two on their gameboard. The goal is to cover five numbers in a row. Discussion focuses on strategies for adding.
Professional Development	**TEACHER NOTES 1, 6** **DIALOGUE BOX 1**	**TEACHER NOTE 7** **DIALOGUE BOX 3**
Materials to View Ahead of Time	**TEACHER PRESENTATIONS:** 🎬 **Classroom Routine** *What Time Is It?* 🎬 **Activity** Revisiting *Today's Number* 🎬 **Discussion** *Today's Number* 🔵 DIFFERENTIATION: ENGLISH LANGUAGE LEARNERS See **Differentiation in This Unit** for session content to preview with students.	**TEACHER PRESENTATIONS:** 🎬 **Classroom Routine** *Today's Number: 10* 🎬 **Activity** Introducing *Five-in-a-Row with Four Cards*
Materials to Gather	🔧 **Demonstration clock** (optional) 🔧 **Student clocks** (1 per pair) **2 large clothespins or clips** **Scrap paper** 🔧 **Connecting cubes** (10 per student) **Number line** **Pocket 100 chart**	🔧 **Connecting cubes** (optional) **Counters** (about 20 per pair)
Materials to Prepare		📄 **C2–C5, Primary Number Cards** Make copies and cut apart. (1 deck without Wild Cards, optional; 1 deck per pair, without Wild Cards) 📄 **G3–G5, *Five-in-a-Row with Four Cards* Gameboards A–C** Make copies, ideally on cardstock, and laminate. (1 per pair) 📄 **G6, *Five-in-a-Row with Four Cards* Directions** Make copies. **Chart: "Strategies for Adding"** Title a piece of chart paper "Strategies for Adding."
Common Core State Standards	**Classroom Routines:** Supports 2.MD.C.7 **Session:** 2.OA.B.2, 2.MD.B.6 **Daily Practice:** Supports 2.MD.C.7	**Classroom Routines:** 2.OA.B.2, 2.MD.B.6 **Session:** 2.OA.B.2, 2.NBT.B.9, 2.MD.B.6 **Daily Practice:** 2.OA.B.2

Present | Videos | Tools | Games | Assessment | MWI | Portfolio | eText | PDF

	SESSION 2.3	**SESSION 2.4**
	DOES ORDER MATTER? The class solves a story problem about combining three quantities. Math Workshop and class discussion focus on whether order matters in addition and on using familiar number combinations to solve problems with multiple addends.	**HOW MANY POCKETS?** Students are introduced to *How Many Pockets?*, another of the year-long Classroom Routines that involves estimating, counting, comparing, and combining large amounts in the course of collecting, representing, and interpreting data. Math Workshop focuses on adding single-digit numbers. The session ends with a brief assessment focused on coins and their values.
Professional Development	**TEACHER NOTE 6** **DIALOGUE BOX 4**	**Part 4: Classroom Routines** in *Implementing Investigations in Grade 2:* How Many Pockets?
Materials to View Ahead of Time	**TEACHER PRESENTATIONS:** **Classroom Routine** *Quick Images: Coins* **Activity** Introducing Problems with Multiple Addends **Discussion** Does Order Matter?	**TEACHER PRESENTATION:** **Classroom Routine** *Today's Number: 25*
Materials to Gather	**Enlarged copies of T2** (from Session 1.3; optional) **Connecting cubes** (green, blue, yellow, and purple) **Materials for *Five-in-a-Row with Four Cards*** (from Session 2.2)	**Number line** (optional) **Connecting cubes** (100) **Large, clear plastic jar** **Masking tape or rubber band** **Materials for Problems about Combining Three Groups** (from Session 2.3) **Materials for Number Strings** (from Session 2.3) **Materials for *Five-in-a-Row with Four Cards*** (from Session 2.2)
Materials to Prepare	**A1, Assessment Checklist: MP8, Look for and express regularity in repeated reasoning** Make copies. (as needed) **Chart Paper** Write the following problem: "Jake is building with cubes. He has a tower of 2 green cubes, a tower of 5 blue cubes, and a tower of 3 yellow cubes. How many cubes does he have?" (optional)	**A2, Quiz 1** Make copies. **Chart: "How many pockets are we wearing today?"** Title a piece of chart paper "How many pockets are we wearing today?" Draw a table with three columns. Label the second column "Pockets" and the third column "People."
Common Core State Standards	**Classroom Routines:** 2.OA.B.2, Supports 2.MD.C.8 **Session:** 2.OA.A.1, 2.OA.B.2, 2.NBT.B.9 **Daily Practice:** 2.OA.B.2	**Classroom Routines:** 2.OA.B.2, 2.NBT.B.5, 2.MD.B.6 **Session:** 2.OA.A.1, 2.OA.B.2, 2.NBT.A.2, Supports 2.MD.C.8 **Daily Practice:** Supports 2.NBT.B.5

Does Order Matter?

	SESSION 2.5	**SESSION 2.6**
	ADDITION FACTS Students are introduced to Fact Cards, a tool they will use over the course of the year to become fluent with addition and subtraction within 20. They begin with a set of mostly familiar addition facts, thinking about categories of problems (e.g., Doubles, Plus 1, Plus 2, Make 10) and sorting them into envelopes of "Facts I Know" and "Facts I Am Still Working On."	**FIVE-IN-A-ROW: SUBTRACTION WITH THREE CUBES** Students learn and play a variation of *Five-in-a-Row* that involves subtraction with 2 dot cubes and a number cube. Discussion focuses on strategies for subtracting.
Professional Development	**TEACHER NOTES 1, 6, 8** **DIALOGUE BOX 5**	**TEACHER NOTE 7** **DIALOGUE BOX 6**
Materials to View Ahead of Time	**TEACHER PRESENTATION:** 📱 **Classroom Routine** *What Time Is It?*	**TEACHER PRESENTATIONS:** 📱 **Classroom Routine** *Today's Number: 14* 🔲 **Activity** Introducing *Five-in-a-Row: Subtraction with Three Cubes*
Materials to Gather	**Envelopes** (2 per student) **Materials for *What Time Is It?*** (from Session 2.1)	🔧 **Connecting cubes** (as needed) **1–6 dot cubes** (2 per pair) **7–12 number cube** (1 per pair) **Counters** (15 per pair)
Materials to Prepare	📄 **C6–C10, Fact Cards: Set 1** Make copies and cut apart. (1 set for display; 1 set per student)	📄 **G7, *Five-in-a-Row: Subtraction with Three Cubes* Gameboard** Make copies, ideally on cardstock, and laminate. (1 for display, optional; 1 per student or pair) 📄 **G8, *Five-in-a-Row: Subtraction with Three Cubes* Directions** Make copies. **Chart: "Strategies for Subtracting"** Title a piece of chart paper "Strategies for Subtracting."
Common Core State Standards	**Classroom Routines:** Supports 2.MD.C.7 **Session:** 2.OA.B.2, 2.NBT.B.9 **Daily Practice:** 2.OA.B.2	**Classroom Routines:** 2.OA.B.2, 2.MD.B.6 **Session:** 2.OA.B.2, 2.NBT.B.9, 2.MD.B.6 **Daily Practice:** 2.NBT.A.3

	SESSION 2.7	SESSION 2.8
	QUICK IMAGES: TEN FRAMES Math Workshop continues. Students learn a variation of *Quick Images* that focuses on images of numbers shown as dots in Ten Frames.	**NUMBER STRINGS** Class discussion focuses on using known addition combinations (e.g., combinations of 10, doubles) to solve problems with several addends in any order. Math Workshop continues. Students solve several problems with multiple addends as an assessment.
Professional Development		**TEACHER NOTE 9**
Materials to View Ahead of Time	**TEACHER PRESENTATIONS:** **Classroom Routine** *What Time Is It?: What Time Will It Be?* **Activity** *Quick Images: Ten Frames*	**TEACHER PRESENTATION:** **Classroom Routine** *Quick Images: Ten Frames*
Materials to Gather	**Calculators** (1 per pair; optional; for the Extension) **Materials for *What Time Is It?*** (from Session 2.1) **Materials for *Five-in-a-Row: Subtraction with Three Cubes*** (from Session 2.6) **Materials for *Fact Cards: Set 1*** (from Session 2.5) **Materials for *Number Strings*** (from Session 2.3) **Materials for *Five-in-a-Row with Four Cards*** (from Session 2.2)	***Quick Images: Ten Frames*** Cards with 3, 4, 5, and 7 dots (from Session 2.7; optional) **Additional 1–6 dot cubes** (1 per pair; optional; for the Extension) **Materials for *Five-in-a-Row: Subtraction with Three Cubes*** (from Session 2.6) **Materials for *Fact Cards: Set 1*** (from Session 2.5) **Materials for *Number Strings*** (from Session 2.3) **Materials for *Five-in-a-Row with Four Cards*** (from Session 2.2) **A1, Assessment Checklist: MP8, Look for and express regularity in repeated reasoning** (from Session 2.3)
Materials to Prepare	**C11–C14, *Beat the Calculator* Cards** Make copies and cut apart. (1 deck per pair; optional; for the Extension) **G9, *Beat the Calculator* Directions** Make copies. (optional; for the Extension) (as needed) **C15, *Quick Images: Ten-Frames* Cards** Copy and cut apart. Store in an envelope for use during this unit and beyond. (optional)	**A3, Number Strings** Make copies or use the Online Assessment.
Common Core State Standards	**Classroom Routines:** Supports 2.MD.C.7 **Session:** 2.OA.B.2 **Daily Practice:** 2.NBT.B.5	**Classroom Routines:** 2.OA.B.2, 2.NBT.B.9 **Session:** 2.OA.B.2, 2.NBT.B.9 **Daily Practice:** 2.OA.B.2

Revisiting Today's Number

MATH FOCUS POINTS

o Using the number line to reason about, and keep track of information about, the magnitude and relationship of numbers

o Using standard notation ($>$, $<$) to express the relationship between two quantities

o Using standard notation ($+$, $-$, $=$) to record expressions or equations

o Generating equivalent expressions for a number

VOCABULARY

o tallies

o taking away

o subtracting

TODAY'S PLAN	MATERIALS
10 Class — CLASSROOM ROUTINES: REVIEW AND PRACTICE ***What Time Is It?***	Teacher Presentation (or use the demonstration clock) Student clocks (1 per pair)
10 Class — **1** ACTIVITY ***Guess My Number* on the Number Line**	Number line 2 large clothespins or clips Scrap paper
10 Class — **2** ACTIVITY **Revisiting *Today's Number***	Teacher Presentation (or use connecting cubes) Connecting cubes (10 per student)
20 Individuals — **3** ACTIVITY ***Today's Number: 7***	*Student Activity Book*, p. 27 Connecting cubes (as needed) Number line Pocket 100 chart
20 Class — **4** DISCUSSION ***Today's Number***	Teacher Presentation (or use connecting cubes) *Student Activity Book*, p. 27 (completed; from Activity 3)
SESSION FOLLOW-UP: REVIEW AND PRACTICE **Daily Practice**	*Student Activity Book*, p. 28

Common Core State Standards	Classroom Routines: Supports 2.MD.C.7 Session: 2.OA.B.2, 2.MD.B.6	Daily Practice: Supports 2.MD.C.7

CLASSROOM ROUTINES: REVIEW AND PRACTICE

What Time Is It?

MATH FOCUS POINT

○ Naming, notating, and telling time to the hour using analog and digital formats

Display the Teacher Presentation (or use the demonstration clock).

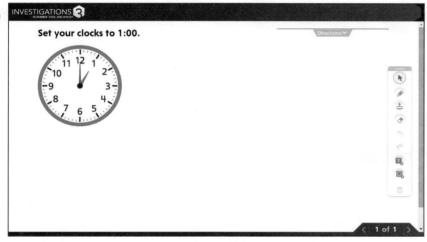

Review the work done in Session 1.6, reiterating the function of the parts of the clock. Then, students practice setting their clocks to the whole-hour times that you suggest, such as 1:00, 6:00, and 12:00. Record the time in digital format. Discuss the arrangement of the hands for 6:00 and 12:00. Students can also pair up and take turns suggesting and setting the time.

1 ACTIVITY

Guess My Number on the Number Line

Play one or two rounds of Guess *My Number* on the number line, this time using the numbers from 0 to 50. For the last round, the secret number should be 7, which will be Today's Number in Activity 2. **TN1**

Remind students that the challenge is to figure out your number in as few guesses as possible. As in Session 1.1, record the clues, and, as each guess is offered, ask students to help you move the clothespins to designate the new range of possible numbers.

After a few guesses have been made, pause and ask students the following question:

What do you know about my number? **TN2**

Encourage students to think about efficiency by discussing guesses that eliminate just a few numbers and guesses that eliminate many numbers. **PD**

TEACHING NOTES

TN1 **Playing and Varying the Activity**
Guess My Number is an engaging activity to play during free times (e.g., just before lunch or recess or the end of the school day) because it is brief and does not require much in the way of materials. These initial experiences focus on "greater than" and "less than," but the activity is flexible—you can change the range of numbers, students can be in charge of choosing the number and leading the discussion, and partners or small groups can also play independently. You can also begin to accept yes/no questions (e.g., "Is it between 10 and 15?", "Is it a teen number?", or "Is your number even?") that offer the opportunity to introduce or revisit vocabulary and concepts.

TN2 **What Do You Know?** This question gives students the opportunity to review and share the information they have collected. It also allows students who might not have been paying attention, or who have difficulty following the verbal information, a chance to catch up on or get back into the activity.

PROFESSIONAL DEVELOPMENT

PD DIALOGUE BOX 1: Guess My Number

We know that my number is more than [23] but less than [45]. What would be a good next guess? Would [24] be a good guess? Why or why not?

Many students see that choosing a number in the middle of the range is an efficient way to eliminate a lot of numbers. If students do not mention this strategy, ask them about it.

What about a number that is about halfway between [23] and [45]? What number would that be? Why might that be a good guess?

Discuss students' ideas and continue until students identify 7 as the secret number.

2 ACTIVITY

Revisiting *Today's Number*

Display the Teacher Presentation (or use connecting cubes).

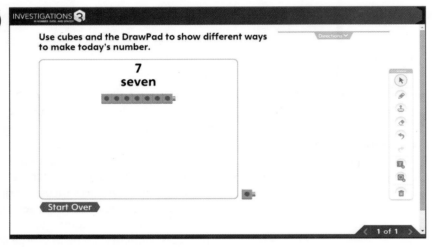

We're going to do *Today's Number* again today. You just figured out that Today's Number is 7. I can write 7 in different ways. I can use a number (write "7"), I can write the word (write "seven"). I can also make 7 with pictures (draw 7 cubes). Another way people sometimes show an amount is with groups of lines or tallies (write ||||| ||).

Explain how to draw 7 tallies, noting how the fifth line crosses the group of 4 and makes it a group of 5. Model how to count them, as needed. **MN**

What are some ways to make 7? You can use cubes and think about combining two or more groups using addition. Or you can think about starting with a larger number and taking away or subtracting a group. Suppose you started with 10 cubes. How could you get to 7? **MWI**

Give students cubes to generate expressions as needed. Record several of the expressions generated, occasionally asking students whether they agree with the different ways listed so far. This allows students to have the opportunity to confirm an idea that they might have had or to respond to an incorrect suggestion. **MPN**

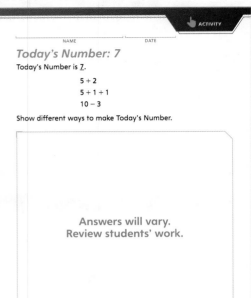

STUDENT ACTIVITY BOOK, P. 27

NAME   DATE

Today's Number: 7

Today's Number is 7.

    5 + 2
    5 + 1 + 1
    10 − 3

Show different ways to make Today's Number.

Answers will vary.
Review students' work.

UNIT 1 | 27 | SESSION 2.1   © Pearson Education 2

MATH NOTE

MN **Tallies** Tallies encourage students to see and use groups of 5, but before they can use them effectively, they first need to understand the representation—that each line represents one, including the fifth line that crosses the first 4 and indicates the bundle or group of 5 objects. Tallies are used again when students investigate the number of pockets in Session 2.4.

MATH WORDS AND IDEAS

MWI Equations and Equivalent Expressions

MATH PRACTICE NOTE

MPN **MP3 Construct viable arguments and critique the reasoning of others.** It is important to regularly ask students to explain the thinking behind an answer, whether it is correct or incorrect. You might ask, for example, "How were you thinking about that problem?"

Model how to use cubes, the number line, and the 100 chart to check whether a given expression really equals 7.

Continue until the list includes a range of expressions, including some that use subtraction.

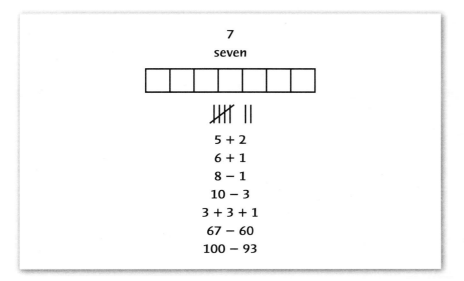

7
seven

5 + 2
6 + 1
8 − 1
10 − 3
3 + 3 + 1
67 − 60
100 − 93

3 ACTIVITY

Today's Number: 7

Students generate expressions that equal 7 on *Student Activity Book* page 27.

ONGOING ASSESSMENT Observing Students at Work

Students generate equivalent expressions for a given number. MPN1 PD MPN2

○ **Can students write an expression that equals 7?** Can they find more than one expression?

○ **Do students generate related expressions** (e.g., 5 + 2 followed by 5 + 1 + 1, or 0 + 7 followed by 1 + 6 followed by 2 + 5)? **MP8**

○ **Do students use more than one operation?** More than two numbers?

As you observe, look for students who use one expression to generate others, to inform the discussion at the end of this session.

 DIFFERENTIATION Supporting the Range of Learners

INTERVENTION **Suggest a Tool** Encourage students who have trouble getting started, or finding more than one or two ways, to use cubes to model the situation. **MPN3**

EXTENSION **Extend Thinking** Challenge students who think they are done to make *Today's Number* with an expression that uses both addition and subtraction. Students can compare their list of expressions with a partner.

MATH PRACTICE NOTES

MPN1 🔍 **MP8 Look for and express regularity in repeated reasoning.** In this routine throughout the year, students may use a pattern to generate a set of expressions. For example, they might notice this pattern using addition— 1 + 6, 2 + 5, 3 + 4—or this pattern using subtraction—8 − 1, 9 − 2, 10 − 3. Ask students to describe their pattern. Does it work with other numbers, or is this something special about 7? Is it special about addition or special about subtraction? Can they explain why? As the year progresses, make note of what different students notice and how their reasoning develops. See the essay **Mathematical Practices in This Unit** for more about MP8.

MPN2 **MP7 Look for and make use of structure.** When students substitute a number with an equivalent expression (e.g., starting with 5 + 2, a student might substitute 2 with 1 + 1 to make 5 + 1 + 1), they are making use of structure.

MPN3 🔍 **MP1 Make sense of problems and persevere in solving them.** Students learn perseverance as they develop strategies for moving forward when they feel confused or stuck.

PROFESSIONAL DEVELOPMENT

PD **TEACHER NOTE 1:** Algebra Connections in This Unit

ENGLISH LANGUAGE LEARNERS **Model Thinking Aloud** Use "think aloud" to review the numerical expressions shown on *Student Activity Book* page 27. Help students understand that there are three different ways shown to make 7 and they must show other ways. **5 + 2** is one way to *combine two groups* to make 7. **5 + 1 + 1** is one way to *combine three groups* to make 7. **10 − 3** is one way to *take away a group* to make 7. What is another way I could make 7?

---

4 DISCUSSION

Today's Number

MATH FOCUS POINTS FOR DISCUSSION

○ Generating equivalent expressions for a number

○ Using standard notation (+, −, =) to record expressions or equations

Gather students to discuss their work on *Today's Number*. Ask students to refer to their copy of *Student Activity Book* page 27 and the list of ways to make 7 generated in Activity 2.

Display the Teacher Presentation (or use connecting cubes).

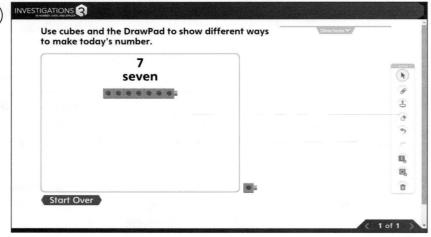

Who has a different way to make 7? One that's not on our list yet?

This question encourages students to look carefully at what has been shared so far and at their own work. It might also trigger discussions about what qualifies as different.

[Carla] says that [she] has [2 + 5] and that's different, because this one is 5 + 2. [She] wrote the same numbers in a different order. **MPN** **PD**

Another idea to focus on is students' use of one expression to generate others.

As I watched you work, I saw something interesting. [Alberto] told me I could share something [he] did. First [Alberto] wrote [4 + 3]. [His] next way to make 7 was [2 + 2 + 3]. What do you think [Alberto] was thinking?

Model and record students' ideas.

MATH PRACTICE NOTE

MPN **MP8 Look for and express regularity in repeated reasoning.** Encourage students to articulate what is the same (the addends and the sum) and different (the order of the addends) about such expressions. Once students agree that 2 + 5 and 5 + 2 both equal 7, ask whether they think this will always work with any two numbers. Consider this the beginning of a year-long conversation about order with addition; students will encounter the idea over the course of the year.

PROFESSIONAL DEVELOPMENT

PD TEACHER NOTE 6: Does the Order Matter?

The teacher records a student's explanation for how he used one expression to generate another related expression.

Then ask for other related expressions. **MN**

What's another way to make 7 that we could write using [4 + 3] as a starting place?

Does someone have another example, where they used one answer to find another?

SESSION FOLLOW-UP: REVIEW AND PRACTICE

Daily Practice

✎ **DAILY PRACTICE** For reinforcement of this unit's content, students complete *Student Activity Book* page 28.

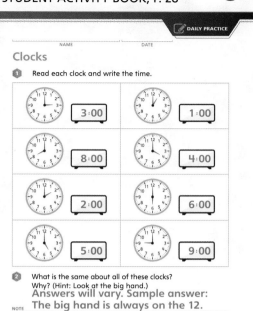

STUDENT ACTIVITY BOOK, P. 28

DAILY PRACTICE

NAME   DATE

Clocks

1 Read each clock and write the time.

3:00   1:00

8:00   4:00

2:00   6:00

5:00   9:00

2 What is the same about all of these clocks? Why? (Hint: Look at the big hand.)
Answers will vary. Sample answer: The big hand is always on the 12.

NOTE   Students practice telling time to the hour.
MN Telling Time to the Hour

UNIT 1 | 28 | SESSION 2.1   © Pearson Education 2

MATH NOTE

MN **Generating Expressions** One of the benefits of this activity is that all students can do it at levels that are appropriate and challenging for them. The expressions that students share provide ideas that others will use the next time they do this activity. As students grow more accustomed to this routine, they will begin to see patterns in the expressions, have favorite kinds of expressions, or use more complicated types of expressions.

Five-in-a-Row with Four Cards

MATH FOCUS POINTS

- Developing fluency with addition within 20
- Naming and comparing strategies for adding two single-digit numbers
- Considering whether order matters in addition

TODAY'S PLAN	MATERIALS
(10) Class CLASSROOM ROUTINES: REVIEW AND PRACTICE *Today's Number: 10*	Teacher Presentation (or use cubes and a number line)
(15) Class **1** ACTIVITY **Introducing *Five-in-a-Row with Four Cards***	*Five-in-a-Row with Four Cards* (or use C2–C5*, G3*, and counters)
(30) Pairs **2** ACTIVITY **Playing *Five-in-a-Row with Four Cards***	G3–G5* (1 per pair) G6* (as needed) Primary Number Cards (1 deck per pair, without Wild Cards) Counters (about 20 per pair)
(15) Class **3** DISCUSSION **Strategies for Adding**	Chart: "Strategies for Adding"*
SESSION FOLLOW-UP: REVIEW AND PRACTICE **Daily Practice and Homework**	*Student Activity Book*, pp. 29–30

* See *Materials to Prepare* in the Investigation 2 Planner.

Common Core State Standards	Classroom Routines: 2.OA.B.2, 2.MD.B.6 Session: 2.OA.B.2, 2.NBT.B.9, 2.MD.B.6	Daily Practice: 2.OA.B.2

CLASSROOM ROUTINES: REVIEW AND PRACTICE

Today's Number: 10

MATH FOCUS POINTS

○ Generating equivalent expressions for a number

○ Finding the two-addend combinations that equal 10

○ Using standard notation (+, −, =) to record expressions or equations

Display the Teacher Presentation (or use cubes and a number line).

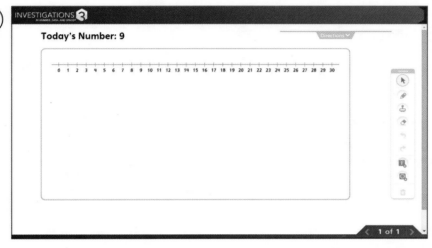

Explain that Today's Number is 10, and ask students to help you find it on the number line and write the number word (i.e., ten). Then explain that, sometimes, there will be specific rules or constraints when students do *Today's Number*.

Today's Number is 10, and your challenge is to find all of the ways to make 10 by adding two numbers. For example, 5 + 5 = 10. I added two numbers, and they equal 10.

Give students time to work. Then compile their combinations, discussing the strategies students used and whether they think they've found them all. **PD**

---

1 ACTIVITY

Introducing *Five-in-a-Row with Four Cards*

Explain that students are going to learn a game called *Five-in-a-Row with Four Cards,* where partners work together to cover five numbers in a row, vertically, horizontally or diagonally. It is similar to games students may have played in Grade 1.

PROFESSIONAL DEVELOPMENT

PD DIALOGUE BOX 3: **Combinations of 10**

Use the Game Presentation (or use a deck of Primary Number Cards (C2–C5) without Wild Cards, G3, and counters) to introduce the game.

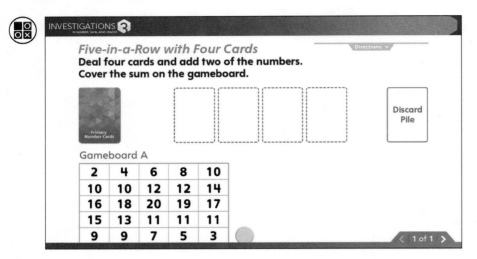

Ask a volunteer to be your partner in a sample game.

Turn over the top four cards.

On each turn, turn over four cards. [Melissa] and I picked [10, 3, 7, and 1]. We can cover the sum of *any two* of these numbers on our gameboard. There are different possibilities. [Melissa], what two numbers do you think we should add?

Record an equation for the pair of numbers chosen (e.g., $3 + 7 = 10$ and/or $7 + 3 = 10$).

Could [Melissa] have made a different choice? What's another problem we could make from these four numbers?

Work together to list the five other possible problems, and record an equation for each. Ask volunteers to share how they would find the sum (e.g., count all; count on mentally, on their fingers, or on the number line; use a fact they know) and record those as well.

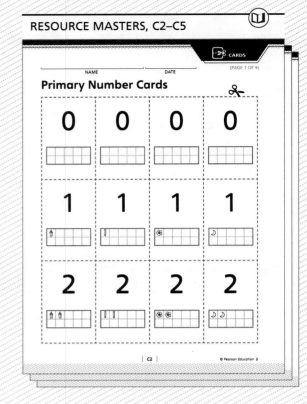

RESOURCE MASTERS, C2–C5

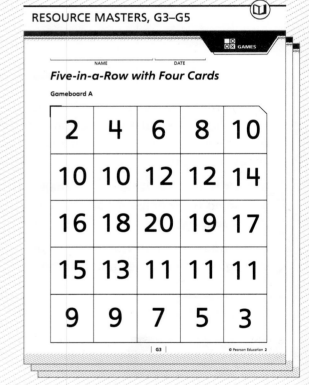

RESOURCE MASTERS, G3–G5

| 10 | 3 | 7 | 1 |

$$3 + 7 = 10 \text{ (or } 7 + 3 = 10)$$
$$10 + 3 = 13$$
$$10 + 7 = 17$$
$$10 + 1 = 11$$
$$3 + 1 = 4$$
$$7 + 1 = 8$$

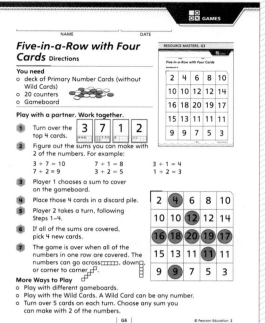

RESOURCE MASTERS, G6

[Melissa] and I could cover a [10, 13, 17, 11, 4, or an 8]. But we can only cover one square on each turn.

Ask your volunteer to choose a sum to cover on the gameboard.

Explain that once a turn is over, the four cards should be placed in a discard pile before turning over four new cards. Again ask students what sums they could make using two of the cards, record these equations, and decide which number to cover.

Remember, the goal is to work together with your partner to cover five squares in a row, horizontally, vertically, or diagonally. So you'll want to think carefully about how to place the counter to get you closer to having five in a row.

Play several rounds, until students are clear how to play, making sure to play one hand that includes a zero. Be sure to explain that:

○ If all of the possible sums are already covered, turn over four new cards.

○ If all the cards in the deck have been used, reshuffle the deck and begin again.

2 ACTIVITY

Playing *Five-in-a-Row with Four Cards*

Partners play *Five-in-a-Row with Four Cards* on Gameboard A, B, or C (G3–G5). Each pair also needs a deck of Primary Number Cards with the Wild Cards removed (C2–C5), and a collection of counters. The directions are available on G6.

ONGOING ASSESSMENT Observing Students at Work

Students practice adding two numbers (0–10). They reason strategically about which sum gives them a better chance of completing a row.

○ **Can students figure out the six possible combinations?** How do they find the sums? Do they count all? Count on? Use knowledge of number combinations? **TN1**

○ **How do students determine which combination of two numbers to use?** Do they seem to choose two of the numbers at random? Do they find all the possible combinations and then choose one strategically?

 DIFFERENTIATION Supporting the Range of Learners

INTERVENTION Adapt the Task Four cards and six possible problems/sums may be a lot for some students to manage. These students can begin by playing *Five-in-a-Row with Three Cards,* which results in only three possible problems/sums.

INTERVENTION Scaffold a Solution Some students may play more thoughtfully, or strategically, if they record the six possible combinations and sums on paper before choosing a square to cover. Demonstrate and use this strategy while playing with a small group.

ENGLISH LANGUAGE LEARNERS Repeat and Clarify Help students understand the meaning of the phrase *five-in-a-row.* Display the *Five-in-a-Row with Four Cards* Gameboards (G3–G5), cover five numbers in a row, and say: **You have *five-in-a-row* when all of the numbers in a row are covered.** Cover five numbers in a column, and again reinforce that there are five in a row. Finally, cover five numbers in a diagonal. Each time, ask the students to count the number of counters and encourage them to show you "five-in-a-row."

3 DISCUSSION

Strategies for Adding

MATH FOCUS POINTS FOR DISCUSSION

○ Naming and comparing strategies for adding two single-digit numbers

○ Considering whether order matters in addition

Gather students for a discussion about addition strategies. Use the context of *Five-in-a-Row* to generate the problems. Display the "Strategies for Adding" Chart. **PD**

Today I was watching [Holly] and [Malcolm] play *Five-in-a-Row.* They added 5 + 6. Think quietly for a minute. What was their total? How do you know? TN2 TN3

$$5 + 6 = ?$$

TEACHING NOTES

TN1 Addition within 20 Fluency with addition (and subtraction) within 10 was an end-of-Grade 1 benchmark; fluency within 20 is expected by the end of Grade 2. This game provides review and practice within 10, and an opportunity to begin developing fluency with sums over 10. If students do not "just know" the combinations within 10, they should be using combinations they know or at least counting on to determine the answer.

TN2 Addition Strategies If students "just know" the answer to this problem, encourage them to explain how they *would* solve the problem if they didn't "just know." The goal of this discussion is to lay out the main strategies for solving addition problems with small numbers: counting all, counting on by 1s, adding one number in parts, and using a known fact. An understanding of these foundational strategies will support students in developing strategies for adding 2- and 3-digit numbers over the course of Grade 2 (e.g., adding one number on in parts, adding by place).

TN3 Explaining Strategies Throughout *Investigations,* students are expected to explain their strategies for solving addition and subtraction problems and to grapple with why (and when) they work. Listen for evidence that they are using properties of operations (e.g., counting on 5 from 6 even though the problem reads 5 + 6 (commutative property) or reasoning from a known fact).

PROFESSIONAL DEVELOPMENT

PD TEACHER NOTE 7: Strategies for Addition and Subtraction

" STUDENTS MIGHT SAY "

"I counted on. 5; 6, 7, 8, 9, 10, 11."

"I did too but I started with 6. 7, 8, 9, 10, 11."

"I broke 6 into 5 + 1. 5 + 5 = 10, and 1 more is 11."

"I just know that 5 + 5 is 10, but it's 5 + 6, so it's 11."

STUDENT ACTIVITY BOOK, P. 29

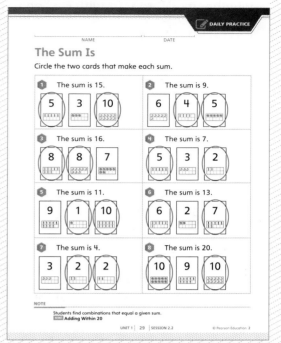

No one shared this strategy, but one way to add is to count all of the parts of the problem. So you could count out 1, 2, 3, 4, 5 things, and then count out 1, 2, 3, 4, 5, 6 things, and then count them all.

Record this strategy under the heading *Count All*.

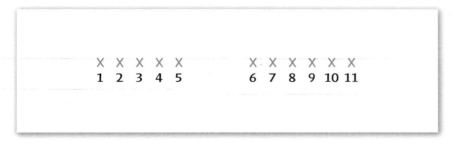

[Simon] and [Monisha] both counted on. [Simon] said 5, because the first number in the problem is 5. And then [he] counted on 6 (draw 6 X's) and said 6, 7, 8, 9, 10, 11.

Record this strategy under the heading *Count On*. Also show what it would look like on the number line.

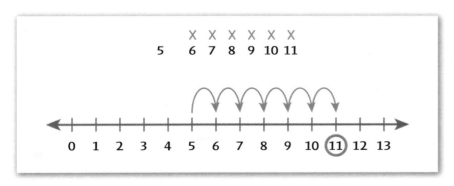

If a student started at 6 and counted on 5, record this as well, and discuss whether it's OK to start with 6 when the problem says 5 + 6. **MPN1**

Finally, discuss any strategies that relied on using a known fact (5 + 5, 6 + 6, 6 + 4).

Some people used a fact they knew. [Tia] and [Rochelle] both knew that 5 + 5 = 10. How did that help them solve the problem?

Record these strategies under the heading *Use a Fact You Know.* **MPN2**

$5 + 6$

$5 + 5 = 10$ $6 + 6 = 12$

$5 + 1$ so $5 + 6 = 11$ (one more)   so $5 + 6 = 11$ (one less)

$5 + 5 = 10$

$10 + 1 = 11$

End by summarizing the strategies. *Math Words and Ideas,* Adding Within 20, offers additional illustrations of them. **MWI**

SESSION FOLLOW-UP: REVIEW AND PRACTICE

Daily Practice and Homework

DAILY PRACTICE For reinforcement of this unit's content, students complete *Student Activity Book* page 29.

HOMEWORK Students generate ways to make Today's Number on *Student Activity Book* page 30.

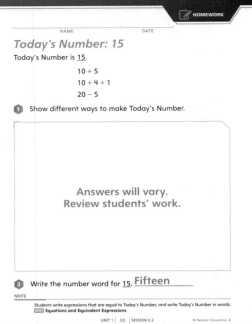

HOMEWORK

NAME   DATE

Today's Number: 15

Today's Number is 15.

$10 + 5$
$10 + 4 + 1$
$20 - 5$

1 Show different ways to make Today's Number.

Answers will vary.
Review students' work.

2 Write the number word for 15. Fifteen

NOTE
Students write expressions that are equal to Today's Number, and write Today's Number in words.
MWI Equations and Equivalent Expressions

UNIT 1 | 30 | SESSION 2.2   © Pearson Education 2

MATH PRACTICE NOTES

MPN1 **MP7 Look for and make use of structure.** Many second graders are comfortable with the idea that you can add numbers in any order, though they may not think to use this fact as they solve addition problems. Highlight instances where doing so is clearly more efficient (e.g., counting on 3 from 8, rather than 8 from 3, to solve 3 + 8). Students will explore order with more than two addends over the next few sessions.

MPN2 **MP8 Look for and express regularity in repeated reasoning.** Deriving 5 + 6 from 5 + 5 or 6 + 6 is based on the principle that if an addend increases (or decreases) by 1 and the other addend remains the same, the sum increases (or decreases) by 1. In the coming sessions, as students repeatedly encounter this idea, encourage them to state it and demonstrate (perhaps with cubes) why it happens. Throughout the year, take note of how students' ability to express general principles develops.

MATH WORDS AND IDEAS

MWI Adding Within 20

Does Order Matter?

MATH FOCUS POINTS

- Using known facts to add two or more numbers
- Developing fluency with addition within 20
- Considering whether reordering three addends results in the same total
- Considering a generalization about reordering addends for all numbers

VOCABULARY

- order
- addends
- combinations that make 10
- doubles

	TODAY'S PLAN	MATERIALS
(10) Class	**CLASSROOM ROUTINES: REVIEW AND PRACTICE** *Quick Images: Coins*	Teacher Presentation (or use enlarged copies of coins from T2)
(20) Class	**1 ACTIVITY** **Introducing Problems with Multiple Addends**	Teacher Presentation (or use chart paper*) Connecting cubes (green, blue, yellow, and purple)
(20)	**2 MATH WORKSHOP** **Adding Two or More Numbers** **2A** Problems about Combining Three Groups **2B** Number Strings **2C** *Five-in-a-Row with Four Cards*	**2A** *Student Activity Book*, pp. 31–32 A1* (as needed) Connecting cubes (as needed) **2B** *Student Activity Book*, pp. 33–38 A1 Connecting cubes (as needed) **2C** Materials from Session 2.2
(20) Class Pairs	**3 DISCUSSION** **Does Order Matter?**	Teacher Presentation (or use *Student Activity Book*, p. 31 and connecting cubes) *Student Activity Book*, p. 31 (completed; from Math Workshop 2A)
	SESSION FOLLOW-UP: REVIEW AND PRACTICE **Daily Practice**	*Student Activity Book*, p. 39

* See *Materials to Prepare* in the Investigation 2 Planner.

Common Core State Standards	**Classroom Routines:** 2.OA.B.2, Supports 2.MD.C.8 **Session:** 2.OA.A.1, 2.OA.B.2, 2.NBT.B.9	**Daily Practice:** 2.OA.B.2

CLASSROOM ROUTINES: REVIEW AND PRACTICE

Quick Images: Coins

MATH FOCUS POINTS

○ Developing and analyzing visual images for quantities up to 10

○ Identifying and recognizing coins and their values

Display the Teacher Presentation (or use enlarged copies of the coins from T2) to display 1 penny, 2 nickels, and 3 dimes.

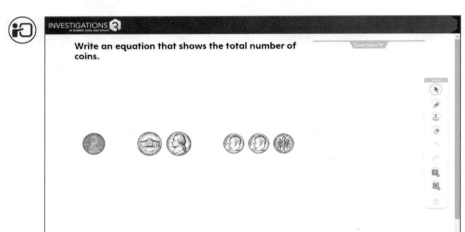

Follow the process introduced in Session 1.3.   **TN**

Focus the discussion on the number of each kind of coin, the total number of coins, and how students remembered the image. Ask questions that require students to both identify (e.g., What's the name of this coin?) and recognize (e.g., Which coin is the penny?) the coins. End by asking students to help you write an equation that shows the total number of coins.

Follow the same process with an image that shows 2 nickels, 3 dimes, and 4 quarters.

TEACHING NOTE

TN *Quick Images* **Routine**

○ Briefly show the image.

○ Students think about what they saw.

○ Show the image again, briefly.

○ Students revise their thinking.

○ With the image showing, volunteers share which and how many coins they saw, how they were arranged, and how they remembered.

1 ACTIVITY

Introducing Problems with Multiple Addends

Display the Teacher Presentation (or write the following story problem) and read the story problem aloud. **TN**

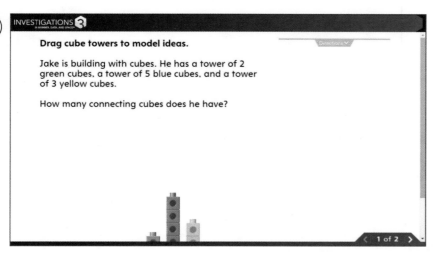

Drag cube towers to model ideas.

Jake is building with cubes. He has a tower of 2 green cubes, a tower of 5 blue cubes, and a tower of 3 yellow cubes.

How many connecting cubes does he have?

1 of 2

Ask several students to retell the story in their own words and to build the cube towers it describes. Then give students time to think about an answer.

Ask students to describe how they solved the problem. Some students add the numbers in order (2 + 5 + 3), while others do not (5 + 2 + 3 or 2 + 3 + 5).

❝ STUDENTS MIGHT SAY ❞

"I know that 2 + 5 = 7 and that 7 + 3 = 10."

"First I added 2 + 3 = 5, and then I did 5 + 5 = 10."

Record expressions that show the original order of numbers in the problem and then each of the students' strategies, rearranging the towers each time to reflect the order in which they were added. (It may help students to see the numbers in the color that corresponds to the cubes.) **MPN**

TEACHING NOTE

TN **Small Numbers** Note that the numbers in this problem are intentionally kept small so that students can focus on whether reordering addends affects the total.

MATH PRACTICE NOTE

MPN **MP2 Reason abstractly and quantitatively.** In order to reason about *why* the addends can be arranged in any order, students must keep the abstract symbols connected to images of the quantities they represent, for example, towers of cubes. The numbers are kept small in this example precisely so that students can make connections to cube representations.

2 + 5 + 3	
2 + 5 = 7 7 + 3 = 10	2 + 5 + 3 = 10
5 + 2 = 7 7 + 3 = 10	5 + 2 + 3 = 10
2 + 3 = 5 5 + 5 = 10	2 + 3 + 5 = 10
5 + 3 = 8 8 + 2 = 10	5 + 3 + 2 = 10

We found a lot of ways to solve this problem. Some of you started with the green, then added the blue and the yellow. Point out the strategy on the list and show the towers in this order. But other people started with the blue (summarize and point to the strategy), and other people started with the green (summarize and point to the strategy).

For each strategy, order the towers to reflect the strategy.

Everyone got the same answer, but you added the numbers in different orders. Why do you think that is? Why does it work, even if you change the order? PD

Discuss students' ideas, using the cube towers to demonstrate their thinking, but keep it brief as students will be thinking and working on this idea in Math Workshop.

I wonder if this would be true for other numbers. MPN1

Explain that students can think about this question during Math Workshop, when they'll be solving story problems, like the one you just solved together, and Number Strings.

Number Strings are similar to the problem we just solved, but there's no story, and sometimes there are three or more addends.

Display $8 + 5 + 2 + 8 = $ __.

Instead of a story problem, Number Strings gives you an expression to solve. You can turn it into a story problem in your head, if that helps you think about and solve the problem. MPN2

Ask a volunteer to make a different color cube tower for each number. Then ask students how they would add these numbers.

Use equations to record several strategies, modeling each equation with the cube towers. Point out strategies that involved using a known fact, and highlight how this seemed to help the students solve the problem more quickly and easily. MPN3

[Katrina] started with 8 and 2. Why do you think [she] did that first? . . . [Chen] added 8 + 8. Why do you think [he] did that?

PROFESSIONAL DEVELOPMENT

PD TEACHER NOTE 6: Does the Order Matter?

MATH PRACTICE NOTES

MPN1 🔍 **MP8 Look for and express regularity in repeating reasoning.** Note that you are asking students to move beyond thinking about only the specific numbers 2, 5, and 3 and to consider the generalization **Will it *always* work to change the order of addends and not change the total?** See the essay, **Mathematical Practices in This Unit**, for more about MP8.

MPN2 **MP2 Reason abstractly and quantitatively.** By creating a story context for an abstract expression, students make meaning for the symbols, which allows them to reason.

MPN3 **MP7 Look for and make use of structure.** When students look for ways to change the order of addends to find the sum of a Number String (for example, if they first look for sums of 10), they are using structure to make the problem easier to solve.

❝ STUDENTS MIGHT SAY ❞

"That's an easy one. I just know the ones that make 10."

"The same with [Chen]'s. The doubles are easy for me."

So [Katrina] and [Paige] know the **combinations that make 10**, and [Chen] and [Yama] said the same things about the **doubles**. They all used facts they know to help them solve this problem. It seems like a good idea to think about the things you already know when you're solving Number Strings.

---

2 MATH WORKSHOP

Adding Two or More Numbers

(20.)

Students choose among the following three activities. Explain that everyone needs to solve Problem 1 on *Student Activity Book* page 31, as it will be the focus of the discussion at the end of the session.

Problems about Combining Three Groups and Number Strings are both activities that provide an opportunity to observe whether and how students look for and express regularity (MP8), one of two highlighted math practices in this unit. Use **Assessment Checklist:** MP8, Look for and express regularity in repeated reasoning (A1) to keep track of your observations over the course of this investigation. Do students notice the regularity that the order of addends can be changed without changing the sum? Are they able to express this idea? Can they explain why this works? Do they apply it in other contexts?

RESOURCE MASTERS, A1

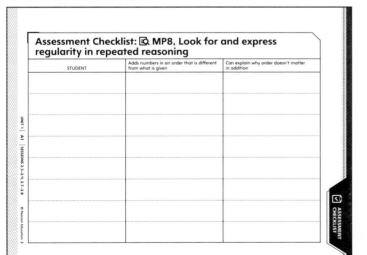

2 A Problems about Combining Three Groups

Students answer the questions on *Student Activity Book* pages 31–32 and show their work. For each problem, they add the numbers in two different orders.

ONGOING ASSESSMENT Observing Students at Work

Students solve problems about adding three numbers and think about whether the order affects the total and why.

○ **How do students add the numbers?** What strategies do they use? Do they combine numbers in the order in which they appear or do they combine numbers out of order? Do they use known combinations? How do they combine subtotals? Are they accurate? 📖 **MP8**

○ **How do they record their work?** Do they record subtotals for each combination? Keep a running total?

○ **Are students convinced that they can add the numbers in any order?** Can they explain why? 📖 **MP8**

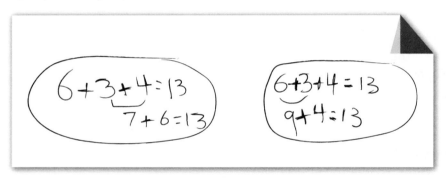

[Problem 1]

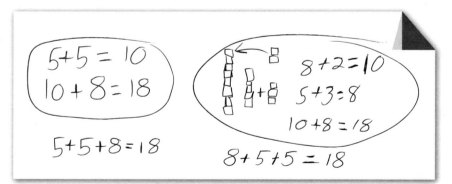

[Problem 2]

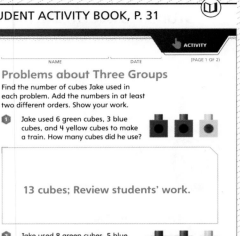

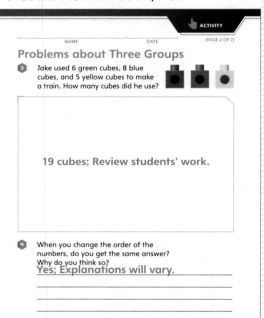

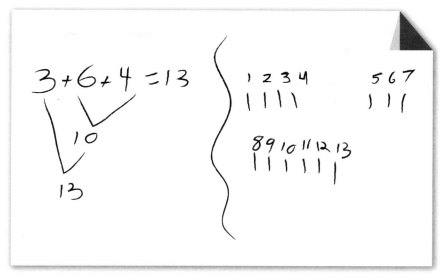

[Problem 1]

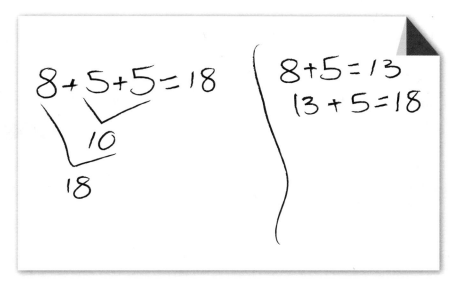

[Problem 2]

 DIFFERENTIATION Supporting the Range of Learners

INTERVENTION **Scaffold a Solution** Help students use cube towers to model the problem and to solve it in at least two different orders. Suggest combinations that students might know (e.g., $5 + 5$ or $6 + 4$) as the first two addends. Encourage students to record an equation for each and then help them connect the towers to the numbers and symbols in the equation.

> For a more comprehensive intervention activity to be done outside of class, see *Does Order Matter?* at the end of this investigation.

EXTENSION **Extend Thinking** Challenge students who finish quickly and are confident that the order does not affect the sum to think about how they would convince someone else that it would work for any numbers. They can investigate whether this is true for more than three numbers and for greater numbers. **MPN**

> For a more comprehensive extension activity to be done outside of class, see *More Than 3 Addends and Larger Numbers* at the end of this investigation.

MATH PRACTICE NOTE

MPN **MP3 Construct viable arguments and critique the reasoning of others;** and **MP8 Look for and express regularity in repeated reasoning.** In Grade 2, convincing arguments generally rely on representations such as cubes to demonstrate why addition (or another operation) behaves this way. Can students picture the cube towers as standing for any number, no matter how large? Can they picture what would happen if there were more than three towers? If there were any number of towers?

ENGLISH LANGUAGE LEARNERS **Model Thinking Aloud** Help students understand what it means to "add the numbers in at least two different orders" by solving Problem 1 on *Student Activity Book* page 31 with them. First have them build the three towers—one with 6 green cubes, another with 3 blue cubes, and another with 4 yellow cubes. Then have students suggest different ways they could connect the towers. **First, connect two towers. Then connect the third tower. How could you do it?** Have students demonstrate each way, and as they do, help them write equations to show the order in which they added.

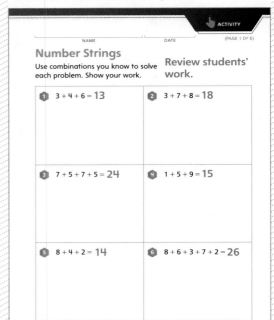

STUDENT ACTIVITY BOOK, P. 33

Number Strings

Use combinations you know to solve each problem. Show your work. — *Review students' work.*

1 $3 + 4 + 6 = 13$

2 $3 + 7 + 8 = 18$

3 $7 + 5 + 7 + 5 = 24$

4 $1 + 5 + 9 = 15$

5 $8 + 4 + 2 = 14$

6 $8 + 6 + 3 + 7 + 2 = 26$

UNIT 1 | 33 | SESSION 2.3   © Pearson Education 2

---

2 B Number Strings

Students solve the problems on *Student Activity Book* pages 33–38. Emphasize looking at the whole problem before they begin and using what they know (e.g., combinations that make 10, doubles) to help them. Students record how they solved each problem and then check their work with a partner. Explain that they have several sessions (until Session 2.8) to finish all 6 sheets.

ONGOING ASSESSMENT Observing Students at Work

Students look for and use what they know to solve a problem with multiple addends. This work reinforces the idea that numbers can be added in any order.

○ **Can students accurately find the total of the Number Strings?**

○ **Are they using familiar combinations (e.g., combinations that make 10 or doubles)? Are they comfortable adding the numbers in any order?** ◳ **MP8**

○ **How do students keep track of and record their work?**

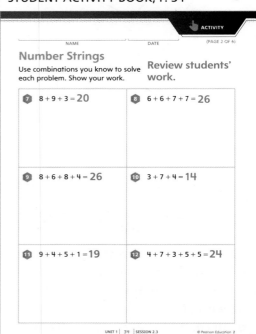

STUDENT ACTIVITY BOOK, P. 34

Number Strings

Use combinations you know to solve each problem. Show your work. — *Review students' work.*

7 $8 + 9 + 3 = 20$

8 $6 + 6 + 7 + 7 = 26$

9 $8 + 6 + 8 + 4 = 26$

10 $3 + 7 + 4 = 14$

11 $9 + 4 + 5 + 1 = 19$

12 $4 + 7 + 3 + 5 + 5 = 24$

UNIT 1 | 34 | SESSION 2.3   © Pearson Education 2

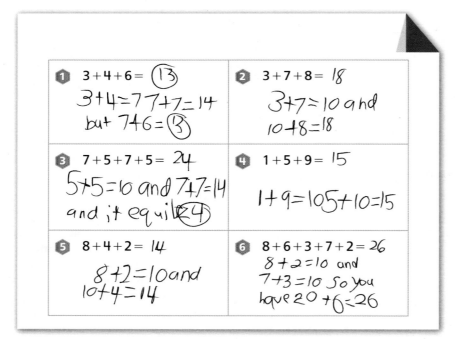

DIFFERENTIATION Supporting the Range of Learners

For another practice activity to be done outside of class, see *More Than 2 Addends* at the end of this investigation.

INTERVENTION Suggest a Tool A few students may need connecting cubes to solve the problem. Others may need cubes to convince themselves that the order in which they add does not affect the outcome. Ask students who have an incorrect total to explain their thinking. Students who missed a step often realize this as they talk it through.

INTERVENTION Clarify the Problem If there are students who exclusively add the numbers in the order they are given, sit together and review the strategies illustrated in *Math Words and Ideas*, Number Strings. Talk together about how the pictured students solved the problem, raising questions about order and efficiency as you do so.

INTERVENTION Scaffold a Solution Ask students whose recording is unclear or incomplete to explain their thinking. Model how to record their strategy with equations. If keeping track of 3, 4, or 5 addends is the issue, model putting a check over each number as it is used. Because some students also lose track of the answer and the original problem after two or more equations have been written, ask **Now we have these two equations under the original problem. Did we add all the numbers? Where is [Katrina]'s answer?** [Katrina] figured out that 8 + 4 + 2 is 14. [She] added the 8 and 2 first and then added the 4, and [she] got 14.

> $$\checkmark \quad \checkmark \quad \checkmark$$
> $$8 + 4 + 2$$
> $$8 + 2 = 10$$
> $$10 + 4 = 14$$
> $$8 + 4 + 2 = 14$$

2C *Five-in-a-Row with Four Cards*

For complete details about this activity, see Session 2.2.

 DIFFERENTIATION Supporting the Range of Learners

EXTENSION Vary the Problem Partners can work together to try to cover more than 5 in a row (e.g., an X or T, the entire outer edge, or the whole board).

STUDENT ACTIVITY BOOK, P. 35

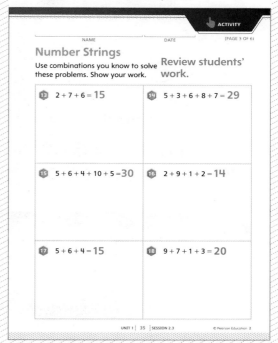

STUDENT ACTIVITY BOOK, P. 36

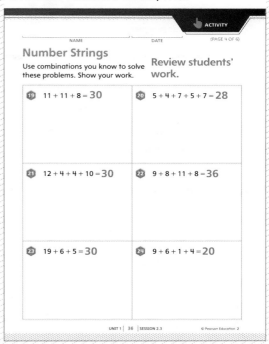

MATH WORDS AND IDEAS

MWI Number Strings

Does Order Matter?

MATH FOCUS POINT FOR DISCUSSION

○ Considering a generalization about reordering addends for all numbers

Gather students to discuss Problem 1 on *Student Activity Book* page 31. Display the Teacher Presentation (or use *Student Activity Book* page 31 and connecting cubes).

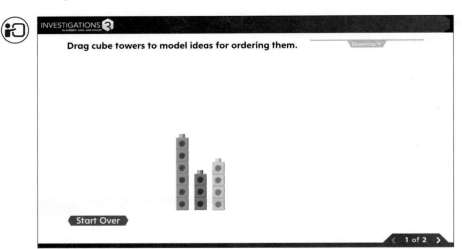

Make cube towers with 6 green, 3 blue, and 4 yellow cubes. Students should agree that Jake used 13 cubes. **PD**

Focus the discussion on the order of the addends. Hold the green and blue cubes together in one hand and the yellow cubes in the other.

Did anyone solve the problem by first finding the number of green and blue cubes and then adding the yellows? Did you find that Jake used 13 cubes?

Record $6 + 3 + 4 = 13$. It may help students to record the numbers in the corresponding colors (e.g., 6 in green, 3 in blue, and 4 in yellow).

Now hold the green and yellow cubes together in one hand and the blue cubes in the other.

Did anyone solve the problem by first finding the combination of 10 (green and yellow) and then adding the blues? Did you find that Jake used 13 cubes?

Record $6 + 4 + 3 = 13$.

Point out that the answer is the same and that it did not matter which way the numbers were added—everyone got 13. Ask students if this is also true for the other problems on *Student Activity Book* pages 31–32.

It seems like we agree that, for these problems, you can change the order of the numbers and you get the same answer. Do you think that's true only for these numbers, or is it true for other numbers?

STUDENT ACTIVITY BOOK, P. 37

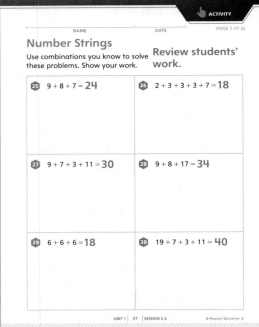

ACTIVITY

NAME   DATE   (PAGE 5 OF 6)

Number Strings
Use combinations you know to solve these problems. Show your work.   Review students' work.

25 $9 + 8 + 7 = 24$ 26 $2 + 3 + 3 + 3 + 7 = 18$

27 $9 + 7 + 3 + 11 = 30$ 28 $9 + 8 + 17 = 34$

29 $6 + 6 + 6 = 18$ 30 $19 + 7 + 3 + 11 = 40$

UNIT 1 37 SESSION 2.3   © Pearson Education 2

STUDENT ACTIVITY BOOK, P. 38

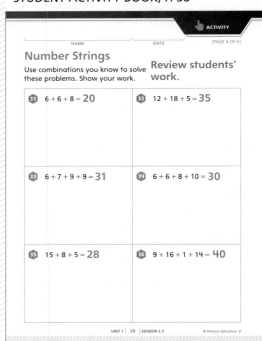

ACTIVITY

NAME   DATE   (PAGE 6 OF 6)

Number Strings
Use combinations you know to solve these problems. Show your work.   Review students' work.

31 $6 + 6 + 8 = 20$ 32 $12 + 18 + 5 = 35$

33 $6 + 7 + 9 + 9 = 31$ 34 $6 + 6 + 8 + 10 = 30$

35 $15 + 8 + 5 = 28$ 36 $9 + 16 + 1 + 14 = 40$

UNIT 1 38 SESSION 2.3   © Pearson Education 2

PROFESSIONAL DEVELOPMENT

PD DIALOGUE BOX 4: **Does the Order Matter?**

" STUDENTS MIGHT SAY "

"The answer is the same in these problems we're doing, no matter what order we add. But I'm not sure it would always work that way."

"It always works. When you add, the order doesn't matter. You still get the same answer."

Let's say that our principal comes to visit. What would you say to convince [her] that you can add numbers in any order and get the same answer? How could you help [her] understand *why* this works? MPN TN

Have students talk to a partner first, and then ask a few pairs to share their thoughts with the class. They can demonstrate their ideas with the cube towers. Ask questions to make sure that students are talking about numbers in general, not just the particular numbers in these problems. Ask them to consider whether their strategies would still work with larger numbers.

SESSION FOLLOW-UP: REVIEW AND PRACTICE

Daily Practice

 DAILY PRACTICE For reinforcement of this unit's content, students complete *Student Activity Book* page 39.

STUDENT ACTIVITY BOOK, P. 39

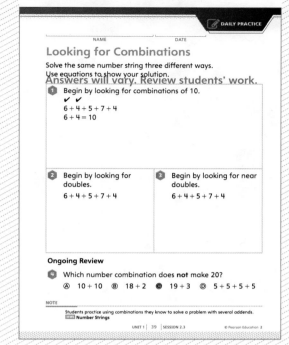

Looking for Combinations

Solve the same number string three different ways.
Use equations to show your solution.
Answers will vary. Review students' work.

1. Begin by looking for combinations of 10.
   ✔ ✔
   $6 + 4 + 5 + 7 + 4$
   $6 + 4 = 10$

2. Begin by looking for doubles.
   $6 + 4 + 5 + 7 + 4$

3. Begin by looking for near doubles.
   $6 + 4 + 5 + 7 + 4$

Ongoing Review

4. Which number combination does **not** make 20?
   Ⓐ $10 + 10$ Ⓑ $18 + 2$ Ⓒ $19 + 3$ Ⓓ $5 + 5 + 5 + 5$

NOTE
Students practice using combinations they know to solve a problem with several addends.
Number Strings

UNIT 1 | 39 | SESSION 2.3   © Pearson Education 2

MATH PRACTICE NOTE

MPN **MP3 Construct viable arguments and critique the reasoning of others.** One aspect of mathematical proof involves being able to convince someone else with reasoning. For example, students may explain that when you move the cube towers around, "You don't take any cubes off and you don't add any more on, so the total has to stay the same."

TEACHING NOTE

TN **Explaining Strategies and Why They Work** In addition to explaining their strategies, this discussion asks students to make mathematical arguments about why they work. Such arguments rely on the commutative and associative properties of addition.

How Many Pockets?

MATH FOCUS POINTS

- o Counting a quantity in more than one way
- o Collecting, counting, representing, and comparing data
- o Using known facts to add two or more numbers
- o Developing fluency with addition within 20
- o Identifying and recognizing coins and their values

VOCABULARY

- o data
- o zero

TODAY'S PLAN	MATERIALS
10 Class **CLASSROOM ROUTINES: REVIEW AND PRACTICE** *Today's Number: 25*	Teacher Presentation (or use a number line)
30 Class **1 ACTIVITY** **Introducing *How Many Pockets?***	Connecting cubes (100) Large, clear plastic jar Masking tape or rubber band Chart: "How many pockets are we wearing today?"*

20
 2 MATH WORKSHOP
 Adding Two or More Numbers
     2A Writing about Pockets
     2B Problems about Combining Three Groups
     2C Number Strings
     2D *Five-in-a-Row with Four Cards*
	2A *Student Activity Book*, p. 40
	 2B Materials from Session 2.3
	 2C Materials from Session 2.3
	 2D Materials from Session 2.2

10 Individuals **3 ASSESSMENT ACTIVITY** **Quiz 1**	A2*
SESSION FOLLOW-UP: REVIEW AND PRACTICE **Daily Practice**	*Student Activity Book*, p. 41

* See *Materials to Prepare* in the Investigation 2 Planner.

Common Core State Standards	**Classroom Routines:** 2.OA.B.2, 2.NBT.B.5, 2.MD.B.6 **Session:** 2.OA.A.1, 2.OA.B.2, 2.NBT.A.2, Supports 2.MD.C.8	**Daily Practice:** Supports 2.NBT.B.5

CLASSROOM ROUTINES: REVIEW AND PRACTICE

Today's Number: 25

MATH FOCUS POINTS

○ Generating equivalent expressions for a number

○ Using standard notation (+, −, =) to record expressions or equations

Display the Teacher Presentation (or use a number line).

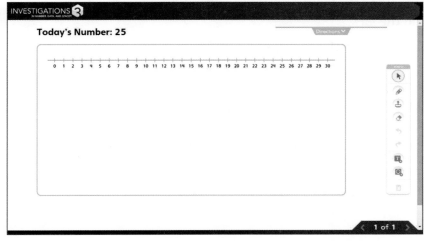

Explain that Today's Number is 25, and ask students to help you find it on the number line and write the number word (i.e., twenty-five). As a class, students generate expressions with three addends that equal 25. Ask students to discuss what strategies (if any) they used to generate their expressions. For example, students might begin with $10 + 10 + 5$ and then adjust the numbers to form a new expression, $9 + 11 + 5$.

1 ACTIVITY

Introducing *How Many Pockets?*

Explain that you are going to be introducing another of the yearlong Classroom Routines: *How Many Pockets?* **PD**

Every ten days or so, all year long, we are going to collect information or data about the total number of pockets our class is wearing. We'll call this Pocket Day.

Take a minute and look around the room. Think about how many people there are. Think about what kind of clothes people are wearing. How many pockets do you think all of the people in our class are wearing today?

Record the estimates and invite students to explain the thinking behind them.

PROFESSIONAL DEVELOPMENT

PD **Part 4: Classroom Routines** in *Implementing Investigations in Grade 2: How Many Pockets?*

One way to count the number of pockets in our class is for each of you to take one cube for each pocket that you are wearing today.

Ask a volunteer to take one cube for each pocket they are wearing, or demonstrate yourself, perhaps putting one cube in each pocket, and then removing and counting them. Then pass out cubes so students can do the same.

Students who are not wearing pockets should not take a cube. Then, show students the large clear jar.

I am going to call out a number. If you are wearing that many pockets, come up and put your cubes in the jar.

If you have zero pockets, come to the front of the room. How many students have no pockets? How many cubes will these students put in the jar?

Use tally marks to keep track of how many students have each number of pockets. **MN**

Pockets	Students
0				
1	ЖЖ
2	

If you have one [two, three, and so on] pocket[s], come to the front of the room. How many students have one pocket? Please put your cubes in the jar. How many students have two pockets? Three pockets?

A student places his cubes—2 cubes for 2 pockets—in the class jar.

MATH NOTE

MN **Tallies** Tallies encourage students to see and use groups of 5. Remind students that each line represents one, including the fifth line that crosses the first four.

Before continuing with four pockets, ask students to estimate the total number of pockets that the class is wearing.

Do you think we are going to have more than 10 pockets? More than 20? More than 30? Why do you think so?

Encourage students to explain their thinking. Then, continue collecting cubes.

When all of the cubes have been collected, hold up the jar so that everyone can see it. Put masking tape or a rubber band around the jar, at the height of the cubes, to mark how full it is.

How can we count the cubes to find out exactly how many pockets we are wearing today?

Explain that, to be sure that the count is accurate, you will count the cubes in two ways. Ask a volunteer to count them by 1s, and then double-check using another way that students suggest (e.g., by 2s, 5s, or 10s). When you have found the total number of pockets the class is wearing, record it on your "How many pockets are we wearing today?" chart. **MPN**

How many pockets are we wearing today?

	Pockets	People
Pocket Day 1	59	22

So on our first Pocket Day, [22] people were wearing a total of [59] pockets. Most of you thought or estimated that there would be more than [30] pockets, and you were correct.

Explain that you will record the number of people and pockets on this chart every time the class does Pocket Day. Also, you will leave the masking tape or rubber band in place so that students can use that information the next time they count their pockets.

MATH PRACTICE NOTE

MPN **MP2 Reason abstractly and quantitatively.** In Grade 1, students learned the sequences for counting by 2s, 5s, and 10s. It is important that they practice counting quantities by 2s, 5s, and 10s to make sure the sequence of number names is associated with the meaning of these counts.

2 MATH WORKSHOP

Adding Two or More Numbers

Students choose among the following four activities.

---

2 A Writing about Pockets

Students write and/or draw about their first Pocket Day on *Student Activity Book* page 40.

> We counted pockets.
> We counted by 10.
> We ended up with 59.

> We counted the pockets.
> We used the cubes.
> We had 59 cubes. We had
> 59 pockets. I had 6 cubes
> and 6 pockets.

---

2 B Problems about Combining Three Groups

For complete details about this activity, see Session 2.3.

Continue to use **Assessment Checklist: MP8,** Look for and express regularity in repeated reasoning (A1) in this activity.

STUDENT ACTIVITY BOOK, P. 40

ACTIVITY

NAME   DATE

Our First Pocket Day

Write about our first Pocket Day.
Think about these questions as you write.

- What was the question we were trying to answer?
- What did we do? What tools did we use?
- What did we find out? How many pockets were there?

Answers will vary; Review students' work.

UNIT 1 | 40 | SESSION 2.4   © Pearson Education 2

2 C Number Strings

For complete details about this activity, see Session 2.3.

Continue to use **Assessment Checklist:** MP8, Look for and express regularity in repeated reasoning (A1) in this activity.

2 D *Five-in-a-Row with Four Cards*

For complete details about this activity, see Sessions 2.2 and 2.3.

 DIFFERENTIATION Supporting the Range of Learners

EXTENSION Vary the Problem Students can play competitively, taking turns, each trying to complete a row of five on their own gameboard.

---

3 ASSESSMENT ACTIVITY

Quiz 1

Explain that students will end the session by solving some problems on their own, so you can get a sense of how much they have learned and grown in their math thinking so far this year.

Distribute Quiz 1 (A2), and review the format with students. Many students will be familiar with Quizzes from Grade 1. Depending on students' prior experience, decide whether to do a sample problem (of your own creation) together to orient students to multiple-choice problems. Similarly, review the format of Problem 4 if needed. Then, read the problems aloud.

These questions provide additional information about Benchmark 1. Use this information along with other information you have collected during this unit when assessing a student's progress towards this Benchmark.

BENCHMARK	QUESTIONS
1: Recognize and identify coins and their values.	1–4

SESSION FOLLOW-UP: REVIEW AND PRACTICE

Daily Practice

 DAILY PRACTICE For reinforcement of this unit's content, students complete *Student Activity Book* page 41.

RESOURCE MASTERS, A2

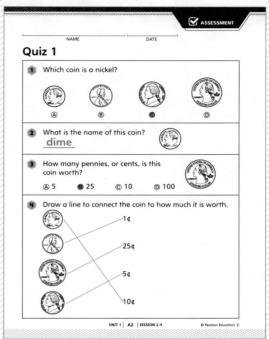

STUDENT ACTIVITY BOOK, P. 41

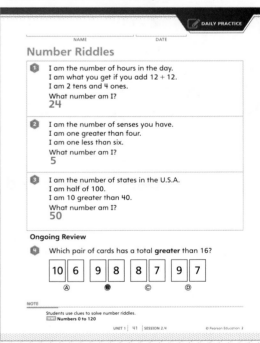

Addition Facts

MATH FOCUS POINT

o Developing fluency with addition within 20

VOCABULARY

o Addition and Subtraction Facts

o doubles

o Plus 1 Facts

o Plus Ones

o sum

o Plus 2 Facts

o Make 10 Facts

TODAY'S PLAN	MATERIALS
10 Class CLASSROOM ROUTINES: REVIEW AND PRACTICE ***What Time Is It?***	Teacher Presentation (or use the demonstration clock) Materials from Session 2.1
5 Class **1** DISCUSSION **Addition and Subtraction Facts**	
20 Class **2** ACTIVITY **Introducing the Fact Cards: Set 1**	C6–C10* Envelopes (2 per student)
35 Pairs **3** ACTIVITY **Which Facts Do I Know?**	Materials from Activity 2
SESSION FOLLOW-UP: REVIEW AND PRACTICE **Daily Practice and Homework**	*Student Activity Book*, pp. 42–43, 45–46

* See *Materials to Prepare* in the Investigation 2 Planner.

Common Core State Standards	**Classroom Routines:** Supports 2.MD.C.7 **Session:** 2.OA.B.2, 2.NBT.B.9	**Daily Practice:** 2.OA.B.2

CLASSROOM ROUTINES: REVIEW AND PRACTICE

What Time Is It?

MATH FOCUS POINT

○ Naming, notating, and telling time to the half hour using analog and digital formats

Display the Teacher Presentation (or use the demonstration clock).

Set the demonstration clock to a whole-hour time such as 4 o'clock. Students record the time in digital format (e.g., 4:00). Repeat several times to get a sense of how comfortable students are with reading the clock to the whole hour. Students can also pair up and take turns setting and recording the time.

---

1 DISCUSSION

Addition and Subtraction Facts

Begin the session by introducing the idea of addition and subtraction facts. **PD1** **PD2**

Sometimes when people think about second-grade math, they talk about learning their "math facts" or "the basic facts" or "the Addition and Subtraction Facts."

Ask students to share any names they know for these problems and any ideas they have about them. Then, explain what the addition facts are.

When people say that, they mean problems like the ones you've been solving when you play games like *Five-in-a-Row* and do activities like Number Strings and similar ones that you'll learn soon that involve subtraction.

PROFESSIONAL DEVELOPMENT

PD1 TEACHER NOTE 8: Learning Addition and Subtraction Facts in Second Grade

PD2 DIALOGUE BOX 5: Introducing the Facts

Explain that knowing the facts is another tool that students will use as they solve problems. Also, talk about what it means to "know your facts."

One part of knowing the facts is knowing the answer quickly. Once you know them, you shouldn't have to stop and figure them out or think about how to solve them.

Another important part of knowing the facts is knowing something about the numbers you are adding or subtracting. This means that you have a picture in your head of about how big these numbers are or an idea about what numbers they are near.

2 ACTIVITY

Introducing the Fact Cards: Set 1

There's lots of ways you're going to work on learning the facts. For example, you have been playing *Five-in-a-Row,* and we've been thinking and talking about combinations we know in *Today's Number* and *Quick Images* and *Number Strings.* We're also going to use a set of cards so that it is easier to keep track of the number facts you know and those that you are still learning.

Hand out a deck of Fact Cards: Set 1 (C6–C10) and two envelopes to each student. `TN`

Explain that they should *not* write the answers on the cards, or anything on the Clue line. They *should* write their initials on the back of each card. They should also write their name on both envelopes and label one "Facts I Know" and the other "Facts I Am Still Working On."

3 + 7 7 + 3 Clue: _____	2 + 6 6 + 2 Clue: _____	L.H.

RESOURCE MASTERS, C6–C10

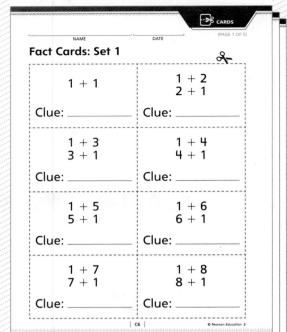

TEACHING NOTE

`TN` **Fact Cards** Set 1 includes 33 addition fact cards, each of which presents the same problem in two ways ($a + b$, $b + a$), except for the doubles; each card includes a "Clue" line. These cards represent the set of addition facts within 10, and the Plus 1, Plus 2, and Doubles with sums above 10. Because fluency with most of these facts was an end-of-Grade 1 benchmark, students should be able to sort most into their "Facts I Know" envelope. Students will receive other sets of cards in this and subsequent units. They will be used throughout Grade 2 as a tool for learning and practicing the facts.

Once students are done labeling their materials, ask what they notice about the cards.

❝ STUDENTS MIGHT SAY ❞

"There's two problems on almost all of them."

"There's no place to write the answer! It should say equals blank or something."

"This says clue. Are we going to write clues?"

[Lonzell] said that there are two problems on almost all of the cards. Take a minute to look through your cards. Find the cards that do not have two problems.

Ask volunteers to share the cards they find, such as these.

1 + 1	2 + 2	5 + 5	7 + 7
Clue: _____	Clue: _____	Clue: _____	Clue: _____

Display the set of cards and discuss them. Most students will recognize and name them as the doubles.

[Juanita] said that these cards show "the doubles." What do you think [she] means? How would you describe the problems that are on these cards? MWI

❝ STUDENTS MIGHT SAY ❞

"They have a number and then plus the same number."

"Yeah. 2 + 2. 3 + 3. 4 + 4. For all of them."

"It's the kind of roll I always hope for when we play [game] at home."

Have students set aside their Doubles cards in a pile. Then, follow a similar process with the Plus 1 Facts.

MATH WORDS AND IDEAS

MWI Learning Addition Facts: Doubles Facts

Just like Doubles are one kind of problem, there are other categories of problems in your fact cards. Look through the cards you have left, and see if you can find the ones I call the Plus Ones. **MWI1**

Display Plus 1 cards as students suggest them. Ask them to think about the answer to one (e.g., $1 + 7$; $7 + 1$), and then turn to a partner and share the solution and their reasoning. Then, ask what students notice about the set.

 STUDENTS MIGHT SAY

 "These have two problems on them."

"It's one problem, then the opposite. They equal the same."

 "Whenever a problem's $+ 1$, it's just like counting. It's the next number."

Discuss students' observations, particularly those that focus on the relationship between the two facts on a card.

[Henry] said that $1 + 7$ and $7 + 1$ have the same sum; they both equal 8. So if you were solving a problem about $1 + 7$, can you solve it by thinking 7 and 1 more is 8?

Encourage students to explain why this would be true, perhaps referring back to the work with the order of cube towers in Sessions 2.3–2.4. **PD**

Would that be true for bigger numbers? For example, what about $1 + 25$?

Follow the same process with the Plus 2 and Make 10 Facts. **MWI2** **MWI3**

Explain that there are some cards in the set that do *not* fit into these four categories (i.e., Doubles, Plus 1, Plus 2, or Make 10), but not many. **TN**

You are going to look through the cards and sort them into two groups. If you look at a card and you just know what the answer is without having to stop and solve the problem, put that card in the "Facts I Know" envelope. Put the cards that you aren't sure about, or have to stop and figure out the answer to, in the "Facts I Am Still Working On" envelope.

Explain that, eventually, once students have had time to practice the facts, they will learn about the Clue line, and how to write clues that might help them remember facts they have trouble with.

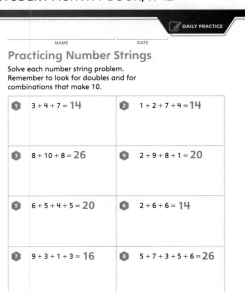

STUDENT ACTIVITY BOOK, P. 42

DAILY PRACTICE

NAME _____ DATE _____

Practicing Number Strings

Solve each number string problem. Remember to look for doubles and for combinations that make 10.

❶ $3 + 4 + 7 = 14$	❷ $1 + 2 + 7 + 4 = 14$
❸ $8 + 10 + 8 = 26$	❹ $2 + 9 + 8 + 1 = 20$
❺ $6 + 5 + 4 + 5 = 20$	❻ $2 + 6 + 6 = 14$
❼ $9 + 3 + 1 + 3 = 16$	❽ $5 + 7 + 3 + 5 + 6 = 26$

NOTE
Students practice solving problems with several addends and using combinations they know.
MWI Number Strings

UNIT 1 | 42 | SESSION 2.5   © Pearson Education 2

MATH WORDS AND IDEAS

MWI1 Learning Addition Facts: Plus 1 Facts

MWI2 Learning Addition Facts: Plus 2 Facts

MWI3 Learning Addition Facts: Make 10 Facts

PROFESSIONAL DEVELOPMENT

PD TEACHER NOTE 6: Does the Order Matter?

TEACHING NOTE

TN **Addition Fact Cards: Set 1** There are 4 cards in Set 1 that are not Doubles, Plus 1, Plus 2, or Make 10 facts:

$3 + 4$	$3 + 5$	$3 + 6$	$4 + 5$
$4 + 3$	$5 + 3$	$6 + 3$	$5 + 4$

3 ACTIVITY

Which Facts Do I Know?

Students sort the Fact Cards: Set 1 into envelopes of facts they know and facts they're still working on.

 ONGOING ASSESSMENT Observing Students at Work

Students practice the addition facts within 10, as well as a few others. **MPN**

○ **Which facts can students recall fluently?** Which do they still need to figure out? **TN**

○ **Do students know that they can use either problem on the card to find the sum?** For example, do they know they can think "7, 8, 9" to solve $2 + 7$?

As you circulate, take cards from students' "Facts I Know" envelopes and see whether you agree that students know these facts. Read aloud one of the problems, varying whether it is the first or second listed on the card. Help students understand what it means to know a fact fluently, and refile any cards as needed.

 DIFFERENTIATION Supporting the Range of Learners

ENGLISH LANGUAGE LEARNERS **Provide Vocabulary Support** Help students understand the term *doubles* as used in this unit. Display: $8 + 8 = 16$ and say: **Doubles means there are two of the same. There are** *two* **8s. The 8s are** *doubles*. Then display: $6 + 6 = 12$ and say: **There are** *two* **6s. The 6s are** *doubles*. Repeat for other *doubles* facts, as needed.

SESSION FOLLOW-UP: REVIEW AND PRACTICE

Daily Practice and Homework

 DAILY PRACTICE For reinforcement of this unit's content, students complete *Student Activity Book* page 42.

 HOMEWORK Students solve the Number Strings on *Student Activity Book* page 43.

📧 **FAMILY LETTER** Send home *Student Activity Book* pages 45–46.

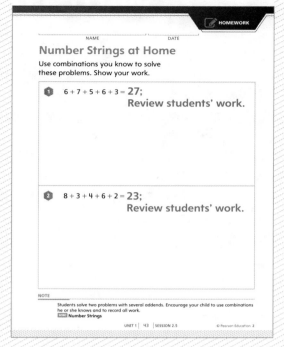

STUDENT ACTIVITY BOOK, P. 43

HOMEWORK

NAME   DATE

Number Strings at Home
Use combinations you know to solve these problems. Show your work.

❶ $6 + 7 + 5 + 6 + 3 = 27$;
                    Review students' work.

❷ $8 + 3 + 4 + 6 + 2 = 23$;
                    Review students' work.

NOTE
Students solve two problems with several addends. Encourage your child to use combinations he or she knows and to record all work.
SMH Number Strings

UNIT 1 | 43 | SESSION 2.5   © Pearson Education 2

MATH PRACTICE NOTE

MPN **MP7 Look for and make use of structure.** An understanding of the ideas discussed in **Teacher Note 1:** Algebra Connections in This Unit will help students learn and remember the addition facts. For example, students who understand commutativity know that if $7 + 1 = 8$, then $1 + 7 = 8$. If they know that $8 + 2 = 10$, then they can reason that $7 + 3 = 10$: "If you take 1 from the 8 and give it to the 2, you've got $7 + 3$; you didn't add any or take any away, so it's still 10."

TEACHING NOTE

TN **Fluency within 10** Students who did not have *Investigations* in K–1 may not be fluent within 10, and others may need some focused practice after summer break (e.g., *One or Two More, Make 10, Tens Go Fish*). *Double Compare* and the *Five-in-a-Row* and *Roll and Record* games provide practice adding a variety of single-digit numbers.

Five-in-a-Row: Subtraction with Three Cubes

MATH FOCUS POINTS

○ Developing fluency with subtraction within 20

○ Naming and comparing strategies for subtracting single-digit numbers

VOCABULARY

○ minus

○ count all

○ count back

○ add up

○ use a known fact

		TODAY'S PLAN	MATERIALS
10 Class		**CLASSROOM ROUTINES: REVIEW AND PRACTICE** ***Today's Number: 14***	Teacher Presentation (or use a number line)
15 Class		**1 ACTIVITY** **Introducing *Five-in-a-Row: Subtraction with Three Cubes***	Five-in-a-Row: Subtraction with Three Cubes (or use G7*, a 7–12 number cube, two 1–6 dot cubes, and counters) Connecting cubes (as needed)
30 Pairs		**2 ACTIVITY** ***Five-in-a-Row: Subtraction with Three Cubes***	G7–G8* 1–6 dot cubes (2 per pair) 7–12 number cube (1 per pair) Counters (15 per pair) Connecting cubes (as needed)
15 Class		**3 DISCUSSION** **Strategies for Subtracting**	Chart: "Strategies for Subtracting"*
		SESSION FOLLOW-UP: REVIEW AND PRACTICE **Daily Practice**	*Student Activity Book*, p. 47

* See *Materials to Prepare* in the Investigation 2 Planner.

Common Core State Standards	**Classroom Routines:** 2.OA.B.2, 2.MD.B.6 **Session:** 2.OA.B.2, 2.NBT.B.9, 2.MD.B.6	**Daily Practice:** 2.NBT.A.3

CLASSROOM ROUTINES: REVIEW AND PRACTICE

Today's Number: 14

MATH FOCUS POINTS

○ Generating equivalent expressions for a number

○ Using standard notation (+, −, =) to record expressions or equations

Display the Teacher Presentation (or use a number line).

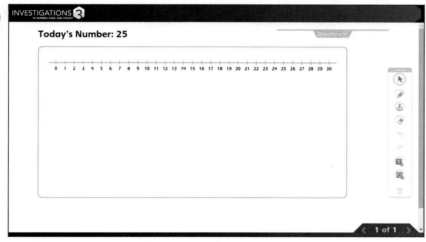

Explain that Today's Number is 14, and ask students to help you find it on the number line and write the number word (i.e., fourteen). As a class, students generate expressions that equal 14. Record students' expressions and discuss the strategies they used. For example, students may begin with 10 + 4 and then adjust the numbers to form a new expression such as 9 + 5 or 10 + 2 + 2. **PD**

PROFESSIONAL DEVELOPMENT

PD DIALOGUE BOX 6: *Today's Number: 14*

1 ACTIVITY

Introducing *Five-in-a-Row: Subtraction with Three Cubes*

Explain that students will play another *Five-in-a-Row* game, but this one will focus on subtraction. The goal remains the same: work together with a partner to cover five numbers in a row, vertically, horizontally, or diagonally.

Display the Game Presentation (or use G7, a 7–12 number cube, two 1–6 dot cubes, and counters) to introduce the game.

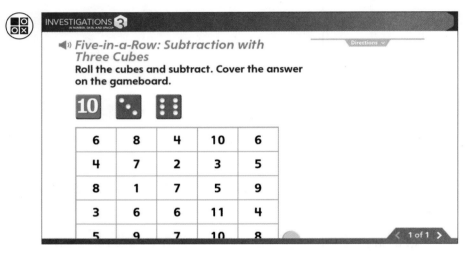

This is similar to *Five-in-a-Row with Four Cards*. This time, you can cover the answer to one of two subtraction problems.

Roll one 7–12 number cube and two 1–6 dot cubes.

In this game, you take away either of the smaller numbers on the dot cubes from the larger number on the number cube. I rolled a 10, a 3, and a 6. So I can use a counter to cover the answer to 10 minus 3, or I can cover the answer to 10 minus 6.

$$10 - 3 = \square$$
$$10 - 6 = \square$$

Let's figure out the answers to these problems, so we can decide which to cover.

Ask a few students to share how they would solve these problems, making cubes available as needed. Some use cubes or their fingers to directly model the problem. Others count back mentally, on their fingers, or on the number line. Still others use an addition fact they know or count up. **MPN**

MATH PRACTICE NOTE

MPN 🔍 **MP8 Look for and express regularity in repeated reasoning.** The relationship between addition and subtraction is an important idea. Students may not yet be able to verbalize how addition and subtraction are related. Comment on this relationship when it arises so that, over time, students will see it in a variety of contexts and forms. Say, for example, [Luis] added to solve the problem, and [Amaya] subtracted. They both got the same answer. Isn't that interesting? Students will revisit this idea throughout the elementary grades.

" STUDENTS MIGHT SAY "

"I would use my fingers. There's 10. So I would go 9 (one finger down), 8 (second finger down), 7 (third finger down). So 7 are left."

"You can count back from 10 on the number line. Find 10 and then go back like this 9, 8, 7."

"7 and 3 makes 10. So 10 minus 3 equals 7."

Play a few more rounds together, covering one answer after each round, until students understand how to play and see that sometimes it makes more strategic sense to choose one problem over another.

2 ACTIVITY

Five-in-a-Row: Subtraction with Three Cubes

Pairs take turns rolling two 1–6 dot cubes and a 7–12 number cube. They solve the two problems that result and use a counter to cover one of the two answers on their *Five-in-a-Row: Subtraction with Three Cubes* Gameboard (G7). The goal is to cover an entire row horizontally or vertically—or five diagonally. Partners can play cooperatively on one gameboard or each on their own. The directions are available on G8.

ONGOING ASSESSMENT Observing Students at Work

Students practice subtracting one number from another.

○ **Can students determine the problems a given roll represents?** For example, if they roll 4, 6, and 12, do they know they need to solve 12 − 4 and 12 − 6?

○ **What strategies do students use to solve the problems?** Do they represent the number on the number cube and remove the number on the dot cube? Do they count back? Count up? Use an addition combination they know? (e.g., "I know 6 + 6 = 12, so 12 − 6 = 6.") Do they use tools such as counters, the dots on the cubes, their fingers, or the number line? What problems do they "just know" the answer to? 📖 **MP8**

○ **How do students decide which numbers to cover on their gameboard?** Are they playing strategically?

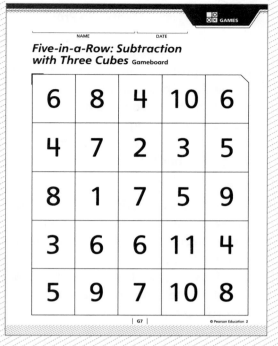

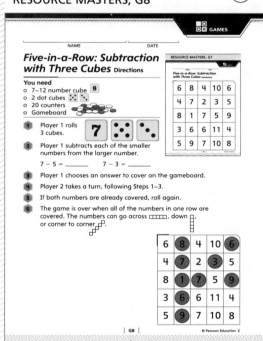

DIFFERENTIATION Supporting the Range of Learners

INTERVENTION Clarify the Problem Some students need support determining the problems to solve after rolling the three cubes. Ask students to tell you which cube shows the largest number. Remind them that there are two possible problems, and ask them to articulate those problems by pairing each of the dot cubes with the number cube. Record each problem and then focus on solving each. **So if we have [8] and take away [4], then how much would we have?** Encourage students to use cubes or counters to model the action of the problem as needed and record the answer so that they can then choose which number to cover on the gameboard.

ENGLISH LANGUAGE LEARNERS Provide Vocabulary Support Help students understand subtraction-related vocabulary. Display 12 cubes and ask a student to take away 6 cubes. Count the remaining cubes with students. **If we *take away* 6 from 12, there are 6 left.** Display: $12 - 6 = \square$. Read the equation aloud with students while pointing to the corresponding numbers/symbols. **12 *minus* 6 *equals* 6.** Ask students to assemble a new set of cubes, and then have them tell you how many to take away. Count the remaining cubes. Record the equation, and ask students to show you each part of the equation using the cube model.

3 DISCUSSION

Strategies for Subtracting

MATH FOCUS POINT FOR DISCUSSION

○ Naming and comparing strategies for subtracting single-digit numbers

Gather students for a discussion about strategies for subtracting. Use the context of *Five-in-a-Row* to generate the problems. Display the "Strategies for Subtracting" chart. `PD` `TN`

Today I was watching [Esteban] and [Nadia] play *Five-in-a-Row: Subtraction with Three Cubes*. They decided to cover the answer to 12 − 7. Think quietly for a minute. What number did they cover? How do you know?

$$12 - 7 = \;?$$

TEACHING NOTE

`TN` **Explaining Strategies** Continue to ask students to explain their strategies for solving addition and subtraction problems and to focus discussions of those strategies on why they work. Note whether students are using strategies that rely on reasoning about the operations (e.g., subtracting one number in parts, using known facts, and/or using the relationship between addition and subtraction).

" STUDENTS MIGHT SAY "

"I used the number line to count back 7 from 12."

"I know 12 − 2 is 10. Then I had to subtract 5 more. 10 − 5 is 5."

"I counted up from 7. 7; 8, 9, 10, 11, 12." (5 fingers are up.)

"I thought 7 plus what makes 12. 7 + 3 is 10, and you need to add 2 more to get to 12. You have to add 5."

"I know 12 − 6 = 6. I have to take away one more, so it's 5."

Just like we talked about with addition, one strategy is to count all of the parts of the problem. So you could count out 1, 2, 3, . . ., 12 things, and then count and cross out the 1, 2, 3, 4, 5, 6, 7 things you're subtracting, and then count the ones that are left.

Record an example of this strategy and label it as *Count All*.

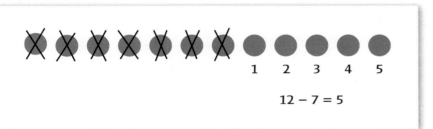

[Carolina] and [Juan] both counted back. [Carolina] counted back on the number line. [She] went one by one. [Juan] took bigger jumps.

Record this strategy and label it as *Count Back*.

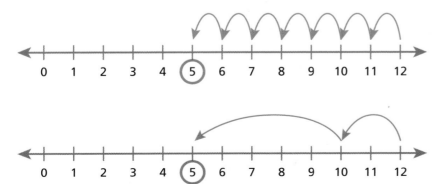

I noticed that [Malcolm] and [Nate] both thought about addition. One way to solve a subtraction problem is by thinking, "What do I have to add to 7 to make 12?" They **added up** to figure that out. [Malcolm] counted up by 1s. [Nate] took bigger jumps.

Again record an example of this strategy and label it as *Count Up or Add Up*.

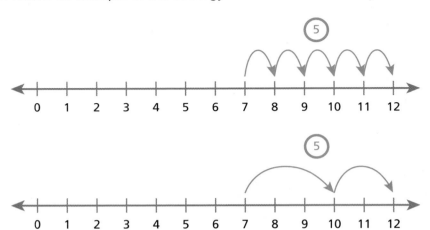

Just like we talked about with addition, sometimes you can **use a fact you know** to help you solve the problem. What did [Anita] "just know"?

Record these strategies and label them as *Using a Fact You Know*.

$$12 - 6 = 6 \qquad 7 + 5 = 12$$
$$\text{so } 12 - 7 = 5 \qquad \text{so } 12 - 7 = 5$$

End by summarizing the strategies. *Math Words and Ideas,* Subtracting Within 20, offers additional illustrations of them. MWI

SESSION FOLLOW-UP: REVIEW AND PRACTICE

Daily Practice

✎ **DAILY PRACTICE** For reinforcement of this unit's content, students complete *Student Activity Book* page 47.

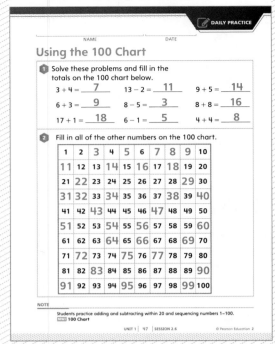

STUDENT ACTIVITY BOOK, P. 47

MATH WORDS AND IDEAS

MWI Subtracting Within 20

Quick Images: Ten Frames

MATH FOCUS POINTS

○ Developing fluency with addition and subtraction within 20

○ Developing and analyzing visual images for quantities up to 10

VOCABULARY

○ Ten Frame

TODAY'S PLAN	MATERIALS

  10

CLASSROOM ROUTINES: REVIEW AND PRACTICE

What Time Is It?: What Time Will It Be?

Teacher Presentation (or set the demonstration clock to 2:00)

Materials from Session 2.1

45

1 MATH WORKSHOP

Adding and Subtracting Single-Digit Numbers

1A *Five-in-a-Row: Subtraction with Three Cubes*

1B Fact Cards: Set 1

1C Number Strings

1D *Five-in-a-Row with Four Cards*

1A Materials from Session 2.6

1B Materials from Session 2.5

1C C11–C14* (optional; for the Extension)

G9*

Materials from Session 2.3

Calculators (1 per pair; optional; for the Extension)

1D Materials from Session 2.2

  15

2 ACTIVITY

Quick Images: Ten Frames

Teacher Presentation (or use the *Quick Images: Ten Frames* Cards with 5 and 10 dots from C15*)

SESSION FOLLOW-UP: REVIEW AND PRACTICE

Daily Practice

Student Activity Book, p. 48

---

* See *Materials to Prepare* in the Investigation 2 Planner.

Common Core State Standards	**Classroom Routines:** Supports 2.MD.C.7 **Session:** 2.OA.B.2	**Daily Practice:** 2.NBT.B.5

What Time Is It?: What Time Will It Be?

MATH FOCUS POINT

○ Naming, notating, and telling time to the hour using analog and digital formats

Record 2:00 in digital format and ask students to display the time on their clocks. Then, display the Teacher Presentation (or set the demonstration clock to 2:00).

In one more hour what time will it be?

Have students set their clocks and talk with their partner about what time it will be and how they know. Repeat with several one-hour intervals. Show students how the large hand travels around the clock one entire circle as the small hand moves to the next number.

Adding and Subtracting Single-Digit Numbers

Students choose among the following four activities.

---

1 A *Five-in-a-Row: Subtraction with Three Cubes*

For complete details about this activity, see Session 2.6.

 DIFFERENTIATION Supporting the Range of Learners

EXTENSION **Vary the Task** Partners can work together to try to cover more than five in a row. For example, they can play until they cover numbers that form an X or T, the entire outer edge, or the whole board.

---

1 B **Fact Cards: Set 1**

Students practice the addition facts in their "Facts I Am Still Working On" envelope. Partners can also work together, quizzing each other and sharing strategies for finding and remembering the sums.

ONGOING ASSESSMENT Observing Students at Work

Students practice the addition facts within 10, as well as a few others.

○ **Do students know that they can use either problem on the card to find the sum?** For example, do they know they can think "7; 8, 9" to solve 2 + 7?

○ **Are students becoming fluent with these facts?** Are they moving cards from the "Facts I Am Still Working On" envelope to the "Facts I Know" envelope? Which combinations are challenging?

 DIFFERENTIATION Supporting the Range of Learners

INTERVENTION **Clarify the Task** As you circulate, select cards from students' "Facts I Know" envelopes and see whether you agree that students know these combinations. Cover one of the problems, varying whether it is the first or second listed on the card. Help students understand what it means to know a combination fluently, and refile any cards as needed.

ENGLISH LANGUAGE LEARNERS **Provide Vocabulary Support** Help students understand the meaning of the two envelopes—*Facts I Know* and *Facts I Am Still Working On*. Point to the corresponding envelope and say: **If you know the fact, put it in this envelope. If you do *not* know the fact, put it in that envelope.** Check students' understanding by asking them a fact and, based on their reply, have them place it in the appropriate envelope. Then observe students as they practice their facts with a partner to confirm that they understand which facts go in which envelope.

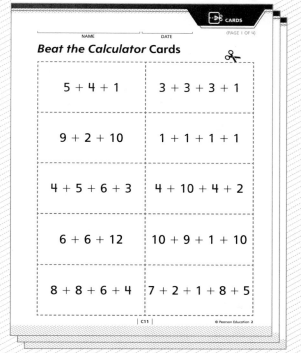

CARDS

NAME   DATE   (PAGE 1 OF 4)

Beat the Calculator Cards ✁

5 + 4 + 1	3 + 3 + 3 + 1
9 + 2 + 10	1 + 1 + 1 + 1
4 + 5 + 6 + 3	4 + 10 + 4 + 2
6 + 6 + 12	10 + 9 + 1 + 10
8 + 8 + 6 + 4	7 + 2 + 1 + 8 + 5

| C11 | © Pearson Education 2

1C Number Strings

For complete details about this activity, see Session 2.3. Continue to use **Assessment Checklist: MP8, Look for and express regularity in repeated reasoning (A1)** in this activity.

 DIFFERENTIATION Supporting the Range of Learners

EXTENSION Adapt the Task Pair students who have completed the Number Strings sheets to play *Beat the Calculator*. Players turn over the top *Beat the Calculator* Card (C11–C14). Player 1 solves the Number String on the card mentally while Player 2 uses a calculator to solve it. Ask students to predict which player will be more efficient, and revisit this question after students have had turns in each role. The directions are available on G9.

1D *Five-in-a-Row with Four Cards*

For complete details about this activity, see Sessions 2.2–2.4.

2 ACTIVITY

Quick Images: Ten Frames

Introduce this new version of *Quick Images*, letting students know that instead of coins, they will be seeing Ten Frames. Ten Frames present visual images of the numbers to ten as dots organized in a 5×2 array. Students should be familiar with them from Grade 1. **MPN**

I'm going to show you a picture of a Ten Frame for 3 seconds. Then I'll cover the picture and ask you to describe what you saw.

Display the Teacher Presentation (or use the *Quick Images: Ten Frames* Cards with 5 and 10 dots from C15).

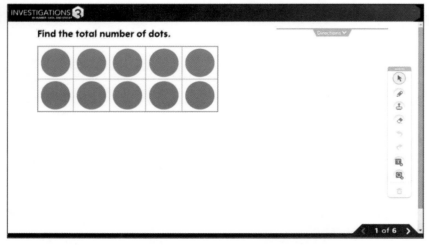

RESOURCE MASTERS, G9

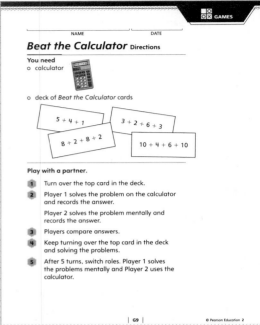

MATH PRACTICE NOTE

MPN MP5 Use appropriate tools strategically; and MP7 Look for and make use of structure. The Ten Frame is a tool that highlights the structure of 10, combinations of ten, teen numbers as ten plus some amount, and 2-digit numbers as groups of ten and some number of ones. Use of the Ten Frame supports students' use of these mathematical structures as they learn to calculate with multidigit numbers.

Use the following process.

○ Briefly show the image.

○ Students think about what they saw.

○ Show the image again, briefly.

○ Students revise their thinking.

○ With the image showing, volunteers share how many dots they saw, and how they remembered.

Next, use the Ten-Frame image with 5 dots and follow the same steps. Ask students how many dots they see and how they know.

 STUDENTS MIGHT SAY

 "Before, 2 rows were full and there were 10; now 1 row is filled, and 5 is half of 10."

 "There are 5 empty spaces, so there are 5 filled spaces."

Use the same process with two more images, one with fewer than five dots and one with more. Each time ask students to share how they figured out the number of dots in the frame. Note whether students are reasoning about how many more or fewer dots than 5 or 10 there are and whether they are using information about the number of empty squares.

SESSION FOLLOW-UP: REVIEW AND PRACTICE

Daily Practice

✎ **DAILY PRACTICE** For reinforcement of this unit's content, students complete *Student Activity Book* page 48.

RESOURCE MASTERS, C15

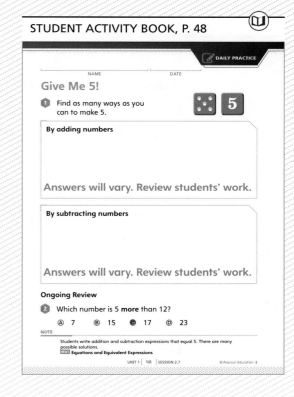

STUDENT ACTIVITY BOOK, P. 48

Give Me 5!

1. Find as many ways as you can to make 5.

By adding numbers

Answers will vary. Review students' work.

By subtracting numbers

Answers will vary. Review students' work.

Ongoing Review

2. Which number is 5 **more** than 12?

Ⓐ 7   Ⓑ 15   Ⓒ 17   Ⓓ 23

NOTE Students write addition and subtraction expressions that equal 5. There are many possible solutions.
Equations and Equivalent Expressions

UNIT 1 | 4B | SESSION 2.7   © Pearson Education 2

Number Strings

MATH FOCUS POINTS

○ Using known facts to add two or more numbers
○ Considering a generalization about reordering addends for all numbers
○ Developing fluency with addition and subtraction within 20

TODAY'S PLAN	MATERIALS

 10 Class **CLASSROOM ROUTINES: REVIEW AND PRACTICE**
Quick Images: Ten Frames

 Teacher Presentation (or use the *Quick Images: Ten Frames* Cards with 3, 4, 5, and 7 dots)

 20 Class **1 DISCUSSION**
Adding Many Numbers

20 **2 MATH WORKSHOP**
Adding and Subtracting Single-Digit Numbers

   2A *Five-in-a-Row: Subtraction with Three Cubes*

   2B Fact Cards: Set 1

   2C Number Strings

   2D *Five-in-a-Row with Four Cards*

2A Materials from Session 2.6

   Additional 1–6 dot cubes (1 per pair; optional; for the Extension)

2B Materials from Session 2.5

2C Materials from Session 2.3

2D Materials from Session 2.2

20 Individuals **3 ASSESSMENT ACTIVITY**
Number Strings

A1 (from Session 2.3)

A3*

SESSION FOLLOW-UP: REVIEW AND PRACTICE
Daily Practice

Student Activity Book, p. 49

* See *Materials to Prepare* in the Investigation 2 Planner.

Common Core State Standards	Classroom Routines: 2.OA.B.2, 2.NBT.B.9 Session: 2.OA.B.2, 2.NBT.B.9	Daily Practice: 2.OA.B.2

CLASSROOM ROUTINES: REVIEW AND PRACTICE

Quick Images: Ten Frames

MATH FOCUS POINTS

○ Developing and analyzing visual images for quantities up to 10

○ Using known facts to add two or more numbers

Display the Teacher Presentation (or use the *Quick Images: Ten Frames* Cards with 3 and 7 dots).

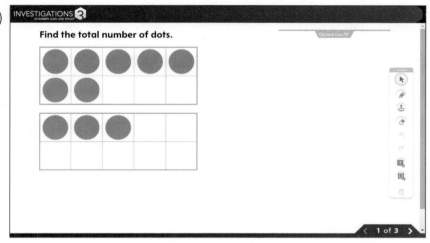

Follow the basic *Quick Images* routine. Students determine the total number of dots and share their strategies. Repeat with the 7-dot and 4-dot images and then the 7-dot and 5-dot images. Focus the discussion on how knowing a combination of 10 (7 + 3) can help with other problems (7 + 4, 7 + 5). Model students' thinking, and use equations to show what's happening in these strategies: **TN** **MPN**

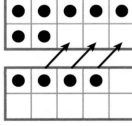

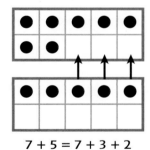

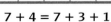

$$7 + 4 = 7 + 3 + 1 \qquad 7 + 5 = 7 + 3 + 2$$

TEACHING NOTE

TN *Quick Images* **Routine**

○ Briefly show the image.

○ Students think about what they saw.

○ Show the image again, briefly.

○ Students revise their thinking.

○ With the image showing, volunteers share how many dots they saw and how they remembered.

MATH PRACTICE NOTE

MPN 🔍 **MP8 Look for and express regularity in repeated reasoning.** In this routine, students work on the idea that adding 1 (or 2) to an addend—e.g., 7 + 3 becomes 7 + 4 (or 5)—increases the sum by 1 (or 2)—10 becomes 11 (or 12). As they repeatedly encounter this principle in this and subsequent units, notice whether students recognize that it can be applied, not just to 7 + 3, but to other addition expressions, as well. Challenge them to express the idea in their own language and explain (perhaps using cubes) why it is true.

---

1 DISCUSSION

Adding Many Numbers

MATH FOCUS POINTS FOR DISCUSSION

○ Using known combinations to add two or more numbers

○ Considering a generalization about reordering addends for all numbers

Display the following number string: $4 + 7 + 8 + 6 + 3 + 2 + 4$.

If I gave this problem to a class of first graders, I bet they would think it looks hard because there are so many numbers. What do you think? . . . You all have ideas about how you would solve this. What advice would you give a first grader about solving a problem like this? What have you learned about solving addition problems with several numbers?

🙶 STUDENTS MIGHT SAY 🙵

"Look for things you know to make the problem easier to solve. There's $8 + 2$ makes 10. Then there are the doubles $4 + 4$, and $7 + 6$ is a near-double."

"You don't have to add the numbers in order."

As students talk about the different combinations they would start with, take the opportunity to consolidate their ideas about whether the order of the addends affects the outcome of addition problems. **MPN**

2 MATH WORKSHOP

Adding and Subtracting Single-Digit Numbers

Students choose among the following activities.

2 A *Five-in-a-Row: Subtraction with Three Cubes*

For complete details about this activity, see Sessions 2.6 and 2.7.

MATH PRACTICE NOTE

MPN **MP7 Look for and make use of structure.** Later in this unit and throughout the year, students' strategies for computation will rely on the idea that in addition, order does not matter. For example, students who add $24 + 33$ by saying, "20 and 30 are 50, and 7 more is 57," are actually breaking the numbers into parts and adding them in a different order.

DIFFERENTIATION Supporting the Range of Learners

EXTENSION **Vary the Problem** Students can play competitively, taking turns, each trying to complete a row of five on their own gameboard.

EXTENSION **Adapt a Material** Students play with one 7–12 number cube and *three* 1–6 dot cubes, generating three possible problems instead of two.

---

2 B Fact Cards: Set 1

For complete details about this activity, see Session 2.5.

---

2 C Number Strings

For complete details about this activity, see Sessions 2.3 and 2.7. Continue to use **Assessment Checklist:** MP8, Look for and express regularity in repeated reasoning (A1) in this activity.

---

2 D *Five-in-a-Row with Four Cards*

For complete details about this activity, see Sessions 2.2–2.4.

---

3 ASSESSMENT ACTIVITY

Number Strings

Students solve several number strings on Number Strings (A3 or the Online Assessment) and show their work. Explain that you would like students to work individually so you can see how their thinking about adding several numbers is progressing.

These problems address Benchmark 2. They also provide a final opportunity to use **Assessment Checklist:** MP8, Look for and express regularity in repeated reasoning (A1) to observe whether and how students look for and express regularity in repeated reasoning. **TN**

BENCHMARK	QUESTIONS
2: Use known combinations to add several numbers in any order.	1–4

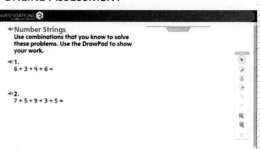

● RESOURCE MASTERS, A3

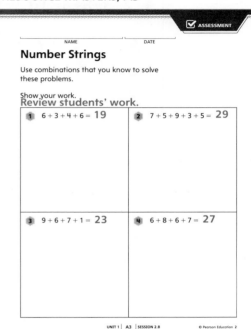

TEACHING NOTE

TN **Assessing Students' Ability to Explain Their Strategy and Why It Works** This activity provides the opportunity to observe how students explain their strategies and to talk with them about why they work. Note how students respond to such questions. For example, do students use examples (e.g., "It equals 19 however you do it. $6 + 3 = 9$, plus 4 equals . . . 13, plus 6 equals 19. But I didn't go in order and I got the same thing: $6 + 6 = 12$, plus 7 equals 19. Or you can add $6 + 4$, then add 9. That's 19 too.") Do they use a mathematical argument? (e.g., "It's like if it's 4 towers of cubes, it doesn't matter which tower you count first or how you snap them into one tower; it's the same total.")

ONGOING ASSESSMENT Observing Students at Work

Students practice addition with multiple addends. This work reinforces the idea that numbers can be added in any order. **PD**

○ **Can students accurately find the totals of the number strings?**

○ **What strategies do they use?** Do they add the numbers in order? Do they use familiar combinations (i.e., pairs that make 10 or doubles)? **MP8**

○ **How do students keep track of and record their work?**

As you circulate, ask students to explain their strategies to you. **TN**

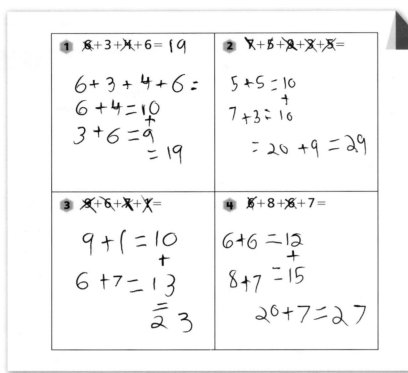

STUDENT ACTIVITY BOOK, P. 49

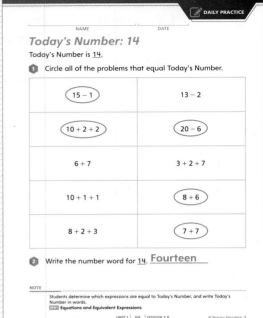

SESSION FOLLOW-UP: REVIEW AND PRACTICE

Daily Practice

DAILY PRACTICE For reinforcement of this unit's content, students complete *Student Activity Book* page 49.

PROFESSIONAL DEVELOPMENT

PD TEACHER NOTE 9: Assessment: Number Strings

TEACHING NOTE

TN **Explaining Strategies** As students describe aloud what they did, they often catch their own mistakes or see that they forgot to record a step on their paper.

Does Order Matter?

MATH FOCUS POINTS

○ Considering whether order matters in addition

○ Considering whether reordering three addends results in the same total

VOCABULARY: order, addend, total

MATERIALS: connecting cubes (10 red, 10 yellow, 10 blue per student)

Read the following problem aloud and ask students to picture it in their minds. Encourage them to remember as many of the details as possible. **Juanita is building with cubes. She has a train of 4 red cubes, a train of 2 green cubes, and a train of 8 blue cubes. How many connecting cubes does she have?**

Have students retell the story in their own words. **What is happening in the story? Is Juanita putting groups of cubes together or taking some cubes away? How many groups is she putting together? How many cubes are in each group? What problem are you trying to solve?** Draw and label the three groups of cubes.

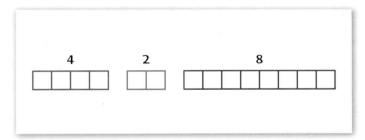

Ask a volunteer to build the three towers with cubes and then demonstrate how to combine the cubes to solve the problem. **Let's record an equation that shows the order in which [Chen] combined the cubes. What towers did [he] combine first? Next? How many cubes are there in all?**

$$4 + 2 + 8 = 14$$

Remind students that the numbers 4, 2, and 8 in the problem are called *addends* because they are being *added* together. **Does it matter in what order the addends are combined?**

Ask another volunteer to add the cubes in a different order, and record an equation. [Jacy] said [she] added the 8 and 2 because that's a 10. Then [she] added the 4 and got 14. Did [Jacy] get the same total as [Chen]? Remind students that the *total* is the sum of all three addends.

$$8 + 2 + 4 = 14$$

Are there other ways to change the order of the addends? Do you think we will get the same total? Why or why not? Test out different orders, asking students to demonstrate each with the cube towers. Confirm with students that the total is the same each time.

Read another cube problem aloud and repeat the process. **Darren is building with cubes. He has a tower of 7 red cubes, a tower of 3 yellow cubes, and a tower of 1 blue cube. How many connecting cubes does he have?**

Have each student build cube towers to represent the problem and then solve the problem twice using a different order for the addends each time. They should record an equation for each solution.

Bring students together to share the different ways they found. Record all equations and discuss why the total remains the same. Confirm that the total is the same each time.

DIFFERENTIATION

ENGLISH LANGUAGE LEARNERS **Repeat and Clarify** Help students remember the meaning of the term *addend* by having them connect the written problem 4 + 2 + 8 with cube towers that they build to represent each addend. **Numbers that are added are called *addends*. In this example 4, 2, and 8 are *addends*.**

ADDITIONAL RESOURCE

Math Words and Ideas Number Strings

More Than 2 Addends

MATH FOCUS POINT

○ Using known facts to add two or more numbers

VOCABULARY: doubles

MATERIALS: 3 number cubes per pair, labeled 1–6, 2–7, 4–9 (made from blank number cubes and labels); 3 cube trains: 4 yellow cubes, 6 blue cubes, 4 red cubes; S15; connecting cubes (as needed)

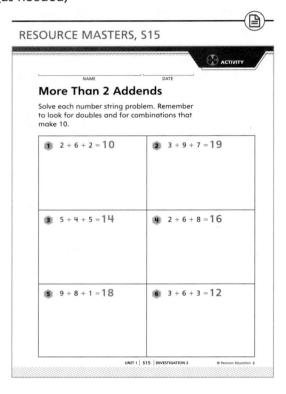

RESOURCE MASTERS, S15

ACTIVITY

NAME   DATE

More Than 2 Addends

Solve each number string problem. Remember to look for doubles and for combinations that make 10.

① $2 + 6 + 2 = 10$	② $3 + 9 + 7 = 19$
③ $5 + 4 + 5 = 14$	④ $2 + 6 + 8 = 16$
⑤ $9 + 8 + 1 = 18$	⑥ $3 + 6 + 3 = 12$

UNIT 1 | S15 | INVESTIGATION 2 | © Pearson Education 2

Display the three cube trains: 4 yellow cubes, 6 blue cubes, and 4 red cubes. Have students verify the number of cubes in each train. Connect the three trains together to make one long train. **What number string can we write that matches our cube train?** Record $4 + 6 + 4$.

Ask students to solve the number string individually, then discuss their methods using the cubes to model each solution. **How did you solve the problem?**

" STUDENTS MIGHT SAY "

"I know $4 + 6$ is 10, so I added that first. Then I added $10 + 4$ to get 14."

"I added $4 + 4$. That equals 8. Then 8 plus 6 is 8; 9, 10, 11, 12, 13, 14."

Highlight strategies that use known combinations. **[Alberto] added the combination that makes 10 first. [Rochelle] added the double 4s first.**

Distribute a set of number cubes to each pair of students. **Take turns rolling the three number cubes. Each person should record a number string with the numbers you get.** Demonstrate a few rounds and model how to record a number string.

Solve the problem and record how you solved it. Compare your solution with your partner's. Students roll, record, and solve at least 6 number strings.

Distribute copies of More Than 2 Addends (S15). Connecting cubes should be available as needed.

DIFFERENTIATION

ENGLISH LANGUAGE LEARNERS Provide Sentence Stems
If students need support explaining how they solved the problems, provide the following sentence stems:

○ *I added _____ and _____ first because _____.*
○ *Then I added _____.*
○ *The sum is _____.*

ADDITIONAL RESOURCE

Math Words and Ideas Number Strings

More Than 3 Addends and Larger Numbers

MATH FOCUS POINT

○ Considering a generalization about reordering addends for all numbers

VOCABULARY: total, order, addend

MATERIALS: S16, connecting cubes and scrap paper (as needed)

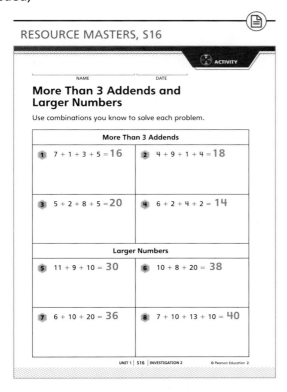

RESOURCE MASTERS, S16

Display $3 + 8 + 7$ and review adding three numbers. **What is the total? In what order did you add the addends? Why? Will the total be the same if we change the order? Why or why not?**

Ask students to consider the order of addends in different situations. **Does it always work to add numbers in an order? When you add four or five numbers together, will the total be the same if you change the order of the addends? What about when you add larger numbers?**

Discuss students' ideas briefly. Then display the following problems:

More Than 3 Addends	Larger Numbers
$2 + 5 + 1 + 2 =$	$20 + 9 + 10 =$
$3 + 6 + 7 + 4 =$	$10 + 18 + 2 =$
$4 + 3 + 5 + 3 + 1 =$	$10 + 15 + 10 + 5 =$

Students work in pairs. They should select one set of problems to investigate. Their task is to find a way to prove that in addition the order of the addends does not affect the sum.

You and your partner can use cubes, sketches, equations, or words to explain why you think this is true or not true when adding a set of numbers.

End the activity by having students share their work.

Students then complete More Than 3 Addends and Larger Numbers (S16).

INVESTIGATION 3

COMPARING QUANTITIES AND COUNTING BY GROUPS

Main Math Ideas

○ Understanding, representing, and solving problems involving addition and subtraction

○ Fluency within 20

○ Understanding and extending the counting sequence

○ Understanding place value

Comparing Quantities and Counting by Groups

SESSION 3.1	SESSION 3.2
INTRODUCING ENOUGH FOR THE CLASS? PROBLEMS Students determine how many children are in their class and use this information to solve an Enough for the Class? problem. Class discussion focuses on strategies for finding the difference between two quantities.	**SUBTRACTION FACTS** The session begins with *Today's Number* and a brief investigation about whether order matters with subtraction. Then, Fact Cards for subtraction are introduced. Students get a new set of cards that include mostly familiar subtraction facts, related to the addition facts they've been practicing (e.g., Minus One, Minus Two, 10 Minus, Minus Half). They sort them into their envelopes of "Facts I Know" and "Facts I Am Still Working On."

	SESSION 3.1	SESSION 3.2
Professional Development	**TEACHER NOTE 10** **DIALOGUE BOX 7**	**TEACHER NOTE 8** **DIALOGUE BOX 8**
Materials to View Ahead of Time	**TEACHER PRESENTATIONS:** 🖾 **Classroom Routine** *What Time Is It?: What Time Will It Be?* 🖾 **Activity** How Many Children Are in Our Class? ⊙ DIFFERENTIATION: ENGLISH LANGUAGE LEARNERS See **Differentiation in This Unit** for session content to preview with students.	**TEACHER PRESENTATIONS:** 🖾 **Classroom Routine** *Quick Images: Ten Frames* 🖾 **Activity** *Today's Number: 7*
Materials to Gather	Materials for *What Time Is It?* (from Session 2.1) 🔧 **Connecting cubes** (as needed) **Class 100 chart** (as needed) **Number line** (as needed) **Self-stick notes** (optional; for the Intervention)	*Quick Images: Ten Frames* **Cards** showing 4, 5, and 6 dots (from Session 2.7; optional) 🔧 **Connecting cubes** **Number line** (optional) **Envelopes** labeled "Facts I Know" and "Facts I Am Still Working On" (from Session 2.5)
Materials to Prepare	**Chart: "How Many Children?"** Title a piece of chart paper "How Many Children?" and divide it into two columns labeled "Children at each table" and "Girls and boys." (optional) **Counting Bag A** Fill a bag labeled "A" with 12 more cubes (in 2 colors) than there are children in the class 📄 **S17, Enough for the Class?** Make copies. (optional; for the Extension)	📄 **C16–C22, Fact Cards: Set 2** Make copies and cut apart. (1 set per student)

| **Common Core State Standards** | **Classroom Routines:** Supports 2.MD.C.7
 Session: 2.OA.A.1, 2.NBT.A.2, 2.NBT.B.9, 2.MD.B.6
 Daily Practice: 2.OA.A.1 | **Classroom Routines:** 2.OA.B.2, 2.NBT.B.9
 Session: 2.OA.B.2, 2.NBT.B.9, 2.MD.B.6
 Daily Practice: 2.NBT.A.3 |

SESSION 3.3	SESSION 3.4
COLLECT 50¢ Students learn *Collect 50¢*, a game about coin equivalencies. Math Workshop includes this game, practicing addition and subtraction facts, and another Enough for the Class? problem. Discussion focuses on coin equivalencies.	**COMPARING TWO NUMBERS** Math Workshop continues to focus on developing fluency with coin equivalencies and addition and subtraction facts and on solving comparison problems with the difference unknown. Class discussion focuses on strategies for comparing two numbers to find the difference.

	SESSION 3.3	SESSION 3.4
Professional Development	**TEACHER NOTE 4**	**DIALOGUE BOX 7**
Materials to View Ahead of Time	**TEACHER PRESENTATIONS:** **Activity** Introducing *Collect 50¢* **Discussion** Coin Equivalencies	
Materials to Gather	**Class 200 chart** (optional) **Coin sets** (1 set per 2–3 students, each with 100 pennies, 20 nickels, 20 dimes, and 8 quarters) **Dollar bill** (optional) **Number line** **Number or dot cubes** (2 per 2–3 students) **Materials for Fact Practice** (from Sessions 2.5 and 3.2)	**Class 200 chart** (optional); **number line; chart paper** **Connecting cubes** (as needed) **Class 100 chart** (as needed) **Materials for *Collect 50¢*** (from Session 3.3) **Materials for Fact Practice** (from Session 3.2) **Materials for Enough for the Class?** (from Sessions 3.1 and 3.3)
Materials to Prepare	**T3, How Many Pennies?** Make copies. (1 per student) **G10, *Collect 50¢* Directions** Make copies. **G11, *Collect 25¢* Directions** Make copies. (optional; for the Intervention) **Counting Bags** Fill 10–15 bags, each with 15–60 cubes in 2 colors. Label the bags B, C, D, and so on. **S17, Enough for the Class?** Make copies. (Several copies per students, for use in Investigation 3) **A4, Assessment Checklist: MP1, Make sense of problems and persevere in solving them** Make copies. (as needed) **Chart: "Coin Equivalencies (Trades)"** Title a piece of chart paper "Coin Equivalencies (Trades)" and make a table with columns labeled "Coin Name," "Coin Value," and "Equivalencies (Trades)." Fill in the coin columns. Leave the trades column blank.	
Common Core State Standards	**Classroom Routines:** 2.NBT.A.2, 2.MD.B.6 **Session:** 2.OA.A.1, 2.OA.B.2, 2.NBT.A.2, 2.MD.C.8 **Daily Practice:** 2.MD.C.8	**Classroom Routines:** 2.NBT.A.2, 2.MD.B.6 **Session:** 2.OA.A.1, 2.OA.B.2, 2.NBT.A.2, 2.NBT.B.6, 2.MD.C.8 **Daily Practice:** 2.OA.A.1

Comparing Quantities and Counting by Groups

SESSION 3.5	SESSION 3.6
GROUPS OF 2, 5, AND 10 Students count out a given number of cubes, group them in three ways (by 2s, by 5s, and by 10s), and fill out a chart about the number of whole towers that can be made and the number of leftovers. Discussion focuses on what happens when a quantity is grouped by 10s.	**TENS AND ONES** Students revisit *How Many Pockets?*. They group cubes into sets of 10 to calculate the total number of pockets, and compare this number to the previous Pocket Day's total. Problems about tens and ones are added to Math Workshop. The session ends with a short assessment about coin values and equivalencies.

	SESSION 3.5	SESSION 3.6
Professional Development	**TEACHER NOTES 3, 11**	**DIALOGUE BOX 9**
Materials to View Ahead of Time	**TEACHER PRESENTATIONS:** (📲) **Activity** Introducing Groups of 2, 5, and 10 (📲) **Discussion** Grouping by 10s	**TEACHER PRESENTATION:** (📲) **Classroom Routine** *Quick Images: Ten Frames*
Materials to Gather	**Class 200 chart** (optional) **Number line** (🔧) **Connecting cubes**	*Quick Images: Ten Frames* Cards showing 5–9 dots (from Session 2.7; optional) **Pocket Data chart** (from Session 2.4) **Pocket Day Jar,** with rubber band still in place (from Session 2.4) and second rubber band to be added (🔧) **Connecting cubes** (100 per class); **coins** (as needed) **Materials for Collect 50¢** (from Session 3.3) **Materials for Fact Practice** (from Session 3.2) **Materials for Enough for the Class?** (from Sessions 3.1 and 3.3)
Materials to Prepare	(📄) **C23, Numbers for Grouping by 2s, 5s, and 10s** Make copies and cut apart. (1 set per pair) **Chart: "Grouping by 2s, 5s, and 10s"** Title a piece of chart paper "Grouping by 2s, 5s, and 10s." Under the title, write, "Our number is ____." Below, draw a four-column table with columns labeled "Number in a Tower," "Number of Towers," "Number of Leftovers," and "Total Number of Cubes." Include three rows for towers of 2, 5, and 10 cubes. (Optional) **Chart: "Grouping by 10s"** Title a piece of chart paper "Grouping by 10s" and draw a table with as many rows as numbers assigned in Session 3.5, with a few empty rows scattered among them.	(☑)(📄) **A5–A6, Quiz 2** Make copies. **Chart: "Students in Our Class"** Title a sheet of chart paper "Students in Our Class" and list all of the students' names on the left side of the chart.
Common Core State Standards	**Classroom Routines:** 2.NBT.A.2, 2.MD.B.6 **Session:** 2.NBT.A.2 **Daily Practice:** 2.MD.C.8	**Classroom Routines:** 2.OA.B.2, 2.NBT.B.9 **Session:** 2.OA.A.1, 2.OA.B.2, 2.NBT.A.2, 2.NBT.B.5, 2.NBT.B.9, 2.MD.C.8 **Daily Practice:** 2.OA.A.1

Present   Videos   Tools   Games   Assessment   MWI   Portfolio   eText   PDF

SESSION 3.7	
	ENOUGH FOR THE CLASS? As an assessment, students solve an Enough for the Class? problem and show their work. Math Workshop follows. Class discussion focuses on a problem about tens and ones.
Professional Development	**TEACHER NOTE 12**
Materials to View Ahead of Time	
Materials to Gather	**Class 200 chart** **Number line** 🔧 **Connecting cubes** (as needed) 🔧 **100 chart** ☑ 📄 **A4, Assessment Checklist: MP1, Make sense of problems and persevere in solving them** (from Session 3.3) **Materials for Problems about Tens and Ones** (from Session 3.6) **Materials for Collect 50¢** (from Session 3.3) **Materials for Fact Practice** (from Sessions 3.2) **Materials for Enough for the Class?** (from Sessions 3.1 and 3.3)
Materials to Prepare	☑ 📄 **A7, Enough for the Class?** Make copies or use the Online Assessment. **Counting Bag Z** Fill a bag with 11–19 more red and blue cubes than the number of students in your class. Label the bag "Z".

Common Core State Standards	**Classroom Routines:** 2.NBT.A.2, 2.MD.B.6 **Session:** 2.OA.A.1, 2.OA.B.2, 2.NBT.B.9, 2.MD.B.6, 2.MD.C.8 **Daily Practice:** 2.MD.C.8

Introducing Enough for the Class? Problems

MATH FOCUS POINTS

○ Counting a quantity in more than one way
○ Solving a comparison story problem with the difference unknown
○ Using numbers, pictures, words, and/or notation to represent a solution to a problem
○ Sharing strategies for solving addition problems

VOCABULARY

○ adding

TODAY'S PLAN | MATERIALS

 10
Class

CLASSROOM ROUTINES: REVIEW AND PRACTICE
What Time Is It?: What Time Will It Be?

 Teacher Presentation (or use the demonstration clock)

Materials from Session 2.1

15
Class

1 ACTIVITY
How Many Children Are in Our Class?

Teacher Presentation (or use the "How Many Children?" chart*)

10
Individuals

Pairs

2 ACTIVITY
Introducing Enough for the Class?

Student Activity Book, p. 50

Counting Bag A*

20
Individuals

Pairs

3 ACTIVITY
Enough for the Class?

Student Activity Book, p. 50

S17* (optional; for the Extension)

Connecting cubes (as needed)

Class 100 chart (as needed)

Number line (as needed)

Self-stick notes (optional; for the Intervention)

15
Class

4 DISCUSSION
Strategies for Enough for the Class?

Student Activity Book, p. 50 (completed; from Activity 3)

Counting Bag A

SESSION FOLLOW-UP: REVIEW AND PRACTICE
Daily Practice

Student Activity Book, p. 51

---

* See *Materials to Prepare* in the Investigation 3 planner.

Common Core State Standards	**Classroom Routines:** Supports 2.MD.C.7 **Session:** 2.OA.A.1, 2.NBT.A.2, 2.NBT.B.9, 2.MD.B.6	**Daily Practice:** 2.OA.A.1

What Time Is It?: What Time Will It Be?

MATH FOCUS POINTS

○ Naming, notating, and telling time to the half hour using analog and digital formats

○ Determining what time it will be when given start and elapsed times that are multiples of 60 minutes

Record 8:00 in digital format and ask students to display the time on their clocks. Then, display the Teacher Presentation (or set the demonstration clock to 8:00).

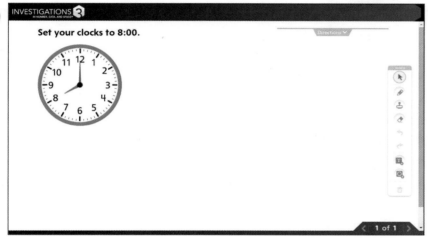

In one more hour what time will it be?

Have students set their clocks and talk with their partner about what time it will be and how they know. Repeat with several one-hour intervals. Show students how the large hand travels around the clock one entire circle as the small hand moves to the next number.

1 ACTIVITY

How Many Children Are in Our Class?

Explain that today's activity requires knowing the number of children in the class. This number will be an important piece of information throughout the year.

We are going to work together to figure out how many children are in our class. We will do this in two different ways. One way is by adding the number of people at each table, and the other way is by adding the number of boys and girls.

Display the Teacher Presentation (or use the "How Many Children?" chart) and together fill in the information. If students are not sitting in table groups, divide them into at least four groups.

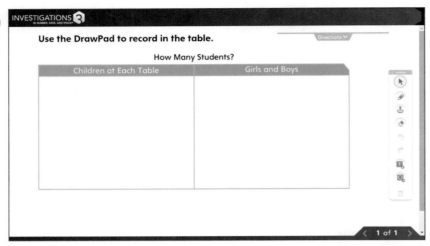

STUDENT ACTIVITY BOOK, P. 50

ACTIVITY

NAME _____ DATE _____

Enough for the Class? Answers will vary.

1. There are _____ children in our class.

2. I counted the cubes in Bag _____.

3. How many cubes are there altogether? _____

4. Are there enough for the class?   YES   NO

5. Were there any extra cubes?   YES   NO
   How many? _____

6. Do you need more cubes?   YES   NO
   How many? _____

7. How did you figure it out? Show your work.
   Explanations will vary;
   Review students' work.

UNIT 1 | 50 | SESSION 3.1   © Pearson Education 2

Do you think we will get the same number of children when we add the boys and girls [12 + 12] as when we add the number of children at each table [5 + 5 + 5 + 5 + 4]?

Encourage students to explain their thinking without solving the problems. While some will be certain that it does not matter how you count (there are the same number of people), others may not yet be confident that the totals should be the same, regardless of the number of groups.

Talk with a partner about how you would solve these two problems. Then solve each problem. MPN1

After a few minutes, collect and record strategies for solving both problems. Finally, count off as one last way of checking their work.

Students share strategies for finding the number of children in the class.

We found out that the number of boys plus the number of girls equals [24]. How could we write this problem as an equation? [Record 12 + 12 = 24.] MPN2

Then we found out that [Table 1 plus Table 2 plus Table 3 plus Table 4 plus Table 5 also equals 24]. How could we write that problem as an equation? [Record 5 + 5 + 5 + 5 + 4 = 24.]

MATH PRACTICE NOTES

MPN1 🔍 **MP1 Make sense of problems and persevere in solving them.** Encourage students who already know the total number of children in the class to check their totals, after adding the subgroups, against the information they know. Encourage students to develop the habit of checking their answers using different methods and asking themselves, "Does this make sense?" As students work to understand their classmates' approaches, they strengthen the mathematical connections to be made in this problem.

MPN2 **MP4 Model with mathematics.** In order to write an equation to represent the context, students must abstract the mathematical elements of the context (number of girls, number of boys, and total number of students in the class) and express their relationship (the total is the sum of the number of boys and the number of girls).

[5 plus 5 plus 5 plus 5 plus 4 equals 24, and 12 plus 12 equals 24.] Because they both equal the same amount, we could also write the problem like this. Record [5 + 5 + 5 + 5 + 4 = 12 + 12]. **MPN1**

Let students know that they will use this information about the total number of students in the class in the next activity.

---

2 ACTIVITY

Introducing Enough for the Class?

Hold up Counting Bag A.

Do you think there are enough cubes in this bag for everyone in the class to have one? How can we find out? MWI1

Some students suggest passing the bag around so that each student can take one. Explain that you'd like them to solve this problem without doing this, but that you will use this strategy to double-check their work at the end of the session.

Remind students about the strategies for accurate counting that you developed together in Session 1.6, and then count the cubes together as a class. Ask for ideas about how you might double-check this count (e.g., by counting by 2s, 5s, or 10s), and use one of the strategies students suggest to do so. Students might also suggest adding the number of [red] and [blue] cubes to get the total. **MWI2**

Are there enough cubes for the class? [Nate] says there are enough. [Leo] says there will be extras. That's the question you're going to solve. How many extras will be left in the bag if everyone takes one cube? MN

Remind students about the available tools (cubes, number line, 100 chart). Explain that they can work alone or together, but everyone needs to record on *Student Activity Book* page 50. Read through the page together and show students where to fill in the letter of the bag (A).

Explain that mathematicians write about how they solve problems in order to communicate their ideas to others. Suggest that students use numbers/ equations, words, and/or pictures to show their thinking. Also, encourage partners to explain their work to each other when they are finished and to help each other make their explanations more clear. **MPN2**

---

3 ACTIVITY

Enough for the Class?

Students compare quantities as they find the difference between the number of cubes and the number of students in the class. They figure out how many extra cubes there are in Counting Bag A and record their work on *Student Activity Book* page 50.

MATH PRACTICE NOTES

MPN1 **MP6 Attend to precision.** Some students may be unfamiliar with an equation such as this one. These students may think that only one number, the answer, can follow the equal sign. Consider this a chance to expose students to a new type of equation format, knowing that students will have many opportunities to see and make sense of a variety of equation formats over the course of the year.

MPN2 **MP6 Attend to precision.** Over the course of the year, as students work to communicate their thinking orally and in writing, they will learn how to communicate more clearly, expanding their familiarity with different representations and technical terms. It is important that students communicate with representations and vocabulary that make sense to them.

MATH WORDS AND IDEAS

MWI1 Enough for the Class

MWI2 Counting by 2s, 5s, and 10s

MATH NOTE

MN **Comparison Problems** When students figure out how many extra cubes there are, or how many more cubes they need for everyone to have one, they are solving comparison problems with the difference unknown. These problems ask students to compare two different amounts, to figure out how many more or how many fewer one quantity has when compared to the other. While problems about finding the difference are often shown with a subtraction equation (e.g., $36 - 24 = ?$), many students think about these problems in terms of how many they need to subtract (e.g., $36 - ? = 24$) or add (e.g., $24 + ? = 36$). For more information, see **Teacher Note 10:** Types of Story Problems.

ONGOING ASSESSMENT Observing Students at Work

Students solve a comparison story problem with the difference unknown and show their work.

○ **How do students figure out how many leftovers are in the bag?** Do they represent the number of students in the class, deal out one cube per student, and count the rest? Do they separate cubes into two groups (i.e., the number of students and the leftovers)? Do they reason based on the number of cubes of each color (e.g., "If there are 18 blues and 14 reds, 18 + 2 is the number of kids, the rest of the reds are leftovers.") Do they count up from the number of students in the class? Do they count back from the number of cubes in the bag?

○ **How do students show their work?** Do they use numbers? Equations? Words? Pictures? A combination?

 DIFFERENTIATION Supporting the Range of Learners

INTERVENTION **Scaffold a Solution** Some students lose track of the parts of the problem (the number of students in the class, the total number of cubes, and the difference between those two quantities) and the relationship among them. Ask these students to restate the problem to see whether they understand what it is they are trying to figure out. Making a cube tower to represent the number of cubes in the bag and another to represent the number of students in the class can help some students model the problem. Label each tower with a self-stick note.

INTERVENTION **Scaffold a Solution** Recording how they solved the problem can be challenging for some students. Encourage those whose explanations are unclear or incomplete to revise their work so that someone else can understand what they did. Take dictation when necessary, showing students how the words you have written could be used to represent the work they have done.

> For a more comprehensive intervention activity to be done outside of class, see *Will Each Person Get One?* at the end of this investigation.

EXTENSION **Adapt the Problem** Students who finish their work with Counting Bag A can figure out whether there are enough cubes for everyone in the class to take 2, and if not, how many more cubes would be needed. They should record their solution on S17.

> For a more comprehensive extension activity to be done outside of class, see *Two or More Bones* at the end of this investigation.

ENGLISH LANGUAGE LEARNERS **Repeat and Clarify** Help students understand the problems on *Student Activity Book* page 50. Read the problems with students and rephrase them using simpler language. For example, for Problem 1, **How many boys and girls in all?** For Problem 3, **How many cubes in all?** For Problem 4, **Compare the number of cubes and children. Are they the same? How are they different?** Pair students and have them discuss their answers to the questions.

RESOURCE MASTERS, S17

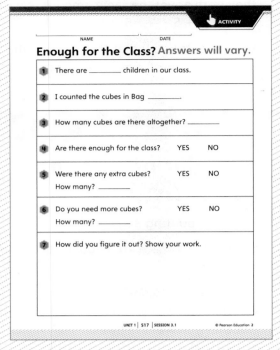

STUDENT ACTIVITY BOOK, P. 51

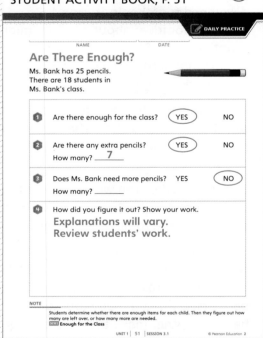

4 DISCUSSION

Strategies for Enough for the Class?

MATH FOCUS POINTS FOR DISCUSSION

○ Solving a comparison story problem with the difference unknown

○ Using numbers, pictures, words, and/or notation to represent a solution to a problem

First let's see what people have for an answer to this problem. [Katrina] thinks 12. Who has a different answer? . . . Did anyone have another answer? MPN

People found a few different answers to this problem. Let's hear how some of you solved the problem and see whether we can figure out why there are different answers. PD

As students share their solutions, record their strategies in order to model for students what a complete explanation looks like. If no one has used the number line or 100 chart to solve this problem, mention them yourself. TN

Last year, some of my students used the number line or the 100 chart to solve Enough for the Class? problems. How do you think they used these tools?

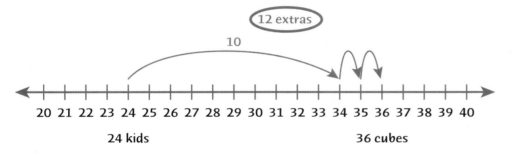

End the discussion by taking Counting Bag A and passing out one cube to each student. The number of cubes left in the bag will provide a concrete model of the problem situation and solution. Encourage students who wish to do so to revise their work.

Explain that students will be solving more Enough for the Class? problems in upcoming sessions.

SESSION FOLLOW-UP: REVIEW AND PRACTICE

Daily Practice

 DAILY PRACTICE For reinforcement of this unit's content, students complete *Student Activity Book* page 51.

MATH PRACTICE NOTE

MPN **MP3 Construct viable arguments and critique the reasoning of others.** Students may find it curious and interesting that there are different answers. Record the range of responses, and encourage students to keep them in mind as they discuss their work. Point out that revising their thinking when presented with new or different ideas is something that mathematicians do. Refrain from acknowledging the correct answer, as it should emerge as students explain their strategies. Remove answers from the list when the original students request it, and explain why that answer no longer makes sense.

PROFESSIONAL DEVELOPMENT

PD1 **DIALOGUE BOX 7:** Are There Enough for the Class?

TEACHING NOTE

TN **The Number Line** The number line can help students conceptualize what a problem is asking (e.g., to find the difference between 24 and 36). It can also help students solve a problem (e.g., "24 to 30 is 6, and 6 more gets me to 36, so there are 12 extra cubes.") and/or communicate their strategy (e.g., "I thought $24 + 10 = 34$ and 2 more is 36. I had to add 12. I can show that on a number line . . ."). Modeling various uses of the number line exposes students to these ideas, and adds another possible tool to their repertoire.

Subtraction Facts

MATH FOCUS POINTS

○ Considering whether reordering the numbers in a subtraction problem results in the same difference

○ Developing fluency with addition and subtraction within 20

TODAY'S PLAN	MATERIALS
⏱ 10 / 👤 Class — **CLASSROOM ROUTINES: REVIEW AND PRACTICE** *Quick Images: Ten Frames*	📺 Teacher Presentation (or use the *Quick Images: Ten Frames* Cards with 4, 5, and 6 dots)
⏱ 20 / 👤 Class — **1 ACTIVITY** *Today's Number: 7*	📺 Teacher Presentation (or use connecting cubes and a number line) 🔧 Connecting cubes
⏱ 20 / 👤 Class — **2 ACTIVITY** **Introducing Fact Cards: Set 2**	📄 C16–C22* Envelopes labeled "Facts I Know" and "Facts I Am Still Working On" (from Session 2.5)
⏱ 20 / 👤 Individuals — **3 ACTIVITY** **Which Subtraction Facts Do I Know?**	Materials from Activity 2
SESSION FOLLOW-UP: REVIEW AND PRACTICE **Daily Practice**	📖 *Student Activity Book*, p. 52

* See *Materials to Prepare* in the Investigation 3 Planner.

Common Core State Standards	Classroom Routines: 2.OA.B.2, 2.NBT.B.9 Session: 2.OA.B.2, 2.NBT.B.9, 2.MD.B.6	Daily Practice: 2.NBT.A.3

CLASSROOM ROUTINES: REVIEW AND PRACTICE

Quick Images: Ten Frames

MATH FOCUS POINTS

○ Developing and analyzing visual images for quantities up to 10

○ Using known facts to add two or more numbers

Display the Teacher Presentation (or use the *Quick Images: Ten Frames* Cards with 6 dots and 4 dots).

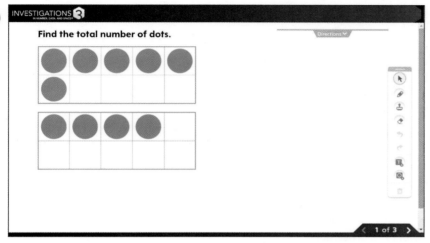

Follow the basic *Quick Images* activity. Students determine the total number of dots and share their strategies. Repeat with the 6-dot and 5-dot images and then the 6-dot and 6-dot images. Focus the discussion on how knowing a combination of 10 (6 + 4) can help with other problems (6 + 5, 6 + 6). Model students' thinking, and use equations to show what's happening in these strategies. **TN** **MPN**

TEACHING NOTE

TN *Quick Images* **Routine**

○ Briefly show the image.

○ Students think about what they saw.

○ Show the image again, briefly.

○ Students revise their thinking.

○ With the image showing, volunteers share how many dots they saw and how they remembered.

MATH PRACTICE NOTE

MPN **MP5 Use appropriate tools strategically;** and **MP7 Look for and make use of structure.** In this activity, the Ten Frame is used to help students recognize how combinations of 10 can be used to solve problems that are near combinations of ten.

Today's Number: 7

Display the Teacher Presentation (or use connecting cubes and a number line).

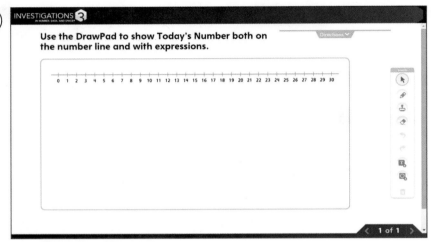

Use the DrawPad to show Today's Number both on the number line and with expressions.

Directions ∨

0 1 2 3 4 5 6 7 8 9 10 11 12 13 14 15 16 17 18 19 20 21 22 23 24 25 26 27 28 29 30

1 of 1

Announce that *Today's Number* is 7, and ask students to find it on the number line. Explain that students are to make 7 with two numbers and use either addition or subtraction. After several minutes, record students' suggestions. Collect expressions until you have some addition, some subtraction, and at least one addition pair that illustrates the commutative property or in which the addends are transposed, such as $2 + 5$ and $5 + 2$. If students do not share such a pair, suggest it yourself.

Because you have explored order with addition in some depth, the question about order with subtraction is likely to come up. Take this opportunity to pose the question for students to begin thinking about whether changing the terms of a subtraction expression changes the result. **MPN**

On the addition cards, there are pairs of combinations. Some of you call these pairs *opposites*. If you see $2 + 5$, what would be the other one in the pair? $(5 + 2)$ Remember that we discovered that, with addition, you can change the order of the numbers and get the same answer: $2 + 5 = 5 + 2 = 7$.

I wonder whether that would also be true for subtraction. Can we take one of the ways you found to make 7, say $9 - 2$, turn it around, and get the same answer?

$$9 - 2 = \underline{\quad}$$
$$2 - 9 = \underline{\quad}$$

Provide connecting cubes and give students a few minutes to think through this problem. Then ask students to share their ideas. Guide students to the conclusion that $9 - 2$ does not equal $2 - 9$. **PD**

MATH PRACTICE NOTE

MPN 🔍 **MP8 Look for and express regularity in repeated reasoning.** Once students have expressed a generalization, it is important to investigate the limits of that generalization. For example, after concluding that they can change the order of addends without changing the sum, students must investigate subtraction to see that changing the order of terms does change the result (except in the special case that the terms are equal). This idea is complex and students will revisit it in later grades. In second grade, it is acceptable to leave the answer to $2 - 9$ unresolved as long as students recognize that $9 - 2$ does not equal $2 - 9$.

PROFESSIONAL DEVELOPMENT

PD DIALOGUE BOX 8: Order and Subtraction

---

2 ACTIVITY

Introducing Fact Cards: Set 2

Just as it is important to quickly know addition combinations with small numbers, it is also important to be able to quickly solve subtraction problems with small numbers. Today, you are going to get sets of subtraction fact cards that are related to the addition facts you've been working on. **PD**

Distribute one deck of Fact Cards: Set 2 (C16–C22) to each student. They will also need their envelopes of "Facts I Know" and "Facts I Am Still Working On." **TN**

As in Session 2.5, students should write their initials on the back of each card. They should *not* write the answers to the problems on the cards and, for now, they should leave the "Clue" line blank.

Look through your cards. What do you notice?

 STUDENTS MIGHT SAY ""

    "They only have one problem on them."

   "I see ones that are about minusing 1, just like the addition ones had ones that were about plussing 1!"

Use students' observations to introduce the categories of facts included in this set. **MPN**

[Holly] said [she] saw cards that were about "minusing 1." Everybody look through your cards. Try to find one that you think shows what [Holly] meant.

Display several examples and discuss what's the same about all of the problems.

Just like we called the +1 cards (record +1) the Plus Ones, let's use [Holly]'s idea and call these the Minus Ones.

Have students gather all the Minus One cards and put them aside.

If the addition cards have Plus Ones, and we found Minus Ones in the subtraction cards, I wonder if there will be Minus Twos, since the addition cards had Plus Twos?

Again, ask students to find examples, and discuss what's the same about all of the problems. They should find and put aside all of the Minus Twos.

RESOURCE MASTERS, C16–C22

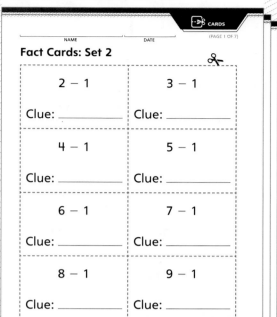

CARDS (PAGE 1 OF 7)

NAME   DATE

Fact Cards: Set 2

2 − 1	3 − 1
Clue: _____	Clue: _____
4 − 1	5 − 1
Clue: _____	Clue: _____
6 − 1	7 − 1
Clue: _____	Clue: _____
8 − 1	9 − 1
Clue: _____	Clue: _____

C16   © Pearson Education 2

PROFESSIONAL DEVELOPMENT

PD TEACHER NOTE 8: Learning Addition and Subtraction Facts in Second Grade

TEACHING NOTE

TN Subtraction Facts: Fact Cards: Set 2

This set includes 53 cards. Though these represent the subtraction facts that relate to Addition Facts: Fact Cards: Set 1, there are more cards in the set because each card includes a single problem. These cards represent the set of subtraction facts within 10, and the Minus One, Minus Two, and Minus Half with initial totals above 10. Because fluency with most of these facts was an end-of-Grade 1 benchmark, students should be able to sort most into their "Facts I Know" envelope. Students will receive other sets of cards in subsequent units. They will be used throughout Grade 2 as a tool for learning and practicing the facts.

MATH PRACTICE NOTE

MPN MP7 Look for and make use of structure. As students identify categories of facts, they are noticing facts that share mathematical structure.

Next, display several of the 10 Minus cards.

10 − 6 Clue: _____	10 − 1 Clue: _____
10 − 3 Clue: _____	10 − 4 Clue: _____

Take a minute to think about what you see here. Then talk to a partner about why you think I put these in a group together.

❝ STUDENTS MIGHT SAY ❞

"It's like the combinations of 10, but it's subtraction."

"They're all 10 minus something."

[Tia] had a great way to describe these problems, [she] said, "They're all 10 minus something." How about we call them the 10 Minuses? **MPN** **MWI1**

Again, students can find and set aside the 10 Minus cards in their sets.

The other category of cards we found in the addition cards were the Doubles. I wonder what the related cards would look like for subtraction?

Ask students to search among their remaining cards to find the set of subtraction cards that are related to the Doubles facts. Once they have selected the cards, ask them to explain why they think a card represents an inverse of a double. Display the related addition cards next to the examples students suggest to help students connect the problems.

8 − 4 Clue: _____	4 + 4 Clue: _____

Ask students to help you decide what to call these facts (e.g., the Minus Half Facts, Doubles Minus, or Minus a Double). It's important that students understand and agree on which problems the name refers to since you and the class will be referencing these cards throughout the year. **MWI2**

Explain that there are some cards in the set that do *not* fit into these four categories. There are a few more than there were with the addition facts, because subtraction cards have only one problem on them. **TN**

MATH PRACTICE NOTE

MPN **MP7 Look for and make use of structure.** When students comment on subtraction facts associated with addition facts, they are approaching a significant mathematical structure—the relationship between a subtraction problem and a missing addend problem.

MATH WORDS AND IDEAS

MWI1 Learning Subtraction Facts: 10 Minus

MWI2 Learning Subtraction Facts: Minus Half

TEACHING NOTE

TN **Subtraction Facts: Fact Cards: Set 2**
There are 19 cards in Set 2 that are not Minus Ones, Minus Twos, 10 Minus or Minus Half Facts: 9 − 3, 8 − 3, 7 − 3, 5 − 3, 4 − 3, 9 − 4, 7 − 4, 6 − 4, 5 − 4, 9 − 5, 8 − 5, 7 − 5, 6 − 5, 9 − 6, 8 − 6, 7 − 6, 9 − 7, 8 − 7, 9 − 8.

3 ACTIVITY

Which Subtraction Facts Do I Know?

Students sort the Fact Cards: Set 2 into their envelopes of facts they know and facts they're still working on.

ONGOING ASSESSMENT Observing Students at Work

Students practice the subtraction facts within 10, as well as a few others. **MPN** **MWI1** **MWI2**

○ **Which subtraction facts can students recall fluently?** Which do they need to figure out? **TN**

○ **Are students able to identify and use related addition facts to solve unknown subtraction facts?**

As you circulate, select cards from students' envelopes of "Facts I Know" and see whether you agree that students know these. Help students understand what it means to know a fact fluently, and refile any cards as needed.

 DIFFERENTIATION Supporting the Range of Learners

INTERVENTION Suggest a Tool Some students may find it helpful to sort their cards into sets (e.g., the Minus Ones, the Minus Twos) and practice each set individually. For students who have a lot of cards in the "Facts I Am Still Working On" envelope, check to see if they are fluent with the related addition facts; fluency with these cards supports fluency with the related subtraction cards.

EXTENSION Adapt the Learning Situation Students who finish sorting their cards can pair up and work together to practice with the cards.

ENGLISH LANGUAGE LEARNERS Provide Opportunities for Practice Have students practice using addition and subtraction vocabulary and naming numbers by asking them to read aloud for you the cards in their "Facts I Know" envelope. For example, "Four plus six equals ten." and "Eight minus (or take away) one equals seven."

SESSION FOLLOW-UP: REVIEW AND PRACTICE

Daily Practice

 DAILY PRACTICE For reinforcement of this unit's content, students complete *Student Activity Book* page 52.

STUDENT ACTIVITY BOOK, P. 52

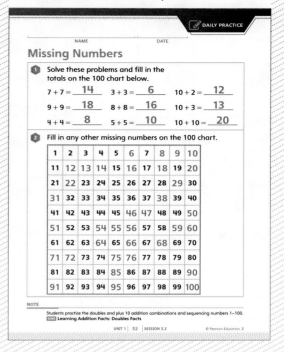

MATH PRACTICE NOTE

MPN **MP1 Make sense of problems and persevere in solving them.** Through using related facts to help with unknown facts, students learn to ask themselves, "What do I know to help me figure out what I don't yet know?"

MATH WORDS AND IDEAS

MWI1 Learning Subtraction Facts: Minus 1

MWI2 Learning Subtraction Facts: Minus 2

TEACHING NOTE

TN Fluency within 10 Students who did not have *Investigations* in Kindergarten and Grade 1 may not be fluent within 10, and others may need some focused practice after summer break (e.g., *One or Two Fewer*). The subtraction variations of *Five-in-a-Row* and *Roll and Record* provide practice subtracting a variety of 1-digit numbers.

Collect 50¢

MATH FOCUS POINTS

○ Combining coins to a total of 50¢

○ Identifying and using coin equivalencies

○ Developing fluency with addition and subtraction within 20

○ Solving a comparison story problem with the difference unknown

VOCABULARY

○ trade

TODAY'S PLAN	MATERIALS

(10) ** **CLASSROOM ROUTINES: REVIEW AND PRACTICE

Today's Number: Skip Counting by 10s

Class

Number line

Class 200 chart (optional)

---

(15) ** **1 ACTIVITY

Introducing *Collect 50¢*

Class

 Collect 50¢ (or use a coin set plus a dollar bill and two 1–6 number cubes)

 T3*

---

(30) **2 MATH WORKSHOP**

Coins, Facts, and Cubes

2A *Collect 50¢*

2B Fact Practice

2C Enough for the Class?

📋 **2A** G10*

📄 G11* (optional; for the Intervention)

📄 T3 (optional; for the Intervention)

🔧 Coin sets (1 set per 2–3 students, each with 100 pennies, 20 nickels, 20 dimes, and 8 quarters)

1–6 number or dot cubes (2 per 2–3 students)

2B Materials from Sessions 2.5 and 3.2

☑ 📄 **2C** A4*

📄 S17*

Counting Bags*

---

(15) ** **3 DISCUSSION

Coin Equivalencies

Class

 Teacher Presentation (or use 26 pennies, 4 nickels, and 2 dimes)

Chart: "Coin Equivalencies (Trades)"*

SESSION FOLLOW-UP: REVIEW AND PRACTICE

Daily Practice and Homework

📖 *Student Activity Book*, pp. 53–54

---

* See Materials to Prepare in the Investigation 3 planner.

Common Core State Standards	**Classroom Routines:** 2.NBT.A.2, 2.MD.B.6 **Session:** 2.OA.A.1, 2.OA.B.2, 2.NBT.A.2, 2.MD.C.8	**Daily Practice:** 2.MD.C.8

Today's Number: Skip Counting by 10s

MATH FOCUS POINTS

○ Counting by 10s

○ Identifying patterns in the multiples of 10

Explain that today students will do a new variation of *Today's Number,* which involves counting by groups of 10s.

Today, instead of writing equations for *Today's Number,* we are going to figure out the total number of fingers in our class as we count by 10s. Let's see what number we end up on once every person has counted. So [Jacy] would say 10 for [her] 10 fingers and [Leo] would say 20. How many fingers is that? Then if you add [Darren]'s fingers, that's 30 . . .

Count around the class by 10s, having students raise both hands as they say their number. For the first several students, use the class number line (or 200 chart if you have one) to keep track of the numbers students say for as high as possible. Count a second time, starting with a different student, this time recording the numbers in a list. Encourage students to look at the list of numbers and share what they notice. **MPN** **TN**

Make note of the ending number to use as a comparison in *Today's Number* in Session 3.4.

1 ACTIVITY

Introducing *Collect 50¢*

Begin by briefly reviewing the names and values of the coins and dollar bill and how many pennies each is worth.

Display the Game Presentation (or use a coin set plus a dollar bill and two 1–6 number cubes) and show only the first column of How Many Pennies? (T3).

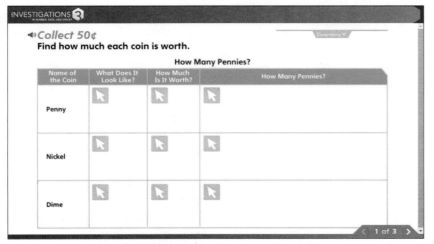

Ask students to find the coin that matches each word, and then reveal the second column. Then ask students what each coin is worth, and reveal the third column. Finally, review how many pennies each coin is worth, and reveal the final column.

Distribute How Many Pennies? (T3) to each student for reference.

Today we are going to play a game called *Collect 50¢.* **Each group will need two number cubes and a set of coins. The object is for each player to collect 50¢.**

Explain that players take turns rolling the number cubes and collecting the number rolled in cents.

I rolled three and three, so how many cents, or pennies, do I need to take?

Take and display six pennies. Explain that if a player has enough pennies, he or she can trade coins in for an equivalent amount. TN1 PD

Six pennies is one way to take six cents. Is there another way I could make six cents?

STUDENTS MIGHT SAY

"You could take one nickel and one penny because a nickel is five cents, and one more penny makes six cents."

So you can take six cents by taking six pennies, or by taking one nickel and one penny. I'm going to trade five of my pennies for a nickel. That way I'll only have two coins to keep track of.

Then ask a volunteer to take a turn and roll two number cubes. Decide together which combination of coins to take. Then take a second turn yourself so that students can see how the number rolled in the second turn is added to the first roll.

This time I rolled four.

Take four pennies, and then show students your collection of coins—one nickel and five pennies—to see whether there are any you can trade. TN2

Talk with the person next to you about how much money I will have now and what coins I should take or trade for.

Play until students understand the game. Remind them to work together to check each other's coins and to figure out how much money each player has after each turn. Also, encourage students to check their collections at the end of each turn to see whether there are any trades they can make and to explain the trades they make to their partner.

RESOURCE MASTERS, T3

TEACHING AIDS

How Many Pennies?

Name	What Does It Look Like?	How Much Is It Worth?	How Many Pennies?
Penny		1 cent or 1¢	
Nickel		5 cents or 5¢	
Dime		10 cents or 10¢	
Quarter		25 cents or 25¢	
Dollar		100 cents, 100¢, or $1.00	100 pennies

| T3 | © Pearson Education 2

TEACHING NOTES

TN1 **Coin Equivalencies** *Collect 50¢* is a first opportunity for students to learn about and use coin equivalencies. Since all rolls can be taken in pennies, students who need it get practice counting a set of objects by 1s. The more often students play this game and have other opportunities to work with and discuss coins and trading, the more they will understand and use equivalencies.

TN2 **When to Trade?** When students play, some take the four cents and *then* look at all the coins to decide whether a trade can be made. Others mentally add four to their previous total and decide which coin(s) should be taken in order to end with that amount.

PROFESSIONAL DEVELOPMENT

PD TEACHER NOTE 4: Money as a Mathematical Tool

2 MATH WORKSHOP

Coins, Facts, and Cubes

Show students the new Counting Bags, and review Enough for the Class? problems. Explain that the following three activities are available and that everyone needs to play at least one round of *Collect 50¢* before the end of Math Workshop.

2 A   *Collect 50¢*

Students play *Collect 50¢* in pairs or groups of three. Each group needs a set of coins and two 1–6 number (or dot) cubes. Players take turns rolling the cubes and collecting the amount rolled, in cents. Coins can be traded for equivalent amounts. The object is for each player to collect 50¢. The directions are available on G10.

ONGOING ASSESSMENT Observing Students at Work

Students count and combine coins and use coin equivalencies to make trades. **TN**

○ **How do students take coins that equal a given amount?** Do they take them all in pennies? Or, do they take a nickel and a penny if they roll 6?

○ **How do students collect and keep track of their total?** Do they count from 1 each time? Do they add the number rolled to the total at the end of their last turn?

○ **Are students able to trade coins for coins of equal value?** Which equivalencies do they seem most comfortable with?

○ **Once students have a mix of coins, how do they calculate their total in cents?**

To encourage thoughtful play, periodically ask players to pause in their game to respond to questions such as these:

○ **How much money do you have right now?**

○ **Look at your coins and the "How Many Pennies?" chart. Are there any trades you could make?**

○ **Could you reach 25¢ on your next turn? How many more do you need to reach 25¢? 50¢?**

RESOURCE MASTERS, G10

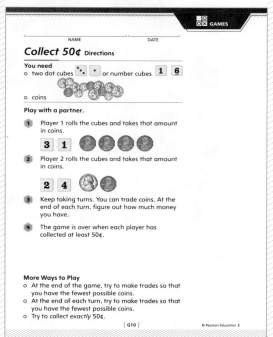

TEACHING NOTE

TN **Trading Coins** Note that as students play this game for the first time, many will be just beginning to think about and make sense of trading. The discussion at the end of this session, and continued experience with this game in upcoming sessions, will help them become more familiar and adept with trading.

Playing *Collect 50¢* helps students become fluent with coin values and coin equivalencies.

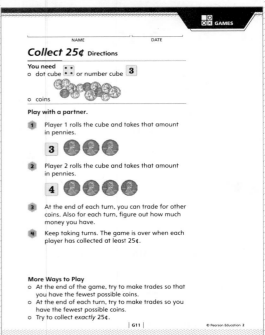

DIFFERENTIATION   Supporting the Range of Learners

INTERVENTION Adapt the Learning Situation Play *Collect 25¢* in a small group with students who are having difficulty. Focus on the coin names, values, and equivalencies. Encourage students to use a copy of How Many Pennies? (T3) to think about possible trades. The directions are available on G11.

Collect 25¢ gives students practice counting pennies and the opportunity to use coin equivalencies with smaller amounts.

INTERVENTION Scaffold a Solution Some students will be able to make trades (e.g., "I can take one of these for five of these.") but will struggle to figure out how much money they have. For example, when asked how much two dimes and three pennies are worth, some students may count "1, 2, 3, 4, 5," while others may count "10, 20, 30, 40, 50." Ask students to name the value of each coin first and work together to find the total. **MPN**

EXTENSION Vary the Problem To encourage trading, challenge students to have the fewest coins possible at the end of each round.

MATH PRACTICE NOTE

MPN **MP7 Look for and make use of structure.** In order to count two dimes and three pennies—10, 20, 21, 22, 23—students must understand the quantity represented by each count and coordinate the relationship between 1 and a group of 10 ones.

ENGLISH LANGUAGE LEARNERS **Model Thinking Aloud** To help students understand the meaning of the term *trade*, have them identify coins that are equal in value. For example, say: **I have 10 pennies. I can** *trade* **10 pennies for different coins with the same value. What is the value of 10 pennies? What other coins have that same value?** After students respond correctly, display the equivalent sets of coins (i.e., 10 pennies, 2 nickels, and 1 dime). **Each group has the same value, 10 cents. Since the value is the same, I can** *trade* **10 pennies for 2 nickels, or I can** *trade* **10 pennies for 1 dime.** Act out the trades with students.

---

2 B Fact Practice

Students practice the set of facts in their "Facts I Am Still Working On" envelope. They also review the cards in their "Facts I Know" envelope. Partners can also work together, quizzing each other and sharing strategies for finding and remembering the answer.

ONGOING ASSESSMENT Observing Students at Work

Students practice addition and subtraction facts within 20.

○ **Which facts can students recall fluently?** Which do they need to figure out?

○ **Are students able to identify and use known facts to solve unknown facts?**

○ **Are students becoming fluent with the facts?** Are they moving cards from the "Facts I Am Still Working On" envelope to the "Facts I Know" envelope? Which facts are challenging?

 **DIFFERENTIATION** Supporting the Range of Learners

INTERVENTION **Clarify the Problem** As you circulate, select cards from students' "Facts I Know" envelopes, and see whether you agree that students know these facts. Help students understand what it means to know a combination fluently, and refile any cards as needed.

2 C   Enough for the Class?

Students determine the number of cubes in a Counting Bag two ways (e.g., counting by 5s and adding the number of blue plus the number of red). Then, they determine whether there are enough cubes for everyone in the class to have one. They figure out how many leftovers there are or how many more cubes they would need. Remind students to record the letter of the bag and their work on Enough for the Class? (S17).

Enough For The Class? problems provide an opportunity to observe whether and how students make sense of problems and persevere in solving them (MP1), one of two highlighted math practices in this unit. Use **Assessment Checklist: MP1, Make sense of problems and persevere in solving them (A4)** to keep track of your observations over the course of this investigation.

RESOURCE MASTERS, A4

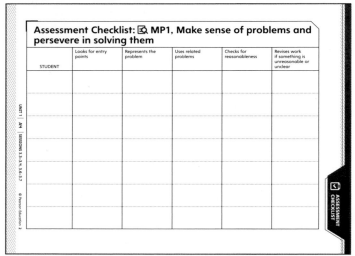

ONGOING ASSESSMENT   Observing Students at Work

Students count, combine, and compare quantities as they find the difference between the number of cubes and the number of students in the class.

○ **Can students make sense of the problem? Do they have a plan for approaching a solution? MP1**

○ **(How) do students determine the number of cubes in the bag?** Do they count by 1s? By groups? Do they add? (e.g., 12 red plus 13 blue cubes makes 25 cubes.) **MN**

○ **When there are more than enough cubes, how do students figure out how many extras there are?** Do they represent the students and deal out the cubes? Do they count up from the number of students in the class to the number of cubes in the bag? Do they count back? Do they separate the cubes into two groups?

○ **When there are not enough cubes, how do students figure out how many more they would need for everyone to have one?** Do they represent the students and deal out the cubes? Do they count up from the number of cubes in the bag to the number of students in the class? Do they count back?

MATH NOTE

MN **I Don't Know How Many Cubes There Are** While Enough for the Class? problems can be viewed as two-step problems that involve combining two amounts and then comparing that total to another amount, they can also be conceptualized and solved in other ways. Typically, some students solve such problems without ever finding the total number of cubes or without comparing the two amounts directly. For example, some count out cubes up to the number of students in the class and then count any additional cubes from one. Others reason about the two amounts, thinking for example, "There are 15 red and 15 blue. We have 12 girls and 12 boys. So there are 3 leftovers of each, and that's 6."

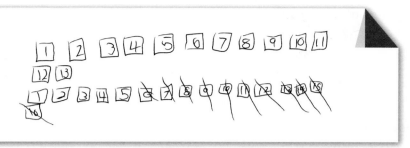

[Problem 7]

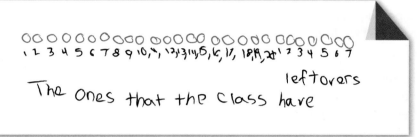

leftovers

The ones that the class have

[Problem 7]

 DIFFERENTIATION Supporting the Range of Learners

For another practice activity to be done outside of class, see *Enough or Not Enough?* at the end of this investigation.

3 DISCUSSION

Coin Equivalencies

MATH FOCUS POINT FOR DISCUSSION

○ Identifying and using coin equivalencies

Bring students together for a brief discussion about *Collect 50¢*. Display the Teacher Presentation (or use a coin set).

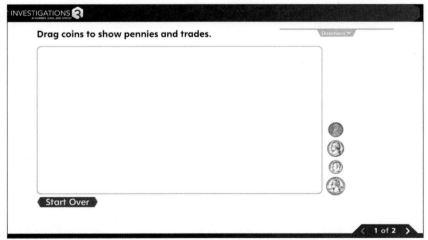

Ask a volunteer to count a set of 22 pennies by 1s while the rest of the class observes.

Ask another volunteer to put the pennies into rows of five.

If the pennies were organized like this, in rows of five, would you count them differently? Would you get the same amount?

Ask a student to count the pennies by 5s. While some students will be sure that there are 22 pennies whether you count them by 1s or by 5s, others may still think that counting objects in different ways can result in different answers.

So imagine this was my game, and I took all of my rolls as pennies. I have 22 pennies. But when [Leigh] was playing *Collect 50¢*, I saw [her] trading pennies for nickels. How many pennies are the same as a nickel?

Ask a student to place a nickel next to the first row of 5 pennies. Do not "trade in" the pennies; leave them in place so that students can see that 5 pennies in each row equal 1 nickel. Do the same for each row of 5 pennies.

So here's my money—22 pennies—and here's [Leigh]'s money. [She] traded [her] pennies along the way and has four nickels and two pennies. Who has more money?

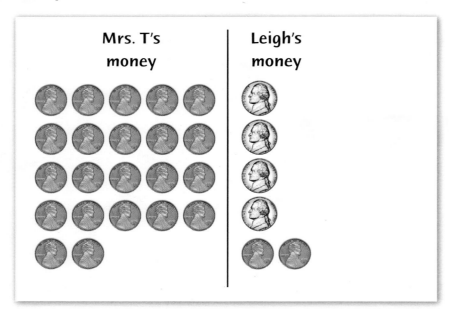

As students come to agreement, use the "Coin Equivalencies (Trades)" chart to discuss the equivalency.

We have thought about the different coins and how many pennies each is worth. But now, as we are playing *Collect 50¢*, people are finding out that you can take coins besides pennies, or you can trade pennies for other coins. For example, we agree that if you roll 5 cents, or have a group of 5 pennies, you can take a nickel instead of 5 pennies.

Fill in the last column of the nickel row on the "Coin Equivalencies (Trades)" chart, sketching the coins.

End by asking students to consider how they would exchange 22 pennies for dimes. Leave the set of 22 pennies and the set of 4 nickels and 2 pennies out so that students can see them.

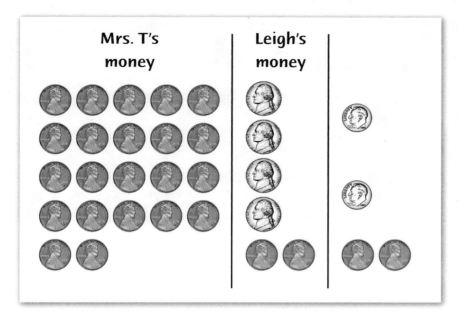

Then, ask students to help you fill in the dime row on the "Coin Equivalencies (Trades)" chart. **TN**

Coin Name	Coin Value	Equivalencies (Trades)
Penny	1 cent	1¢ ⓵¢
Nickel	5 cents	5¢ ⑤¢ ①¢ ①¢ ①¢ ①¢ ①¢
Dime	10 cents	10¢ ⑩¢ ⑤¢ ⑤¢ ⑤¢ ①¢ ①¢ ①¢ ①¢ ①¢
Quarter	25 cents	25¢ ㉕¢

SESSION FOLLOW-UP: REVIEW AND PRACTICE

Daily Practice and Homework

✏️ **DAILY PRACTICE** For reinforcement of this unit's content, students complete *Student Activity Book* page 53.

✏️ **HOMEWORK** Students determine the value of sets of coins on *Student Activity Book* page 54. They write equations to show their answers.

STUDENT ACTIVITY BOOK, P. 53

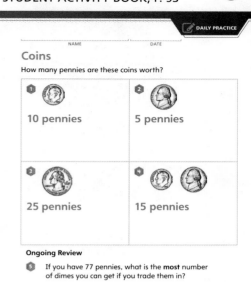

STUDENT ACTIVITY BOOK, P. 54

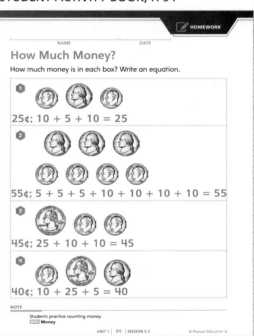

TEACHING NOTE

TN **Coin Equivalencies** It is not necessary to make a complete chart at this time. Students will be playing this game during Math Workshop over the next few days and can add new combinations as they find them. Keep this chart posted as a classroom resource.

Comparing Two Numbers

MATH FOCUS POINTS

- ○ Combining coins to a total of 50¢
- ○ Identifying and using coin equivalencies
- ○ Developing fluency with addition and subtraction within 20
- ○ Solving a comparison story problem with the difference unknown

TODAY'S PLAN	MATERIALS

CLASSROOM ROUTINES: REVIEW AND PRACTICE

Today's Number: Skip Counting by 5s

Number line

Class 200 chart (optional)

1 MATH WORKSHOP

Coins, Facts, and Cubes

   1A *Collect 50¢*

   1B Fact Practice

   1C Enough for the Class?

1A Materials from Session 3.3

1B Materials from Session 3.2

1C Materials from Sessions 3.1 and 3.3

2 DISCUSSION

Strategies for Enough for the Class?

Labeled counting bag (from Math Workshop 1C)

Chart paper

🔧 Connecting cubes (as needed)

🔧 Class 100 chart (as needed)

Number line (as needed)

SESSION FOLLOW-UP: REVIEW AND PRACTICE

Daily Practice

📖 *Student Activity Book*, p. 55

Common Core State Standards	**Classroom Routines:** 2.NBT.A.2, 2.MD.B.6 **Session:** 2.OA.A.1, 2.OA.B.2, 2.NBT.A.2, 2.NBT.B.6, 2.MD.C.8	**Daily Practice:** 2.OA.A.1

Today's Number: Skip Counting by 5s

MATH FOCUS POINTS

○ Counting by 5s

○ Identifying patterns in the multiples of 5

Remind students of their experience in the previous session with counting the number of fingers in the room by counting around the class by 10s.

Yesterday we counted by 10s around the class and we figured out that we had [240] fingers. Today we are going to count the number of fingers again but, instead of counting by 10s, we are going to count by 5s. Do you think we will land on [240] again?

Count around the class, having students raise one hand and then the other as they count by 5s. For the first several students, use the class number line (or 200 chart if you have one) to keep track of the numbers students say for as high as possible. Count a second time, starting with a different student, this time recording the numbers in a list. Encourage students to look at the list of numbers and share what they notice.

Make note of the ending number to use as a comparison in *Today's Number* in Session 3.5.

1 MATH WORKSHOP

Coins, Facts, and Cubes

Choose a counting bag with no more than 40 connecting cubes in it to discuss at the end of this session. Ask students to check the work they have done so far to see whether they have already completed the Enough for the Class? problem for this bag. If not, they should begin here.

1 A *Collect 50¢*

For complete details about this activity, see Session 3.3.

 DIFFERENTIATION Supporting the Range of Learners

INTERVENTION **Scaffold a Solution** Work in a small group with students who consistently take the rolled amount in pennies to discuss equivalencies and to scaffold trades for other coins. Use *Math Words and Ideas*, Coin Values and Equivalencies to present several examples of equivalencies, and work together to generate others. Play a few rounds of *Collect 50¢* and discuss with students what combinations of coins could be taken for each roll. **MWI**

MATH WORDS AND IDEAS

MWI Money

EXTENSION **Extend Thinking** Players collect exactly 50¢, which requires figuring out how many more cents they need to make exactly 50¢.

---

1 B **Fact Practice**

For complete details about this activity, see Session 3.2. **TN**

 DIFFERENTIATION Supporting the Range of Learners

INTERVENTION **Scaffold a Solution** Meet with students who have Fact Cards in their "Facts I Am Still Working On" envelope. Ask them to choose a card they find particularly difficult, and think together about a hint they could write on the Clue line that will help them learn and remember this fact. For example:

3 + 6 6 + 3 Clue: _6; 7, 8, 9_	3 + 6 6 + 3 Clue: _Think 3+3+3_
3 + 6 6 + 3 Clue: _Think 6+4, minus 1_	3 + 6 6 + 3 Clue: _Think 3+7, minus 1_

If students struggle to think of a hint, pose a related problem and ask how it could help. So, I notice that 3 + 5 / 5 + 3 is not a fact you're still working on. What's the sum? How could knowing that 3 + 5 = 8 help with 8 − 3? Let's look at it with cubes. Here's 3 + 5 = 8.

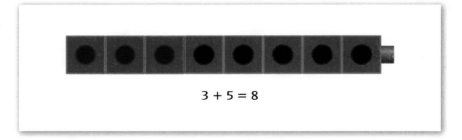

3 + 5 = 8

TEACHING NOTE

TN **The Facts** The Facts within 20 are benchmarked in Unit 8. Practice with them is built in, particularly in the Classroom Routine *Practicing the Facts*, which is introduced in Session 4.4. However, for this unit, it's good to have a sense of where students are with these facts (most of which were assessed at the end of Grade 1) so you can provide early, systematic, and focused support.

Can you use my tower to show 8 − 3?

Vary the types of hints you discuss, encouraging students to record ones that make sense to them and will help them learn that fact fluently.

```
┌─────────────────────────────────────────────┐
│  ┌──────────────────┐  ┌──────────────────┐  │
│  │     8 − 3        │  │     8 − 3        │  │
│  │                  │  │                  │  │
│  │ Clue: 8; 7,6,⑤   │  │ Clue: 3+5=8      │  │
│  └──────────────────┘  └──────────────────┘  │
└─────────────────────────────────────────────┘
```

---

1 C Enough for the Class?

For complete details about this activity, see Sessions 3.1 and 3.3. Continue to use **Assessment Checklist: MP1, Make sense of problems and persevere in solving them (A4)** in this activity.

---

2 DISCUSSION

Strategies for Enough for the Class?

MATH FOCUS POINT FOR DISCUSSION

○ Solving a comparison story problem with the difference unknown

Display the cubes from the chosen counting bag, and ask students to take out their completed sheet Enough for the Class? for that bag. Begin the discussion by collecting the answers students found. Then discuss students' strategies for solving the problem. **PD**

Record students' strategies on chart paper and model them with cubes, the number line, or the 100 chart, where appropriate. Repeat or elaborate on each strategy, or ask a volunteer to do so, to give students another chance to make sense of a strategy that might be different from their own. **MPN1**

Use the following questions to guide the discussion:

○ **How did you solve this problem?** **MPN2**

○ **Did anyone solve the problem in a different way?**

○ **Is [Jeffrey]'s strategy similar to another one on our chart?**

PROFESSIONAL DEVELOPMENT

PD DIALOGUE BOX 7: Are There Enough for the Class?

MATH PRACTICE NOTES

MPN1 🔍 **MP1 Make sense of problems and persevere in solving them.** Through class discussion, students work to understand classmates' approaches to solving complex problems and identify correspondences between different approaches.

MPN2 **MP7 Look for and make use of structure.** Most likely, some students will count on or add up to solve this problem, while others count back or subtract in parts. Point this out to the class as something of interest. Later in the year, students will examine the relationship between addition and subtraction, exploring why both strategies should result in the correct answer.

Enough for the Class?
24 kids
9 blue, 12 red

1 2 3 4 5 6 7 8 9 10 11 12 13 14 15 16 17 18 19 20 21 22 23 24

3 kids didn't get cubes

12; 13, 14, 15, 16, 17, 18, 19, 20, 21. 21 cubes.
24 kids, so we need 3 more.

9 + 12
Take 1 from the 12 and give it to the 9.
10 + 11 = 21
3 kids didn't get cubes.

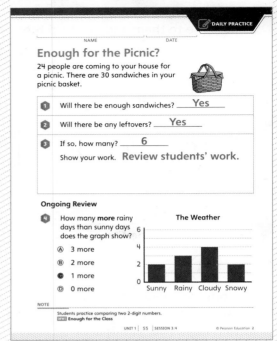

DAILY PRACTICE

NAME   DATE

Enough for the Picnic?
24 people are coming to your house for a picnic. There are 30 sandwiches in your picnic basket.

1 Will there be enough sandwiches? ___Yes___

2 Will there be any leftovers? ___Yes___

3 If so, how many? ___6___
   Show your work. Review students' work.

Ongoing Review

4 How many **more** rainy days than sunny days does the graph show?

   Ⓐ 3 more
   Ⓑ 2 more
   ● 1 more
   Ⓓ 0 more

The Weather

Sunny Rainy Cloudy Snowy

NOTE
Students practice comparing two 2-digit numbers.
Enough for the Class

UNIT 1 | 55 | SESSION 3.4   © Pearson Education 2

SESSION FOLLOW-UP: REVIEW AND PRACTICE

Daily Practice

✎ **DAILY PRACTICE** For reinforcement of this unit's content, students complete *Student Activity Book* page 55.

SESSION 3.5

Groups of 2, 5, and 10

MATH FOCUS POINTS

○ Counting by groups of 2, 5, and 10

○ Recognizing that the first digit of a 2-digit number designates the number of groups of 10 and the second digit designates the number of ones

TODAY'S PLAN	MATERIALS
(10) Class — **CLASSROOM ROUTINES: REVIEW AND PRACTICE** *Today's Number: Skip Counting by 5s and 10s*	Number line Class 200 chart (optional)
(15) Class — **1 ACTIVITY** **Introducing Groups of 2, 5, and 10**	Teacher Presentation (or use the "Grouping by 2s, 5s, and 10s" chart* and connecting cubes)
(30) Pairs — **2 ACTIVITY** **Grouping by 2s, 5s, and 10s**	*Student Activity Book*, p. 56 C23* Connecting cubes
(15) Class — **3 DISCUSSION** **Grouping by 10s**	Teacher Presentation (or use the "Grouping by 10s" chart* and connecting cubes) *Student Activity Book*, p. 56 (completed; from Activity 2)
SESSION FOLLOW-UP: REVIEW AND PRACTICE **Daily Practice**	*Student Activity Book*, pp. 57–59

* See *Materials to Prepare* in the Investigation 3 planner.

Common Core State Standards	**Classroom Routines:** 2.NBT.A.2, 2.MD.B.6 **Session:** 2.NBT.A.2	**Daily Practice:** 2.MD.C.8

CLASSROOM ROUTINES: REVIEW AND PRACTICE

Today's Number: Skip Counting by 5s and 10s

MATH FOCUS POINTS

○ Counting by 5s and 10s

○ Identifying patterns in the multiples of 5 and 10

Remind students of the number they ended with when they counted by 10s in Session 3.3, and ask whether they think the total will be the same today, and why. Note whether they realize that the number of students in school affects the total.

Again, frame the activity as being about counting fingers. Count around the class by 10s, having students raise both hands as they say their number. Ask a student to keep track of the numbers said on the class number line (or 200 chart if you have one) for as high as possible, while you record them in a list.

What if we count the fingers again, but this time we count first one hand, and then the other? So [Anita] would hold up one hand and say 5, and then [she] would hold up [her] other hand, and say 10. [Henry] would hold up one hand and say 15, and then hold up the other and say 20.

Count around the class by 5s, in the same order. Keep track of the numbers said on the class number line (or 200 chart if you have one). See if students notice that the second number they say is the same number they said when counting by 10s.

Count by 5s a second time. This time, record the numbers in a list next to the counting by 10 numbers.

Encourage students to look at the lists of numbers and share what they notice. **MPN**

MATH PRACTICE NOTE

MPN ⊟ **MP8 Look for and express regularity in repeated reasoning.** Asking students to look for and describe patterns helps them learn to look for mathematical structure and communicate with precision. Asking them to think about why the pattern works encourages them to develop mathematical reasoning and construct arguments.

Introducing Groups of 2, 5, and 10

Display the Teacher Presentation (or use the "Grouping by 2s, 5s, and 10s" chart and connecting cubes). Begin by calling attention to the prepared "Grouping by 2s, 5s, and 10s" chart. **MWI1** **MWI2**

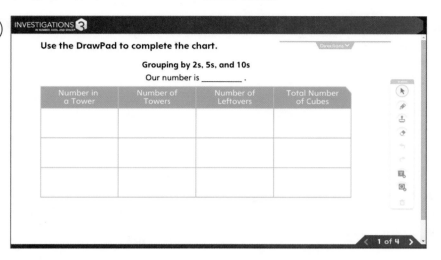

Today, we are going to look at different numbers and see what happens when we make groups of two, groups of five, or groups of ten.

Explain that you're going to give pairs a number card, with a number to investigate, and that you will demonstrate with the number 38. Fill in 38 for "our number" at the top of the chart.

Your first job is to work together to count out 38 cubes. When you agree that you have 38 cubes, put them into groups, or towers, of two.

Ask a volunteer to take 38 cubes and put them into groups of two. Ask another volunteer to count the number of towers (19) and the number of leftovers (0). Record this information on your table. Ask a volunteer to double-check that you still have 38 cubes. Make a check mark next to the 38 cubes in the last column to demonstrate that you double-checked your count. **MPN**

Follow the same process for grouping 38 cubes by 5s and by 10s. Together, record the information on the class chart.

Grouping by 2s, 5s, and 10s
Our number is 38 .

Number in a Tower	Number of Towers	Number of Leftovers	Total Number of Cubes
2	19	0	38 ✓
5	7	3	38 ✓
10	3	8	38 ✓

Explain that students will now work with a partner to investigate other numbers.

I will give you a number. Just like we did, write that number above the table on *Student Activity Book* page 56 and then count out that many cubes.

MATH WORDS AND IDEAS

MWI1 Counting by Groups

MWI2 Counting by 2s, 5s, and 10s

MATH PRACTICE NOTE

MPN 🔍 **MP1 Make sense of problems and persevere in solving them.**
Developing the habit of double-checking will serve students throughout the grades.

Then, you will put your cubes in groups of 2, record, and double-check your count. Next you will put the cubes in groups of 5, and finally, in groups of 10.

2 ACTIVITY

Grouping by 2s, 5s, and 10s

(30) (👥)

Partners work together to count out the number of cubes shown on a card from Numbers for Grouping by 2s, 5s, and 10s (C23). Pairs record information about what happens when they put cubes in groups of 2, 5, and 10 on *Student Activity Book* page 56. **TN**

ONGOING ASSESSMENT Observing Students at Work

Students organize objects into equal groups and then count the groups and leftovers.

○ **Can students accurately count out the total amount?** Do they count by 1s? By groups? Do they use the towers and singles to count by groups (5, 10, 15, 20, 25, 30, 35, 36, 37, 38)? Do they count by 1s? How do they double-check? **PD** 🔍 **MP1**

○ **Do students record information accurately?**

○ **Do students recognize that a 2-digit number represents the number of towers of ten plus the number of leftovers?**

Students use cubes to figure out how many groups of 2s, 5s, and 10s are in given numbers.

 DIFFERENTIATION Supporting the Range of Learners

INTERVENTION Scaffold a Solution Some students count groups accurately, but continue counting by the group as they transition to the leftovers. For example, they might count a set of 32 as 10, 20, 30, 40, 50 instead of 10, 20, 30, 31, 32. Ask these students about their counting, and to tie the numbers they are saying to the cubes in front of them. Model counting the cubes, pausing after the last group of 10 and focusing specifically on the set of leftover cubes. **So we have 30 cubes. Let's add one more. How many? And one more?** Give students a related group, for example 36 cubes, and observe how they count. Find ways to provide more practice, perhaps assigning additional number cards at other times of the day and in future sessions.

MATH PRACTICE NOTE

MPN 🔍 **MP8 Look for and express regularity in repeated reasoning.** When students notice that grouping by 10s results in the digits of the original number, they are making connections to the meaning of place value: The first digit of a 2-digit number represents the number of tens and the second digit represents the number of ones that comprise the 2-digit number.

MATH NOTE

MN Groups of 2s, 5s, and 10s In this activity, students are dividing the given number into equal groups of 2, 5, and 10, and recording the number of groups and the number of leftover cubes.

TEACHING NOTE

TN Assigning Numbers Give each pair a number appropriate for them, taking into account the class supply of connecting cubes. There are enough numbers for 15 pairs. Most pairs will investigate more than one number, and it is all right to assign the same number to more than one pair.

PROFESSIONAL DEVELOPMENT

PD TEACHER NOTE 3: Counting by Groups

EXTENSION Adapt the Problem Some students may be interested in exploring even greater numbers, such as 71, 72, and 73 (which offer an interesting comparison to 17, 27, and 37).

ENGLISH LANGUAGE LEARNERS Provide Sentence Stems Help pairs get started completing *Student Activity Book* page 56 by talking through each step as students build the towers and fill in their tables for the first problem. Provide sentence stems for students to complete to help them summarize what they did. For example: *I have _____ [12] towers of [2]. I have _____ [1] cube leftover. The total number of cubes is _____ [25].*

3 DISCUSSION

Grouping by 10s

MATH FOCUS POINT FOR DISCUSSION

○ Recognizing that the first digit of a 2-digit number designates the number of groups of 10 and the second digit designates the number of ones

Display the Teacher Presentation (or use the "Grouping by 10s" chart and connecting cubes).

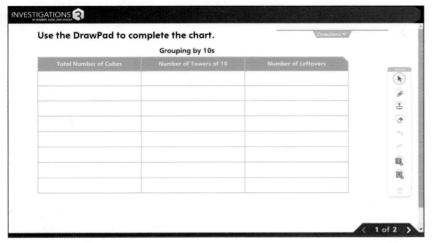

I heard some of you talking about a pattern you noticed when you grouped your number into towers of ten cubes. Before we talk about the pattern, let's share some of our numbers so that we can look at them together.

Ask several pairs to read their information for grouping by 10s—the total number of cubes, the number of towers of 10, the number of leftovers—as you record on the class chart.

Grouping by 10s		
Total Number of Cubes	Number of Towers of 10	Number of Leftovers
13	1	3
17	1	7
23	2	3

After you have filled three rows, ask another pair to tell you only the number of towers and the number of leftovers. Then ask students what they think the total number of cubes was. **PD**

[Nate] and [Juan], the class thinks you had [27] cubes altogether. Are they right?

After a few more examples, ask students to describe the pattern they have noticed.

Some of you can figure out the total number of cubes from the number of towers of ten and the number of leftovers. How do you figure it out?

" STUDENTS MIGHT SAY "

"The towers and the singles (or leftovers) give you the number. Together they make the number. Here is a 2 and here's a 7, so the number is 27."

"The number of towers is the first number in the total number. And the number of leftovers is the other number."

"The number of towers is the number of 10s, and the other is the number of singles."

Ask students to check their rows for making towers of ten to see whether the pattern worked. If someone finds a number that does not work, have the class look at that number together; count out that number of cubes by 1s, create towers of ten, and then count the towers and singles to show that the pattern works for that number.

Does the same pattern happen with towers of two or five?

Looking at their tables, students should see that the pattern did not hold when they made towers of two and five.

SESSION FOLLOW-UP: REVIEW AND PRACTICE

Daily Practice

 DAILY PRACTICE For reinforcement of this unit's content, students complete *Student Activity Book* pages 57–58.

 FAMILY LETTER Send home *Student Activity Book* page 59.

STUDENT ACTIVITY BOOK, P. 57

STUDENT ACTIVITY BOOK, P. 58

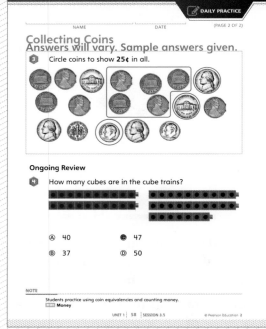

PROFESSIONAL DEVELOPMENT

PD TEACHER NOTE 11: Place Value in Second Grade

Tens and Ones

MATH FOCUS POINTS

○ Collecting, counting, representing, and comparing data

○ Solving problems about 10s and 1s

○ Recognizing that the first digit of a 2-digit number designates the number of groups of 10 and the second digit designates the number of ones

○ Developing fluency with addition and subtraction within 20

○ Solving a comparison story problem with the difference unknown

TODAY'S PLAN	MATERIALS
10 **CLASSROOM ROUTINES: REVIEW AND PRACTICE** Class *Quick Images: Ten Frames*	 Teacher Presentation (or use the *Quick Images: Ten Frames* Cards with 5, 6, 7, 8, and 9 dots)
25 **1 ACTIVITY** Class **Pocket Day**	Pocket Data chart (from Session 2.4) Pocket Day Jar, with rubber band still in place (from Session 2.4) 🔧 Connecting cubes (100 per class) Rubber band Chart: "Students in Our Class"*

25 **2 MATH WORKSHOP**
Tens and Ones
   2A Problems about Tens and Ones
   2B *Collect 50¢*
   2C Fact Practice
   2D Enough for the Class?
	📖 **2A** *Student Activity Book*, pp. 61–64
	🔧 Connecting cubes (as needed)
	🔧 Coins (as needed)
	2B Materials from Session 3.3
	2C Materials from Session 3.2
	2D Materials from Sessions 3.1 and 3.3

10 **3 ASSESSMENT ACTIVITY** Individuals **Quiz 2**	☑ 📄 A5–A6*
SESSION FOLLOW-UP: REVIEW AND PRACTICE **Daily Practice and Homework**	📖 *Student Activity Book*, pp. 65–66

* See *Materials to Prepare* in the Investigation 3 Planner.

Common Core State Standards	**Classroom Routines:** 2.OA.B.2, 2.NBT.B.9 **Session:** 2.OA.A.1, 2.OA.B.2, 2.NBT.A.2, 2.NBT.B.5, 2.NBT.B.9, 2.MD.C.8	**Daily Practice:** 2.OA.A.1

CLASSROOM ROUTINES: REVIEW AND PRACTICE

Quick Images: Ten Frames

MATH FOCUS POINTS

○ Developing and analyzing visual images for quantities up to 10

○ Using known facts to add two or more numbers

Display the Teacher Presentation (or use the *Quick Images: Ten Frames* Cards with 8 dots and 5 dots).

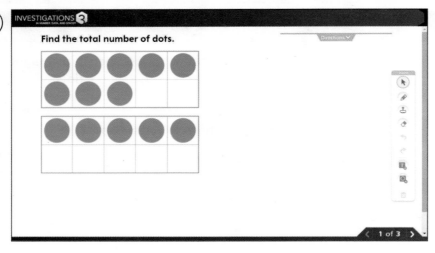

Follow the basic *Quick Images* activity. Students determine the total number of dots and share their strategies. Repeat with the 6-dot and 9-dot images and then the 7-dot and 8-dot images. Focus the discussion on how knowing a combination of 10 can help with other problems. Model students' thinking, and use equations to show what's happening in these strategies. **TN**

---

1 ACTIVITY

Pocket Day

Display the Pocket Data chart. Ask students whether they think the class is wearing more pockets than on their first Pocket Day, fewer pockets, or about the same number of pockets. Encourage them to explain their reasoning (e.g., attendance or a change in the weather).

The last time we collected pocket data, our class was wearing [59] pockets and the cubes filled the jar up to this line. (Point to the rubber band on the jar.) **How many pockets do you think all the people in our class are wearing today? PD**

Record the estimates, and ask students to compare them with the first day's total.

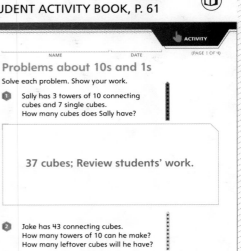

STUDENT ACTIVITY BOOK, P. 61

ACTIVITY

NAME   DATE   (PAGE 1 OF 4)

Problems about 10s and 1s

Solve each problem. Show your work.

1. Sally has 3 towers of 10 connecting cubes and 7 single cubes. How many cubes does Sally have?

37 cubes; Review students' work.

2. Jake has 43 connecting cubes. How many towers of 10 can he make? How many leftover cubes will he have?

4 towers, 3 leftover cubes; Review students' work.

UNIT 1 | 61 | SESSION 3.6   © Pearson Education 2

TEACHING NOTE

TN *Quick Images* Routine

○ Briefly show the image.

○ Students think about what they saw.

○ Show the image again, briefly.

○ Students revise their thinking.

○ With the image showing, volunteers share how many dots they saw, and how they remembered.

PROFESSIONAL DEVELOPMENT

PD DIALOGUE BOX 9: Our Second Pocket Day

[Alberto] thinks we are wearing [65] pockets today because no one's absent. If we put [65] cubes in the jar and made a line, as we did last time, would the line be higher? Lower? At about the same place?

Pass around bins of cubes, asking each student to take the same number of cubes as he or she has pockets. Tell them they need to remember the number of pockets they are wearing; you will be asking for it later in the session.

Take the jar from student to student and have them place their cubes in it. Put a new rubber band around the jar, indicating how full it is today.

Let's compare the two lines on our jar. Would you say we are wearing more pockets or fewer pockets today than on the first day? Or are we wearing about the same number of pockets?

Show students the prepared "Students in Our Class" chart listing their names.

Today we are going to collect pocket data a different way. When I call your name, tell us how many pockets you have and I'll record that information on this list.

Begin at the top of the list of names, and ask each student for his or her data. Record the number of pockets next to the student's name. Ask students to double-check that the number next to their name represents the correct number of pockets.

Today we are going to figure out how many pockets we are wearing by adding the numbers on this list. Think of this as one giant addition problem. Let's start by looking for combinations that make 10. **TN** **MPN**

As students point out combinations of pockets that make 10, the teacher uses equations to record them next to the list of names, crossing out the numbers used to keep track.

When no more combinations of 10 can be made, help students identify which numbers have not yet been added and again ask how these numbers could be combined. If you have anyone without any pockets, discuss how to count the zeros.

STUDENT ACTIVITY BOOK, P. 62

ACTIVITY

NAME   DATE   (PAGE 2 OF 4)

Problems about 10s and 1s

3   Franco has 62 pennies. If he trades the pennies for as many dimes as he can, how many dimes will he have? How many pennies will be left?

6 dimes, 2 pennies left; Review students' work.

4   Baseball cards come in packs of 10. Kira has 3 packs and 8 single cards that her brother gave her. How many baseball cards does she have altogether?

38 cards; Review students' work.

UNIT 1 | 62 | SESSION 3.6   © Pearson Education 2

TEACHING NOTE

TN **Addition Models** The strategy of joining known combinations will make sense to many students; however, it may take time and practice for some students to use this strategy on their own.

MATH PRACTICE NOTE

MPN **MP1 Make sense of problems and persevere in solving them.** An important habit for solving complex problems is to ask, "What do I know that can make the problem simpler?" When given a long string of numbers to add, grouping addends that make 10 is one such approach.

So, now we have many groups of 10 and some left over. Let's think about a way to add all these 10s. Does anyone know what 10 + 10 is?

Write 10 + 10 = 20 and cross out two groups of 10. Next, add another group of 10 to the 20, cross out another group of 10, and write 20 + 10 = 30. Continue with this procedure until all the groups of 10 are crossed out. **TN**

Finally, add any remaining numbers to calculate the total number of pockets, and write that equation.

Remove the rubber band marking the first day's data and leave the rubber band showing today's data. Ask several volunteers to put the cubes from the jar into towers of 10, and a tower with any leftovers. Set the jar aside.

We have a bunch of towers of 10 and some left over. Let's count them by 10s and see if we get the same total.

Ask students to count with you, raising each tower of 10 as you count it. You may hear discrepancies when you get to the final tower of less than 10. Discuss this, and count again as needed. Note whether any students relate the process of counting by 10s to your process for adding the numbers on your list.

Once you agree on the number of pockets, record this information on the class Pocket Data chart and compare today's data with the data from the first Pocket Day.

How many pockets are we wearing today?

	Pockets	People
Pocket Day 1	59	22
Pocket Day 2	72	22

Are students wearing more or fewer pockets this time? Why might this be?

Revisit the estimates and the reasons for them.

2 MATH WORKSHOP

Tens and Ones

 (25)

Math Workshop continues with one new activity. Briefly introduce *Student Activity Book* pages 61–64, Problems about Tens and Ones. Then, set students to work.

2 A   Problems about Tens and Ones

Students solve problems about tens and ones, and show their work on *Student Activity Book* pages 61–64. Connecting cubes and coins should be available for this work as needed.

STUDENT ACTIVITY BOOK, P. 63

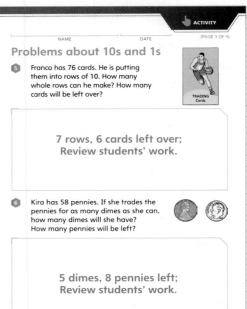

ACTIVITY

NAME   DATE   (PAGE 3 OF 4)

Problems about 10s and 1s

5. Franco has 76 cards. He is putting them into rows of 10. How many whole rows can he make? How many cards will be left over?

> 7 rows, 6 cards left over;
> Review students' work.

6. Kira has 58 pennies. If she trades the pennies for as many dimes as she can, how many dimes will she have? How many pennies will be left?

> 5 dimes, 8 pennies left;
> Review students' work.

UNIT 1 | 63 | SESSION 3.6   © Pearson Education 2

STUDENT ACTIVITY BOOK, P. 64

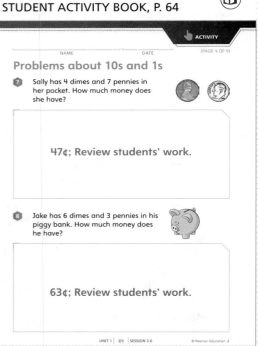

ACTIVITY

NAME   DATE   (PAGE 4 OF 4)

Problems about 10s and 1s

7. Sally has 4 dimes and 7 pennies in her pocket. How much money does she have?

> 47¢; Review students' work.

8. Jake has 6 dimes and 3 pennies in his piggy bank. How much money does he have?

> 63¢; Review students' work.

UNIT 1 | 64 | SESSION 3.6   © Pearson Education 2

TEACHING NOTE

TN   **Adding Groups of 10** You may need to guide this part of the calculation, particularly as the size of the numbers increase. For example, when adding 20 + 10, use 10 cubes, 10 fingers, or 10 jumps on the number line or 100 chart to determine (or confirm) the total amount. Note that students will have many opportunities to work with, count by, and add groups of 10 throughout Grade 2.

ONGOING ASSESSMENT Observing Students at Work

Students practice working with tens and ones.

○ **Are students thinking in terms of ones or groups of tens and ones?** Can they work in both directions? For example, when given a number, can they say how many tens and ones? When told how many tens and ones, can they say the total number?

○ **Are students confident with problems based in contexts other than cubes (e.g., money, items in packages of ten, and so on)?**

○ **How do students show their work?** Do they show every single item? Do they just represent the groups and leftovers? That is, if they draw cubes, do they draw an empty rectangle to represent ten, or do they show every single cube? **TN**

Pay particular attention to students' strategies for Problem 3, which will be the focus of the discussion at the end of Session 3.7. Look for students who 1) count out 62 individual items and then group them into 10s, or 2) start with groups and count up by 10s to break 62 into as many 10s as possible.

 DIFFERENTIATION Supporting the Range of Learners

INTERVENTION Suggest a Tool Remind students of the patterns discussed in Session 3.5, and refer them to the posted "Grouping by 10s" chart. Some students may need to model the problems with cubes.

ENGLISH LANGUAGE LEARNERS Repeat and Clarify Help students understand what is being asked in each of the problems on *Student Activity Book* pages 61–64 by reading the problems, one sentence at a time, with students. Rephrase the problems using simpler language, as needed. For example, for Problem 1, say: **Sally has 3 towers. Each tower has 10 cubes. She also has 7 cubes. How many cubes does she have in all?** Pause after each sentence and have students restate it. Encourage students to use manipulatives, such as cubes or coins, or to draw sketches to represent and solve each problem.

---

2 B *Collect 50¢*

For complete details about this activity, see Session 3.3.

 DIFFERENTIATION Supporting the Range of Learners

EXTENSION Vary the Problem As the end of the game approaches, if a player rolls a number that will place him or her over 50¢, the player *subtracts* the amount and continues playing until he or she accumulates *exactly* 50¢.

RESOURCE MASTERS, A5

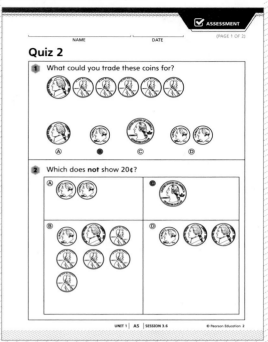

RESOURCE MASTERS, A6

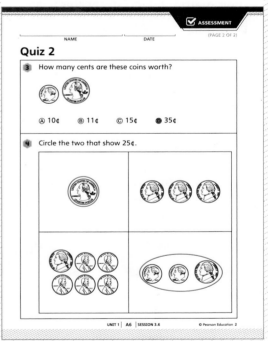

TEACHING NOTE

TN Representing Tens and Ones
Although some students may need to draw every single item or cube, others may benefit from seeing ways to record without doing so (e.g., drawing long rectangles or lines labeled "ten" to represent groups of ten).

2 C　Fact Practice

For complete details about this activity, see Session 3.2.

2 D　Enough for the Class?

For complete details about this activity, see Sessions 3.1 and 3.3. Continue to use **Assessment Checklist: MP1, Make sense of problems and persevere in solving them (A4)** in this activity.

3　ASSESSMENT ACTIVITY

Quiz 2

 (10)

Explain that students will end the session by solving some problems on their own so you can get a sense of how much they have learned and grown in their math thinking so far this year.

Distribute Quiz 2 (A5–A6), review the format with students, and read the problems aloud.

These questions provide additional information about Benchmark 1. Use this information along with other information you have collected during this unit when assessing a student's progress towards this Benchmark.

BENCHMARK	QUESTIONS
1: Recognize and identify coins and their values.	1–4

SESSION FOLLOW-UP: REVIEW AND PRACTICE

Daily Practice and Homework

DAILY PRACTICE For reinforcement of this unit's content, students complete *Student Activity Book* page 65.

HOMEWORK Students count the pockets on people in their families and record the data on *Student Activity Book* page 66.

STUDENT ACTIVITY BOOK, P. 65

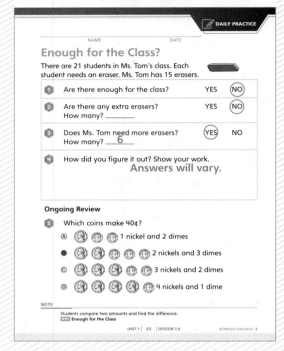

STUDENT ACTIVITY BOOK, P. 66

SESSION 3.7
Enough for the Class?

MATH FOCUS POINTS

○ Solving a comparison story problem with the difference unknown

○ Solving problems about 10s and 1s

○ Recognizing that the first digit of a 2-digit number designates the number of groups of 10 and the second digit designates the number of ones

○ Developing fluency with addition and subtraction within 20

TODAY'S PLAN	MATERIALS

 10 Class

CLASSROOM ROUTINES: REVIEW AND PRACTICE

Today's Number: Skip Counting by 5s and 10s

Class 200 chart

Number line

---

 20 Class Individuals

1 ASSESSMENT ACTIVITY

Enough for the Class?

 A4 (from Session 3.3)

 A7*

Counting Bag Z*

Connecting cubes (as needed)

Number line

100 chart

 35

2 MATH WORKSHOP

Tens and Ones

2A Problems about Tens and Ones

2B *Collect 50¢*

2C Fact Practice

2D Enough for the Class?

2A Materials from Session 3.6

2B Materials from Session 3.3

2C Materials from Session 3.2

2D Materials from Sessions 3.1 and 3.3

---

 15 Class

3 DISCUSSION

A Problem about Tens and Ones

 Student Activity Book, p. 62 (completed; from Session 3.6)

SESSION FOLLOW-UP: REVIEW AND PRACTICE

Daily Practice

Student Activity Book, p. 67

---

* See *Materials to Prepare* in the Investigation 3 Planner.

Common Core State Standards	**Classroom Routines:** 2.NBT.A.2, 2.MD.B.6 **Session:** 2.OA.A.1, 2.OA.B.2, 2.NBT.B.9, 2.MD.B.6, 2.MD.C.8	**Daily Practice:** 2.MD.C.8

CLASSROOM ROUTINES: REVIEW AND PRACTICE

Today's Number: Skip Counting by 5s and 10s

MATH FOCUS POINTS

○ Counting by 5s and 10s

○ Identifying patterns in the multiples of 5 and 10

Remind students of the numbers they ended with when they counted by 10s in Sessions 3.3 and 3.5. Ask whether students think the total will be the same today, and why. Note whether they realize that the number of students in school affects the total.

Again, frame the activity as being about counting fingers. Count around the class by 10s, having students raise both hands as they say their number. Ask a student to keep track of the numbers said on the class 200 chart or number line while you record them in a list.

What if we count the fingers again, but this time we count first one hand, and then the other? So [Lonzell] would hold up one hand and say 5, and then [he] would hold up [his] other hand, and say 10. [Leigh] would hold up one hand and say 15, and then hold up the other and say 20.

Count around the class by 5s, in the same order. Keep track of the numbers said on the class number line or 200 chart for as high as possible. See if students notice that the second number they say is the same number they said when counting by 10s. Record the final number.

Count by 5s a second time. This time, record the numbers in a list next to the counting by 10 numbers.

Encourage students to look at the lists of numbers and share what they notice.

● RESOURCE MASTERS, A7

☑ ASSESSMENT

NAME _____   DATE _____

Enough for the Class?

1. There are _____ children in our class.

2. There are _____ red cubes and _____ blue cubes in the bag.

3. How many cubes are there altogether? _____

4. Are there enough for the class?   YES   NO

5. Were there any extra cubes?   YES   NO
How many? _____

6. Do you need more cubes?   YES   NO
How many? _____

7. How did you figure it out? Show your work.
Answers will vary. Review students' work.

UNIT 1 | A7 | SESSION 3.7   © Pearson Education 2

1 ASSESSMENT ACTIVITY

Enough for the Class?

Explain that students are going to solve an Enough for the Class? problem and show their work. They will work individually so that you can get a sense of how they are growing in their thinking.

To solve an Enough for the Class? problem, students find the difference between the number of cubes and the number of students in their class. (Benchmark 3). This is also the last chance to use Enough for the Class? as an opportunity to assess MP1: Make sense of problems and persevere in solving them. Continue to use **Assessment Checklist:** MP1, Make sense of problems and persevere in solving them (A4) to keep track of your observations. **TN1 TN2**

BENCHMARK	QUESTIONS
3: Solve a comparison story problem with the difference unknown.	1–7

Show students the counting bag of blue and red cubes labeled Z. As a class, count and record the number of blue cubes and the number of red cubes.

There are [17] blue cubes and [18] red cubes in this bag. Your job is to figure out if there are enough cubes in the bag for everyone in the class to have one. If there are, how many leftover cubes would there be? If there are not, how many more cubes would we need so that everyone could have one?

Distribute A7 (or the Online Assessment), and have students record the number of cubes of each color.

You can use any of our math tools, such as the number line, the 100 chart, or the connecting cubes, to help you solve this problem. Make sure that you record your answer and explain how you solved the problem.

Tell students that you are interested in all of their strategies and explanations for solving this problem and that you will look carefully at each person's writing.

ONGOING ASSESSMENT Observing Students at Work

Students combine two numbers and then compare two numbers to find the difference. **PD**

○ **How do students find the total number of cubes in the bag?** Do they recreate the situation with cubes and count them all? Do they count on from one of the numbers? Do they add the numbers mentally or on paper?

○ **How do students determine whether there are enough cubes?** How do they figure out how many leftovers there will be? What tools do they use (e.g., cubes, the number line, the 100 chart)?

○ **How do they show their thinking on paper?** Do they use numbers? Pictures? Words? A combination of these?

TEACHING NOTES

TN1 Assessing Students' Use of the Number Line Some students use a number line as they work on Enough for the Class? problems. Pay attention to how students use this tool. Do they use it to represent the problem and what it's asking? Do they use it to solve the problem, perhaps jumping from the number of students in the class to the number of cubes in the bag (or vice versa)? Do they label every number? Every 10th? Only the numbers they used in solving the problem? Are their jumps relatively proportional (e.g., a jump of 10 looks larger than a jump of 1)?

TN2 Assessing Students' Ability to Explain Their Strategy This problem also provides the opportunity to observe students' growing ability to explain their strategies for solving addition and subtraction problems. Look for evidence that they are using strategies that rely on reasoning about the operations and place value (e.g., "There are 35 cubes and 24 kids. $35 - 10 = 25$, minus 1 more is 24. So there are 11 extra cubes." Or "24 kids use 24 cubes. The rest are extra: $24 + 10 = 34$ and 1 more is 35, that's 11.").

PROFESSIONAL DEVELOPMENT

PD TEACHER NOTE 12: Assessment: Enough for the Class?

When students have finished writing, have them read their explanations to you. Do not tell them whether they are correct or incorrect, but point out places that are unclear or where information seems to be missing and have them revise their work. MPN TN

 DIFFERENTIATION Supporting the Range of Learners

ENGLISH LANGUAGE LEARNERS **Allow Varied Responses** Students may find it challenging to explain how they solved the problem. Allow students to draw pictures and/or use their first language, along with gestures, to make their point. To determine students' mathematical knowledge, pose the following questions: **How many cubes are in the bag? Can everyone in the class have 1 cube? Are there leftover cubes?**

2 MATH WORKSHOP

Tens and Ones

(35)

As students finish the assessment, they choose among the following activities. Students need to have completed Problem 3 on *Student Activity Book* page 62 for the discussion at the end of this session.

---

2 A Problems about Tens and Ones

For complete details about this activity, see Session 3.6.

---

2 B *Collect 50¢*

For complete details about this activity, see Session 3.3.

---

2 C Fact Practice

For complete details about this activity, see Session 3.2.

---

2 D Enough for the Class?

For complete details about this activity, see Sessions 3.1 and 3.3.

MATH PRACTICE NOTE

MPN ▣ **MP1 Make sense of problems and persevere in solving them.** Commenting on students' work in this manner places the focus on the clarity of their thinking. This forces students to look again at their work and learn to ask themselves, "Does this make sense to me?" Also, it helps them see that an important part of mathematics is communicating your thoughts to others.

TEACHING NOTE

TN **Analyzing Responses** This set of papers can give you information about the understanding of individual students and also about the class as a whole. Consider comparing this to the work students did in Session 3.1.

3 DISCUSSION

A Problem about Tens and Ones

MATH FOCUS POINT FOR DISCUSSION

○ Recognizing that the first digit of a 2-digit number designates the number of groups of 10 and the second digit designates the number of ones

Briefly discuss Problems 1 and 2 from *Student Activity Book* page 61, asking one student to share a solution and another student to model the problem with cubes.

Then spend the rest of this discussion on Problem 3 (*Student Activity Book* page 62): trading 62 pennies for dimes. Call on students who used the following strategies to share their work: 1) representing 62 ones and then grouping them into tens or 2) breaking 62 into groups of 10 and then counting the groups. Then focus discussion on how the two strategies are connected.

Franco has 62 pennies. If he trades the pennies for as many dimes as he can, how many dimes will he have? How many pennies will be left?

Some students draw 62 circles or tallies, or count out 62 pennies or cubes. Most organize them in some way. Then they circle or create groups of ten. They count the groups of ten, each of which represents a dime, and count the leftover pennies.

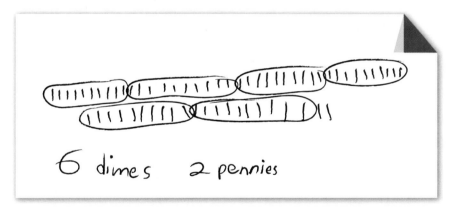

Other students count by 10s or break 62 into as many groups of ten as possible. They may count in their heads or use manipulatives. They count the groups of ten (i.e., dimes) and the leftovers (i.e., the pennies).

As they work on and discuss this problem, it can be challenging for students to go back and forth between thinking about six dimes and 60 cents. In fact, one or several students are likely to record their answer as 60 dimes and two pennies. If this issue doesn't come up naturally, raise it yourself and clarify that each dime is ten cents.

60 dimes 2 pennies

SESSION FOLLOW-UP: REVIEW AND PRACTICE

Daily Practice

 DAILY PRACTICE For reinforcement of this unit's content, students complete *Student Activity Book* page 67. For Problem 1, students are not expected to make an organized list.

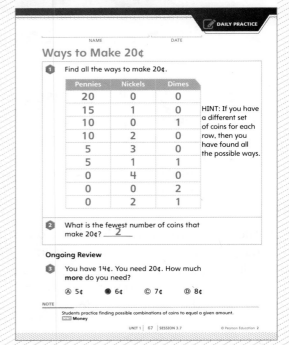

STUDENT ACTIVITY BOOK, P. 67

DAILY PRACTICE

NAME   DATE

Ways to Make 20¢

1   Find all the ways to make 20¢.

Pennies	Nickels	Dimes
20	0	0
15	1	0
10	0	1
10	2	0
5	3	0
5	1	1
0	4	0
0	0	2
0	2	1

HINT: If you have a different set of coins for each row, then you have found all the possible ways.

2   What is the fewest number of coins that make 20¢? ___2___

Ongoing Review

3   You have 14¢. You need 20¢. How much **more** do you need?

   Ⓐ 5¢   ● 6¢   Ⓒ 7¢   Ⓓ 8¢

NOTE

Students practice finding possible combinations of coins to equal a given amount.
Money

UNIT 1 | 67 | SESSION 3.7   © Pearson Education 2

Will Each Person Get One?

MATH FOCUS POINT

○ Solving a comparison story problem with the difference unknown

MATERIALS: bags containing 8–16 connecting cubes (1 per pair; each with a different number of connecting cubes), 1 extra bag containing 7 connecting cubes, T4

Simplify an Enough for the Class? situation (Session 3.1) as follows. **There are 10 people sitting at a table.** Display a blank Ten Frame (T4). **I'm going to draw a face for each person. How many faces should I draw?** Explain that the faces represent the people at the table. Count to verify that there are exactly 10 faces. Hold up the bag of 7 cubes. **Let's find out if there are enough cubes in this bag for each person at the table to get one.**

Pour the cubes from the bag and have students count to verify the total. Then, starting at the top left, place one cube on each face as everyone counts: **1, 2, 3, . . . 7.**

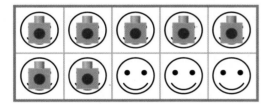

Are there enough cubes for each person at the table to get one? How many more do we need? How can we find out?

STUDENTS MIGHT SAY

"Count how many faces don't have cubes."

"I can see that 3 faces don't have a cube."

So, if we have 10 people and 7 cubes, there are not enough cubes in the bag for each person to get one.

Repeat the problem using the bag of 16 cubes. Remind students that there are still 10 people at the table. Determine the number of cubes in the bag. **Are there enough cubes for the people at the table to each have one? How do you know?** Ask students to share their thinking about how to figure out how many extra cubes there are. Try each strategy.

 STUDENTS MIGHT SAY

"Put the cubes on the Ten Frame and if you cover the smiley faces for the 10 people you have enough. Then count the extras."

"16 is enough because 16 is more than 10. And it's, 11, 12, 13, 14, 15, 16 . . . 6 more."

Distribute a bag of cubes and a copy of T4 to each pair of students. Have them work together to draw 10 faces on one blank Ten Frame. They count the number of cubes in their bag and determine if there are enough cubes for the 10 people to each get one. Then they determine how many more cubes they need or how many extras there are.

DIFFERENTIATION

ENGLISH LANGUAGE LEARNERS **Model Thinking Aloud** Help students understand the meaning of the word *enough* as used in this context, by first modeling a situation where there is *enough* of something for everyone. For example, show students a set of cubes and give each student one cube. **We have the same number of cubes as people. Everyone can have one. We have *enough*.** Then model *not enough* with another set of cubes.

ADDITIONAL RESOURCE

Math Words and Ideas Enough for the Class

Enough or Not Enough?

MATH FOCUS POINTS

○ Solving a comparison story problem with the difference unknown

○ Using numbers, pictures, words, and/or notation to represent a solution to a problem

MATERIALS: connecting cubes (as needed), S18

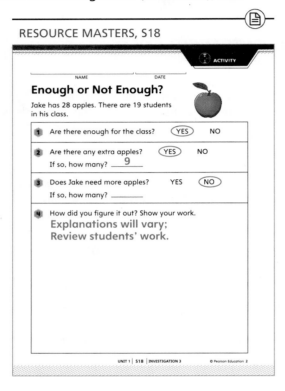

RESOURCE MASTERS, S18

Display and read the following problem aloud. **Mrs. Reed has 23 stickers. There are 13 boys and 14 girls in her class. Are there enough stickers for each student in her class to get one?**

Review the information in the problem. **What does the problem tell us? What do we know? What do we need to find out?**

Discuss the steps for solving the problem. **First, we need to find out how many students are in Mrs. Reed's class. How could we do that? Next, we need to compare the number of students with the number of stickers. How could we do that?**

" STUDENTS MIGHT SAY "

"Make a cube tower for the stickers and a cube tower for the students. It shows there are more students."

"Look on the number line. 23 is less than 27, so I know there are not enough stickers."

How many more stickers does Mrs. Reed need? How did you find out? Record students' solution strategies.

Present a second problem for students to solve on their own. **There are 32 basketballs. There are 15 boys and 12 girls in gym class. Are there enough basketballs for each student to get one?**

After students have solved the problem, bring them together to discuss their solutions. **Are there enough basketballs for each student to get one? How many extras are there? How did you find out?** Record strategies as they are shared.

Distribute copies of Enough or Not Enough? (S18).

DIFFERENTIATION

ENGLISH LANGUAGE LEARNERS **Provide Vocabulary Support** Help students understand the vocabulary used in the context of this activity. For example, explain that when you are *comparing* the numbers of students and stickers, you are trying to find out which group has more. **Are there *more* stickers or *more* students?** There are *more* students. There are *fewer* stickers. So there are *not enough* stickers for each student to get one. Also, review the meaning of the term *extras*.

Two or More Bones

MATH FOCUS POINTS

○ Solving a comparison story problem with the difference unknown

○ Using numbers, pictures, words, and/or notation to represent a solution to a problem

MATERIALS: connecting cubes (30–55 per student), S19 (2 per student)

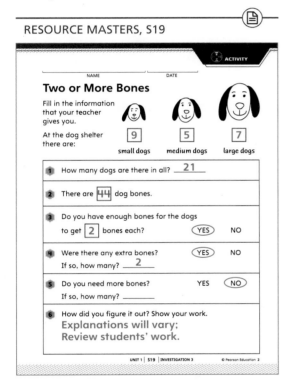

RESOURCE MASTERS, S19

Draw 3 simple, different-sized dogs and label them as shown.

Distribute a copy of Two or More Bones (S19) to each student. Read the following problem aloud. **A shelter has dogs for adoption. This picture shows how many small, medium, and large dogs there are. You have 44 dog bones. Do you have enough for each dog at the shelter to get 2 bones each?** Direct students to fill in the information about this problem in the boxes on S19. Then, students figure out the total number of dogs, whether there are enough bones for each dog to get 2, and whether any more are needed or whether there are any leftovers.

Students work individually to solve the problem. After students solve the problem, ask volunteers to share their solutions. Students will likely have a variety of approaches for solving this problem. Encourage students to listen to each strategy and decide if their approach was the same or different.

" STUDENTS MIGHT SAY "

 "I used cubes for the dog bones. First I counted out 44 cubes. Then I put the cubes into towers of 2 because each dog gets 2 bones. I put 9 towers of 2 in a group for the small dogs, 5 for the medium dogs, and 7 for the large dogs. Then I had one tower of 2 left over. 44 − 2 is 42."

 "I started with the small dogs. I knew if each small dog got 1 bone, that would be 9 bones altogether, but each dog gets 2 bones, so I did 9 + 9. That's 18. I did the same thing for the medium dogs and the large dogs. Then I added the bones for all the dogs together. I got 42."

Distribute another copy of S19 to each student. Use the same story above but tell students that this time each dog gets 3 bones. This resource can be used repeatedly by changing one or more of the variables in the problem.

DIFFERENTIATION

ENGLISH LANGUAGE LEARNERS Partner Talk Have students work in pairs to solve the problem. Students may find it challenging to explain their solutions. Encourage students to first use drawings, cubes, or other manipulatives to help them solve the problem. Have students practice explaining their solution to a partner and encourage them to use the vocabulary they've learned. When it is time to share with others, ask students to present their drawings or models, and help them with their explanations, as necessary.

INVESTIGATION 4

SOLVING ADDITION AND SUBTRACTION STORY PROBLEMS

Main Math Idea

○ Understanding, representing, and solving problems involving addition and subtraction

Solving Addition and Subtraction Story Problems

	SESSION 4.1	SESSION 4.2
	INTRODUCING STORY PROBLEMS Students are introduced to a set of steps for making sense of and solving story problems. Initially the focus is on visualizing the action of a problem and retelling it to a partner. The class identifies the known and unknown information and thinks about whether there will be more or less at the end of the story. Pairs solve the problem and strategies are briefly discussed and modeled. Then, students solve problems individually and record their solutions so that someone else can understand their thinking. Discussion focuses on methods for solving an add to story problem with result unknown.	**STRATEGIES FOR SOLVING A SUBTRACTION STORY PROBLEM** Students visualize and retell two story problems. The focus is on making sense of what is happening and discussing what is known and unknown before solving the problems with a partner and discussing strategies. Then, students solve problems individually and record their solutions so that someone else can understand their thinking. Discussion focuses on methods for solving a take from story problem with result unknown.
Professional Development	**TEACHER NOTES 7, 10, 13, 14** **DIALOGUE BOX 10**	**TEACHER NOTE 14** **DIALOGUE BOX 11**
Materials to View Ahead of Time	⊙ DIFFERENTIATION: ENGLISH LANGUAGE LEARNERS See **Differentiation in This Unit** for session content to preview with students.	**TEACHER PRESENTATION:** 📱 **Classroom Routine** *Quick Images: Ten Frames*
Materials to Gather	**Materials for *What Time Is It?*** (from Session 2.1) **Number line** 🔧 **100 chart** 🔧 **Connecting cubes** (as needed)	***Quick Images: Ten Frames* Cards** showing 7, 8, and 9 dots (from Session 2.7; optional) **Number line** 🔧 **100 chart** 🔧 **Connecting cubes** (as needed)
Materials to Prepare	📄 **T7, Clocks: 2:30** Make copies. (as needed) **Chart: "Strategies for Solving 12 + 10"** Title a piece of chart paper "Strategies for Solving 12 + 10."	📄 **C15, *Quick Images: Ten Frames* Cards** Make 1 extra copy of the *Quick Images: Ten Frames* Cards showing 7, 8, and 9 dots. (optional) **Chart: "Strategies for Solving 16 – 7"** Title a piece of chart paper "Strategies for Solving 16 – 7."
Common Core State Standards	**Classroom Routines:** Supports 2.MD.C.7 **Session:** 2.OA.A.1, 2.NBT.B.9, 2.MD.B.6 **Daily Practice:** 2.OA.A.1	**Classroom Routines:** 2.OA.B.2, 2.NBT.B.9 **Session:** 2.OA.A.1, 2.NBT.B.9, 2.MD.B.6 **Daily Practice:** 2.OA.A.1

	SESSION 4.3	SESSION 4.4
	STRATEGIES FOR SOLVING AN ADDITION STORY PROBLEM Students continue to solve story problems first as a class and then individually. Visualizing and restating the problem, and discussing what information is known and unknown, are now becoming a familiar set of steps for students to use when they solve story problems. Students continue to think about how to record their solutions so that someone else can understand their thinking. Discussion focuses on methods for solving a put together/take apart story problem with total unknown.	**STRATEGIES FOR SUBTRACTING** Students solve story problems in the whole group and then individually. Discussion focuses on strategies for solving a take from story problem with result unknown.
Professional Development	**TEACHER NOTE 14** **DIALOGUE BOX 12**	
Materials to View Ahead of Time	**TEACHER PRESENTATION:** **Classroom Routine** *What Time Is It?*	
Materials to Gather	**Materials for *What Time Is It?*** (from Session 2.1) **Number line** 🔧 **100 chart** 🔧 **Connecting cubes** (as needed)	**Students' envelopes of "Facts I Know" and "Facts I Am Still Working On"** (from Sessions 2.5 and 3.2) **Number line** 🔧 **100 chart** 🔧 **Connecting cubes** (as needed)
Materials to Prepare	**Chart: "Strategies for Solving 16 + 24"** Title a piece of chart paper "Strategies for Solving 16 + 24".	

| **Common Core State Standards** | **Classroom Routines:** Supports 2.MD.C.7
 Session: 2.OA.A.1, 2.NBT.B.9, 2.MD.B.6
 Daily Practice: 2.OA.A.1 | **Classroom Routines:** 2.OA.B.2
 Session: 2.OA.A.1, 2.NBT.B.9, 2.MD.B.6
 Daily Practice: Supports 2.MD.C.7 |

Solving Addition and Subtraction Story Problems

	SESSION 4.5
	SOLVING STORY PROBLEMS Students complete an assessment focused on solving put together/take apart story problems with the total unknown, and add to and take from story problems with the result unknown.
Professional Development	**TEACHER NOTE 15**
Materials to View Ahead of Time	**TEACHER PRESENTATION:** 🔁 **Classroom Routine** *Today's Number: 18*
Materials to Gather	**Number line** (as needed) 🔧 **100 chart** 🔧 **Connecting cubes**
Materials to Prepare	☑ 📄 **A8–A10, Solving Story Problems** Make copies or use the Online Assessment.

Common Core State Standards	**Classroom Routines:** 2.OA.B.2, 2.MD.B.6 **Session:** 2.OA.A.1, 2.NBT.B.9, 2.MD.B.6 **Daily Practice:** 2.OA.A.1

Introducing Story Problems

MATH FOCUS POINTS

○ Visualizing, representing, and solving put together/take apart story problems with the total unknown, and add to and take from story problems with the result unknown

○ Introducing standard notation (+ and =) to represent addition situations

○ Using numbers, symbols, pictures, and/or words to represent a solution

○ Sharing strategies for solving an add to story problem with result unknown

VOCABULARY

○ half hour	○ plus sign	○ count on
○ half	○ add	○ add one number in parts
○ two-thirty	○ equal sign	
○ half past	○ equals	
○ equation	○ count all	

TODAY'S PLAN | MATERIALS

 10 Class **CLASSROOM ROUTINES: REVIEW AND PRACTICE**
What Time Is It?

T7*
Materials from Session 2.1

---

10 Class **1** ACTIVITY
Story Problems Aloud

---

10 Class **2** ACTIVITY
Introducing How Many Children?

 Student Activity Book, p. 68

---

20 Individuals **3** ACTIVITY
How Many Children?

 Student Activity Book, pp. 68–69
Number line
🔧 100 chart
🔧 Connecting cubes (as needed)

---

20 Class **4** DISCUSSION
Strategies for Combining

 Student Activity Book, p. 68 (completed; from Activity 3)
Number line
🔧 100 chart
🔧 Connecting cubes (as needed)
Chart: "Strategies for Solving 12 + 10"*

SESSION FOLLOW-UP: REVIEW AND PRACTICE
Daily Practice

Student Activity Book, p. 70

* See *Materials to Prepare* in the Investigation 4 Planner.

Common Core State Standards	**Classroom Routines:** Supports 2.MD.C.7 **Session:** 2.OA.A.1, 2.NBT.B.9, 2.MD.B.6	**Daily Practice:** 2.OA.A.1

CLASSROOM ROUTINES: REVIEW AND PRACTICE

What Time Is It?

MATH FOCUS POINTS

○ Naming, notating, and telling time to the half hour using analog and digital formats

Record 2:00 in digital format and ask students to display the time on their clocks. Introduce students to the half hour by asking:

What would the clock look like if the minute hand went half way around the clock, or 30 minutes past 2:00?

Display and discuss the representation of 2:30 on both clocks (T7).

Sometimes people refer to this time as two-thirty or half-past two.

Briefly discuss the different ways to name the time, connecting the language to the time notation of 2:30 and to the arrangement of the hands on the clock.

Repeat with 1:00/1:30, 6:00/6:30, and 12:00/12:30. In pairs, students set their clocks to the half-hour time and then look at the arrangement of the hands. Throughout the discussion, refer to times in a variety of ways, including "one thirty," "30 minutes past 1 o'clock," and "half-past one."

1 ACTIVITY

Story Problems Aloud

Explain that you are going to tell a story. Encourage students to close their eyes and imagine the story in their minds as you tell it. **PD** **TN** **MPN1**

Franco has 8 apples and 7 oranges. How many pieces of fruit does Franco have in all? MN

Explain that you don't want students to solve the problem yet.

First, turn and talk to a partner. Tell your partner my story. Explain what you think is happening in my problem.

After a few minutes, ask volunteers to retell the story in their own words.

Think again about the story people have been telling. Will the answer to this problem be more than 8 or less than 8? Why do you think so? MPN2

Ask partners to briefly discuss how they would solve the problem. Model and discuss one or two strategies.

PROFESSIONAL DEVELOPMENT

PD TEACHER NOTE 13: Story Problems in Second Grade

TEACHING NOTE

TN **Addition or Subtraction?** Do not label the stories you tell as "addition" or "subtraction." Part of students' work is to analyze what is happening and then to decide how to proceed.

MATH PRACTICE NOTES

MPN1 **MP1 Make sense of problems and persevere in solving them.** Story problems are a central component of students' mathematical studies. In this session, students learn how to enter a problem: Picture the story in your mind. Then ask yourself, what do I know about the quantities involved? That is, students work to understand the context and reason about what happens to the quantities in the action of the story. Through that process, students come to the problem's solution. See the essay Mathematical Practices in This Unit for more about MP1.

MPN2 **MP1 Make sense of problems and persevere in solving them.** By considering whether the story results in more or less pieces of fruit than at the start, students anticipate characteristics of the answer. Once they solve the problem, they can consider their solution in relation to what they anticipated. Developing the habit of asking this question—From the context of the problem, what do I know about the answer?—is an essential component of making sense of problems.

MATH NOTE

MN **Size of Numbers** The size of the numbers in Activity 1 of Sessions 4.1–4.4 is purposefully kept small, so that students can solve the problems mentally and focus instead on what's happening in the problems.

Follow the same process with another story. Because each story represents a different problem type, also encourage students to compare and think about how the stories are similar and different. PD1 MN1 MWI1

Kira has 12 crayons. She gave 4 to Jake. How many crayons does Kira have now?

2 ACTIVITY

Introducing How Many Children?

Display Problem 1 from *Student Activity Book* page 68. Follow the same process as in Activity 1: read the story aloud, encouraging students to visualize what is happening in the problem and to retell it.

What is happening in this problem? Don't solve it yet. Just explain what you see in your mind.

After a couple of volunteers have shared their thinking, ask these questions:

○ **In this problem, what are we trying to find out?** (how many children altogether)

○ **What information do we already know?** (how many children were playing at the beginning, and how many children joined them)

○ **Will the answer be more than 12 or less than 12? Why do you think so?**

○ **What equation could we write to represent what is happening in this problem?**

Ask pairs to talk about an equation for this problem. Record their suggestions, using this as an opportunity to review addition notation and the meaning of the symbols. PD2 MN2 MWI2

Mathematicians write equations, with numbers and symbols, to show what is happening in a problem. Write "12." What does the 12 stand for in our problem? . . . Then 10 more children joined the game. Write " + 10." We can use the plus sign to show that another group is being added . . . Mathematicians use this sign, the equal sign, to show that two things are the same or equal. You're going to figure out how many children are playing altogether, or what 12 + 10 equals. MPN

$$12 + 10 = \underline{}$$

Throughout, encourage students to explain what the 12 and the 10 stand for. Such questions encourage students to think about this problem as being about two groups coming together to make a whole.

So the 12 is the group of children playing at the start and the 10 is the group of children that joined. We are trying to find out how many children there are when you put the two groups together.

UNIT 1: Coins, Number Strings, and Story Problems | **193** | SESSION 4.1: Introducing Story Problems

---

PROFESSIONAL DEVELOPMENT

PD1 TEACHER NOTE 10: Types of Story Problems

PD2 TEACHER NOTE 14: Using Notation to Record Strategies

MATH NOTES

MN1 **Types of Story Problems** The three problems discussed in this session represent a problem with no action (put together/take apart), one that involves the action of removing or separating (take from), and another at the end-of-session discussion that involves the action of combining (add to). In each, the end amount is what students are trying to find (total unknown, result unknown). Students are not expected to know or name these problem types. Instead, the expectation is that they can solve a problem, whatever its type. For more information, see **Teacher Note 10:** Types of Story Problems.

MN2 **Equations That Show What the Problem Is Asking** Given previous discussions about order in addition, students may also suggest: $10 + 12 = \underline{}$. Acknowledge that this would give you the same answer, but the problem talks about 12 children being joined by 10 more. Be sure to emphasize that students can use either equation when *solving* the problem.

MATH PRACTICE NOTES

MPN **MP4 Model with mathematics.** Representing a story problem with an equation is one form of modeling with mathematics. In an equation, the mathematical aspects of the problem have been abstracted from the context and expressed in relationship to each other. Pictures, diagrams, or representations with cubes can also model story problems.

MATH WORDS AND IDEAS

MWI1 Story Problem Routine

MWI2 An Addition Story Problem about Children

3 ACTIVITY

How Many Children?

Distribute *Student Activity Book* pages 68–69.

Now you are going to solve this problem, and some others, on paper. Remember to write an equation and to check your answers. Be sure to show how you solved the problems on *Student Activity Book* pages 68–69. Someone else should be able to look at your work and understand what you did to solve it.

Remind students of the tools available (connecting cubes, number line, 100 chart). Students should work on their own but feel free to discuss their strategies with others. Explain what students should do if they need help reading Problems 2–4. **TN**

ONGOING ASSESSMENT Observing Students at Work

Students solve add to and take from story problems with result unknown, and put together/take apart story problems with the total unknown, and show their work.

- ○ **Can students retell the stories and explain the situation?** Do they know whether there will be more or fewer [children] at the end of the story? Can they write an equation that represents what is happening? 🔍 **MP1**

- ○ **Can students solve the problems correctly?** What strategies do they use? Do they draw or count all? Count on or back? Do they count by 1s or by groups? Do they reason numerically (e.g., "12 + 10 is the same as 10 + 10 + 2" or "32 − 2 = 30 and then it's easy to subtract 5.")?

- ○ **How do students record their strategy?** Do they use equations? Pictures? Words? A combination? Can you follow their thinking by looking at their written work? Does it match their verbal explanation?

[Problem 1]

RESOURCE MASTERS, T7

TEACHING NOTE

TN **Reading Support** Some Grade 2 students may need support reading problems, particularly early in the year. Let students know that story problems will always involve the same four names (Kira, Jake, Franco, Sally) to make the reading easier. Also review strategies for getting help, such as asking a friend or an assigned reading helper, which might be a student or an adult.

$$12-2=10 \quad 18+10=20$$
$$20+2=22$$

[Problem 1]

[Problem 3]

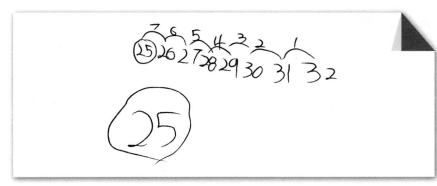

[Problem 3]

$$32-2=30$$
$$30-5=25$$

[Problem 3]

Focus your observations on students' strategies (e.g., count all, count on, break the numbers apart) for Problem 1 to prepare for the end-of-session discussion. **PD**

STUDENT ACTIVITY BOOK, P. 68

ACTIVITY
(PAGE 1 OF 2)

NAME _____ DATE _____

How Many Children?

Solve each problem. Show your work.
Write an equation.

1 There were 12 children playing tag on the playground. Then 10 more children joined the game. How many children are playing tag now?

22 children; Review students' work.

2 There were 22 children playing tag on the playground. Then 10 more children joined the game. How many children are playing tag now?

32 children; Review students' work.

UNIT 1 | 68 | SESSION 4.1   © Pearson Education 2

STUDENT ACTIVITY BOOK, P. 69

ACTIVITY
(PAGE 2 OF 2)

NAME _____ DATE _____

How Many Children?

3 32 students were sitting at the lunch table. 7 of them went to get a school lunch. How many students are still sitting at the table?

25 students; Review students' work.

4 Our class went on a trip to the zoo. There were 23 students and 9 adults on the trip. How many people went on the zoo trip?

32 people; Review students' work.

UNIT 1 | 69 | SESSION 4.1   © Pearson Education 2

PROFESSIONAL DEVELOPMENT

PD TEACHER NOTE 7 **Strategies for Addition and Subtraction**

DIFFERENTIATION Supporting the Range of Learners

INTERVENTION Clarify the Problem If students are having difficulty getting started, see whether they can retell the story. Do they understand that they are looking for the total number of children? Suggest that they model the problem with cubes.

INTERVENTION Scaffold a Solution If students are having difficulty recording their strategy, ask them to explain it in words. You can help them get started. You started with 12, and then you counted on. The first thing you said was 12. Can you write that on your paper? Now, how can you show that you counted on from 12? What numbers did you say? How many did you count on?

EXTENSION Extend Thinking Challenge students who solve the problems easily and record their work clearly to think about and try to describe the relationship between Problems 1 and 2. They may find ways to double-check their answers or a second way to solve the problems.

ENGLISH LANGUAGE LEARNERS Partner Talk To help students prepare for the class discussion, have them rehearse with a partner how they solved Problem 1. If necessary, write the steps as students dictate or point to information. Then have students practice reading the steps to partners.

4 DISCUSSION

Strategies for Combining

MATH FOCUS POINTS FOR DISCUSSION

○ Sharing strategies for solving an add to story problem with unknown result

○ Using numbers, symbols, pictures, and/or words to represent a solution to a problem

Gather students to share and record strategies for Problem 1. **PD**

Begin by telling students that you noticed that they solved the problem in different ways. Ask them to listen as classmates share their strategies and to think about whether their methods were similar or different. **MPN** **TN1**

As students share, record their strategies on a chart, providing models of recording. Name the strategies by the math idea, helping students see the difference between a strategy and a tool. **TN2** **TN3**

[Henry] counted all of the children. [He] counted out a group of 12 and a group of 10 and then counted all of the cubes, or children, on the playground. Did anyone else count all of the children?

After a strategy is shared, rephrase and/or model it for the class with connecting cubes, on the number line or 100 chart, or ask another student to do so. **TN4**

[Bruce] and [Yama] counted on. They knew there were 12 kids, so they counted on from 12. [Bruce] used pictures, and [Yama] used [her] fingers.

PROFESSIONAL DEVELOPMENT

PD DIALOGUE BOX 10: An Addition Story Problem

MATH PRACTICE NOTE

MPN **MP3 Construct viable arguments and critique the reasoning of others.** Listening to classmates' strategies and identifying how their classmates' thinking is similar to and different from their own is an aspect of critiquing the reasoning of others.

TEACHING NOTES

TN1 **Explaining Strategies** Continue to ask students to explain their strategies for solving addition and subtraction problems, and to focus discussions of those strategies on why they work. Listen for evidence that they are using properties of operations and place value in their work (e.g., "I thought $10 + 10$ is 20, and 2 more is 22.")

TN2 **Naming Strategies** Naming strategies by the math involved is a way to make the strategy used and the mathematics involved more explicit for students.

TN3 **Strategies and Tools** Some students will count on in their heads, while others may use their fingers, the 100 chart, the number line, or numbers and equations. While these strategies often seem different to students, the mathematics they are using is the same. It will take time for students to realize that the tool they use is not the same as the strategy they use. For example, "I used the 100 chart" does not explain whether a student used it to count all, count on, or to add the numbers in some other way.

TN4 **How Did [Henry] Solve the Problem?** This is an opportunity to explain the strategy again or to pose questions about it that may illuminate issues that keep other students from understanding and therefore adopting it. For example, counting on is often confusing for students who struggle to answer questions like, "How do you know where to start?", "How do you know where to stop?", and "What is the answer when you're finished?" A class discussion offers the opportunity to pose and answer such questions, to demonstrate the strategy, and to ask all students to try it out.

Point out that these students do not count out a set of 12. Connect this strategy to the first, highlighting the efficiency of counting on.

[Katrina] broke apart the 12. What did [she] break it into? (10 and 2) Why do you think [she] did that? . . . So [she] **added one number in parts**. To add the 12, first [she] added the 10, and then [she] added the 2.

Again, model the strategy and compare it to the others. Help students distinguish between using equations to show what the problem is asking, and using equations to show a solution strategy.

[Katrina] used equations in [her] work, but not the same ones we wrote earlier. Those showed what the problem was asking. These show how [she] solved the problem.

Did anyone have a way that is different from the ways I've written here?

Ask students to look at how they solved the problem and decide which of the strategies that you have recorded is closest to it. As you point to each strategy, ask students to raise their hands to indicate which strategy they used. This is a way of validating all students' work and also getting a sense of what kinds of strategies are being used by your class as a whole.

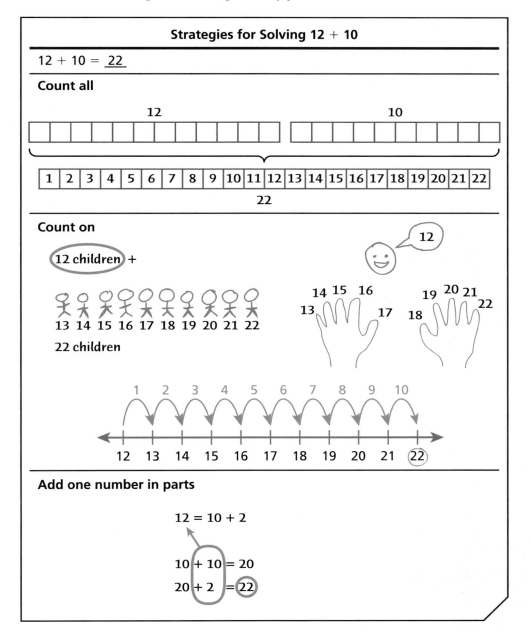

Keep the chart of students' strategies posted for students to refer to throughout the rest of this investigation. You can also use *Math Words and Ideas*, An Addition Story Problem about Children, to review and summarize strategies for this problem. [MWI]

End by reviewing the equation you wrote in Activity 2, filling in the answer, and connecting what each number represents in the story.

Then, briefly introduce vertical notation for the same problem. Follow the same process, connecting what each number represents in the story. [MN] [TN]

$$\begin{array}{r} 12 \\ + 10 \\ \hline 22 \end{array}$$

SESSION FOLLOW-UP: REVIEW AND PRACTICE

Daily Practice

DAILY PRACTICE For reinforcement of this unit's content, students complete *Student Activity Book* page 70.

STUDENT ACTIVITY BOOK, P. 70

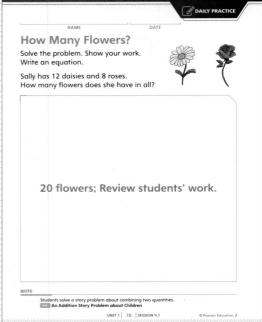

DAILY PRACTICE

NAME   DATE

How Many Flowers?
Solve the problem. Show your work.
Write an equation.

Sally has 12 daisies and 8 roses.
How many flowers does she have in all?

20 flowers; Review students' work.

NOTE
Students solve a story problem about combining two quantities.
[MWI] An Addition Story Problem about Children

UNIT 1 | 70 | SESSION 4.1   © Pearson Education 2

MATH WORDS AND IDEAS

[MWI] An Addition Story Problem about Children

MATH NOTE

[MN] **Vertical Notation** While both forms of notation represent the problem situation, note that mathematicians only refer to the first as an equation. Vertical notation involves stacking numbers so that like places of the numbers are aligned.

TEACHING NOTE

[TN] **Strategy Discussions** The purpose of this first strategy discussion is to establish the general process for describing and representing students' strategies. Students revisit addition strategies in a discussion at the end of Session 4.3. They discuss subtraction strategies in Sessions 4.2 and 4.4.

SESSION 4.2

Strategies for Solving a Subtraction Story Problem

MATH FOCUS POINTS

○ Visualizing, representing, and solving put together/take apart story problems with the total unknown, and add to and take from story problems with the result unknown

○ Introducing standard notation (− and =) to represent subtraction situations

○ Using numbers, symbols, pictures, and/or words to represent a solution to a problem

○ Sharing strategies for solving a take from story problem with unknown result

VOCABULARY

○ equation
○ minus sign
○ subtract
○ equals
○ count all
○ count back
○ subtract one number in parts
○ add up
○ use known fact

		TODAY'S PLAN	MATERIALS
10 Class		**CLASSROOM ROUTINES: REVIEW AND PRACTICE** ***Quick Images: Ten Frames***	Teacher Presentation (or use two copies of the *Quick Images: Ten Frames* Cards with 7, 8, and 9 dots from C15*)
10 Class		**1** ACTIVITY **Story Problems Aloud**	
10 Class		**2** ACTIVITY **Introducing How Many Cards?**	*Student Activity Book*, p. 71

20 Individuals		**3** ACTIVITY
		 How Many Cards, Cans, and Pennies?
			Student Activity Book, pp. 71–72
			 Number line
			  100 chart
			  Connecting cubes (as needed)

20 Class		**4** DISCUSSION **Strategies for Subtracting**	*Student Activity Book*, p. 71 (completed; from Activity 3) Number line 100 chart Connecting cubes (as needed) Chart: "Strategies for Solving 16 − 7"*
		SESSION FOLLOW-UP: REVIEW AND PRACTICE **Daily Practice and Homework**	*Student Activity Book*, pp. 73–74

* See *Materials to Prepare* in the Investigation 4 Planner.

Common Core State Standards	**Classroom Routines:** 2.OA.B.2, 2.NBT.B.9 **Session:** 2.OA.A.1, 2.NBT.B.9, 2.MD.B.6	**Daily Practice:** 2.OA.A.1

CLASSROOM ROUTINES: REVIEW AND PRACTICE

Quick Images: Ten Frames

MATH FOCUS POINTS

○ Developing and analyzing visual images for quantities up to 10

○ Using known facts to add two or more numbers

Display the Teacher Presentation (or use the *Quick Images: Ten Frames* Cards with 7 dots and 7 dots).

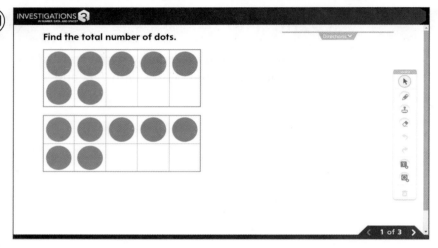

Follow the basic *Quick Images* routine. **TN**

Students determine the total number of dots and share their strategies. Repeat with the 8-dot and 8-dot images and then the 9-dot and 9-dot images. Some students may be fluent with their doubles; others may use a combination they know (e.g., $7 + 7 = 7 + 3 + 4$, or thinking of $9 + 9$ as $10 + 10$ and then removing the extra 2 they added). Model students' thinking, and use equations to show what's happening in these strategies.

---

1 ACTIVITY

Story Problems Aloud

As in Session 4.1, begin by telling and discussing two story problems. Follow the same routine, encouraging students to close their eyes and imagine the story in their minds.

Jake sees some pencils in the classroom. There are 9 pencils on the floor and 8 pencils in a jar. How many pencils are there in the classroom?

Ask students to discuss the problem with a partner, and then have several students retell the story to the whole group.

Think again about the story people have been telling. Will the answer to this problem be more than 9 or less than 9? Why do you think so?

TEACHING NOTE

TN *Quick Images* **Routine**

○ Briefly show the image.

○ Students think about what they saw.

○ Show the image again, briefly.

○ Students revise their thinking.

○ With the image showing, volunteers share how many dots they saw and how they remembered.

Ask partners to briefly discuss how they would solve the problem. Model and discuss one or two strategies.

Follow the same process with the following story.

Kira has 7 apples. Sally gave her 5 more apples. How many apples does Kira have now?

2 ACTIVITY

Introducing How Many Cards?

Display Problem 1 from *Student Activity Book* page 71. Follow the same process as in Activity 1: read the story aloud, encouraging students to visualize what is happening in the problem and then to retell it.

What is happening in this problem? Don't solve it yet. Just explain what you see in your mind.

After a couple of volunteers have shared their thinking, ask these questions:

○ **In this problem, what are we trying to find out?** (how many cards Kira has left)

○ **What information do we already know?** (how many cards she had, how many cards she gave away)

○ **Will the answer be more than 16 or less than 16? Why do you think so?**

○ **What equation could we write to represent what is happening in this problem?**

Ask pairs to talk about an equation that represents what is happening in this problem. Record their suggestions, using this as an opportunity to review subtraction notation and the meaning of the symbols. MN PD

Let's write an equation to show what is happening in the problem. Write "16." What does the 16 stand for in our problem? . . . Then she gave 7 cards away. Write " − 7." We can use the minus sign to show that a group is being removed or subtracted . . . You're going to figure out how many baseball cards Kira had left, or what 16 − 7 equals.

$$16 - 7 = \underline{\quad}$$

Encourage students to explain what the 16 and the 7 stand for. Such questions encourage students to think about this problem as being about removing one group from a larger whole and determining how many are left in the other group.

We know the starting amount—Kira had 16 baseball cards. We know she gave away 7 of the cards. We are trying to figure out how many she has left.

MATH NOTE

MN The Relationship Between Addition and Subtraction Most students will suggest $16 - 7 = \underline{\quad}$ as the equation that represents what is happening in this story problem. A few may suggest $7 + \underline{\quad} = 16$. These students may be thinking about how they would *solve* the problem, which is fine and interesting, but explain that you'd like to wait to discuss their equation in the discussion about strategies at the end of the session.

PROFESSIONAL DEVELOPMENT

PD TEACHER NOTE 14: Using Notation to Record Strategies

3 ACTIVITY

How Many Cards, Cans, and Pennies?

For this activity students will use *Student Activity Book* pages 71–72.

Now you are going to solve this problem, and some others, on paper. Remember to write an equation and to check your answers. Be sure to show how you solved the problems on *Student Activity Book* pages 71–72. Someone else should be able to look at your work and understand what you did to solve each problem.

Remind students of the tools available (connecting cubes, number line, 100 chart) and what they should do if they need help reading a problem. **MPN**

ONGOING ASSESSMENT Observing Students at Work

Students solve take from and add to story problems with result unknown, and put together/take apart story problems with the total unknown, and show their work.

○ **Can students retell the stories and explain the situation?** Do they know whether there will be more or fewer [cards, cans, pennies] at the end of the story? Can they write an equation that represents what is happening? **MP1**

○ **Can students solve the problems correctly?** What strategies do they use? Do they draw or count all? Count on or back? Do they count by 1s or by groups? Do they reason numerically (e.g., "$16 - 6 = 10$, but it's minus 7, so I have to subtract 1 more," or "$7 + 10$ is 17, so $7 + 9$ is 16")?

○ **How do students record their strategy?** Do they use equations? Pictures? Words? A combination? Can you follow their thinking by looking at their written work? Does it match their verbal explanation?

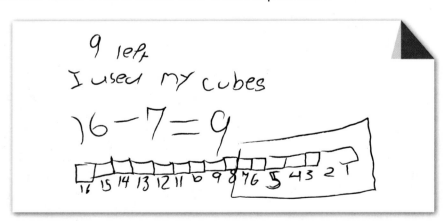

[Problem 1]

MATH PRACTICE NOTE

MPN **MP5 Use appropriate tools strategically.** As students work on story problems individually and in pairs, they learn to select tools that will help them solve the problem. These tools allow students to develop images of the quantities and the relationships among them.

I Circled the 7 on
rhe Hundreds chart
and tnat was the
giving away group
then I counted
up to 16 8¹ 9² 10³
11⁴ 12⁵ 13⁶ 14⁷ 15⁸
16⁹   ⑨

[Problem 1]

〲〲〲〲 〲〲〲〲 〲〲〲〲 | |

〲〲〲〲 〲〲〲〲 〲〲〲〲 |

17 + 16 = 33

[Problem 3]

I couned by 1 like this 18 19 20 21 22 23
24 25 26 27 28 29 30 31 32 ㉝
My answer is 33

[Problem 3]

10 + 10 = 20
6 + 7 = 13
20 + 13 = 33 cans

[Problem 3]

STUDENT ACTIVITY BOOK, P. 72

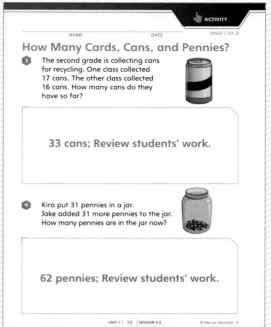

ACTIVITY

NAME   DATE   (PAGE 2 OF 2)

How Many Cards, Cans, and Pennies?

3 The second grade is collecting cans for recycling. One class collected 17 cans. The other class collected 16 cans. How many cans do they have so far?

33 cans; Review students' work.

4 Kira put 31 pennies in a jar. Jake added 31 more pennies to the jar. How many pennies are in the jar now?

62 pennies; Review students' work.

UNIT 1 | 72 | SESSION 4.2   © Pearson Education 2

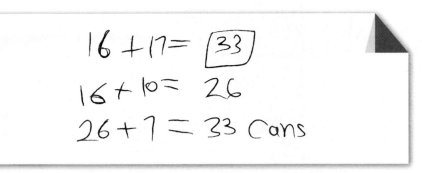

[Problem 3]

As you observe, make note of which strategies students use (e.g., count all, count back, add on, use something you know) to inform the discussion at the end of this session.

 DIFFERENTIATION Supporting the Range of Learners

INTERVENTION **Clarify the Problem** If students are having difficulty getting started, see whether they can retell the story. Do they understand that they are trying to determine the number of cards Kira has left? Suggest that they model the problem with cubes. **MPN1**

INTERVENTION **Scaffold a Solution** If students are having difficulty recording their strategy, ask them to explain how they solved the problem. Then repeat or rephrase their process and help them record their steps. **You started with 16, and then you counted back. The first thing you said was 16. Can you write that on your paper? Now, how can you show that you counted back from 16? What numbers did you say? How many did you count back?**

EXTENSION **Extend Thinking** Challenge students who solve the problems easily and record their work clearly to think about and try to describe the relationship between Problems 1 and 2. They may find ways to double-check their answers or a second way to solve the problems. **MPN2**

ENGLISH LANGUAGE LEARNERS **Partner Talk** In preparation for the class discussion, have students explain to a partner how they solved Problem 1 on *Student Activity Book* page 71. Consider pairing English Language Learners with students whose first language is English. Encourage students to draw sketches to explain their thinking/solutions, and remind them to write an equation and to check their work.

4 DISCUSSION

Strategies for Subtracting

MATH FOCUS POINTS FOR DISCUSSION

○ Sharing strategies for solving a take apart story problem with unknown result

○ Using numbers, symbols, pictures, and/or words to represent a solution to a problem

---

MATH PRACTICE NOTES

MPN1 🔍 **MP1 Make sense of problems and persevere in solving them.** Students learn that they must first make sense of the problem before selecting a strategy to solve it.

MPN2 🔍 **MP8 Look for and express regularity in repeated reasoning.** Throughout the year, story problems are often given in pairs, related by a particular mathematical structure. By comparing the problems, students may notice those structures and may be able to explain them using pictures, cubes, or other representations of the problem.

Much as you did at the end of Session 4.1, gather students to share and record strategies for solving Problem 1. **PD**

Begin by commenting on the variety of solution strategies you saw and encouraging students to listen as classmates share and to think about whether their classmates' methods are similar to or different from their own.

As students share, record their strategies on a chart, providing models of recording. Name the strategies by the math idea, helping students see the difference between a strategy and a tool.

[Juan] counted out 16 cubes. Then [he] counted and broke off 7 of those cubes. Then [he] counted how many were left. [He] counted all of the parts of the problem.

After a strategy is shared, rephrase and/or model it for the class with connecting cubes, on the number line or 100 chart, or ask another student to do so.

[Lonzell] started at 16 and [he] counted back 7.

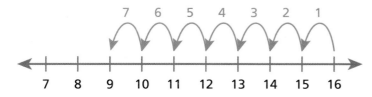

Point out that this strategy does not involve counting out the 16 baseball cards Kira started with but instead begins with knowing there are 16 cards. **MN1**

Did anyone else count back? . . . [Monisha] said [she] "went back" too, but made bigger jumps. [Monisha], can you show us? [She] subtracted the 7 in parts. First [she] subtracted 6, and then [she] subtracted 1 more. **MWI**

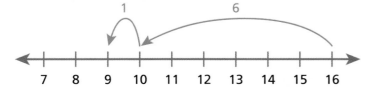

Some students turn this problem into a missing addend problem, thinking "How many do I have to add to 7 to get 16?" They might count up by 1s, add up in chunks (e.g., "7 + 3 + 6 = 16"), or use a related fact they already know (e.g., "7 + 10 = 17, so 7 + 9 = 16"). **MPN**

[Simon] said [he] thought about addition—how much [he] would have to add to 7 to get to 16. He got 9 by counting by 1s from 7 to 16. People call this strategy adding up. Did anyone else add up to solve this problem? Yama got 9 by adding 3 to the 7 to get 10 and then adding 6 more to get to 16. **MN2**

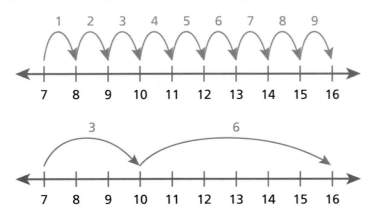

PROFESSIONAL DEVELOPMENT

PD DIALOGUE BOX 11: A Subtraction Story Problem

MATH NOTES

MN1 **Counting Back** This strategy involves counting back from the known whole amount (16) while also keeping track of the objects being removed from the whole (7) and knowing that the last number said (9) indicates the leftover part of the whole. When students use this strategy, they have to think about both numbers in the problem and the number sequence of counting back (or counting on) and must have a reliable way to keep track of both.

MN2 **Using Addition or Subtraction** Point out that some students used addition to solve the problem while others used subtraction. Encourage students to think about whether any subtraction problem can be thought of as a missing addend problem, and vice versa. The relationship between addition and subtraction will be addressed throughout Grade 2.

MATH WORDS AND IDEAS

MWI Story Problem Routine

MATH PRACTICE NOTE

MPN **MP8 Look for and express regularity in repeated reasoning.** The relationship between addition and subtraction is a key concept but a difficult one for many Grade 2 students. Throughout the year, when a problem has been solved using subtraction by some students and finding a missing addend by others, encourage students to think about how they could get the same result using different operations.

[Esteban] used equations in [his] work but not the same ones we wrote earlier. Those showed what the problem was asking. These equations show how [he] solved the problem. He used a known fact to help him. PD

$$7 + 10 = 17$$
$$\text{so } 7 + \underline{9} = 16$$

After several students have shared their strategies, discuss strategies not yet mentioned.

Did anyone use a way that is different from the ways I've written here?

Ask students to look at how they solved the problem and decide which of the strategies you recorded is closest to it. As you point to each strategy, ask students to raise their hands to indicate which strategy they used. This is a way of validating all students' work and also of getting a sense of what kinds of strategies are being used by your class as a whole.

Keep the chart of students' strategies posted for students to refer to throughout the rest of this investigation. You can also use *Math Words and Ideas*, A Subtraction Story Problem: Giving Away Baseball Cards, to review and summarize strategies for this problem. MWI

End by reviewing the equation you wrote in Activity 2, filling in the answer, and connecting what each number represents to the numbers in the story.

Then, briefly introduce vertical notation for the same problem. Follow the same process, connecting what each number represents to the numbers in the story.

$$\begin{array}{r} 16 \\ -\ 7 \\ \hline 9 \end{array}$$

SESSION FOLLOW-UP: REVIEW AND PRACTICE

Daily Practice and Homework

✎ **DAILY PRACTICE** For reinforcement of this unit's content, students complete *Student Activity Book* page 73.

✎ **HOMEWORK** On *Student Activity Book* page 74, students solve an addition story problem.

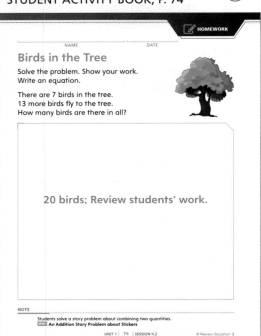

STUDENT ACTIVITY BOOK, P. 73

DAILY PRACTICE

NAME   DATE

Fish and Sharks

Solve each problem. Show your work.
Write an equation.

1. Franco and Kira went to the aquarium. Franco counted 16 blue fish. Kira counted 14 yellow fish. How many fish did they count altogether?

   30 fish; Review students' work.

2. In the shark tank, Kira counted 13 sharks and Franco counted 13 other sharks. How many sharks did they count in all?

   26 sharks; Review students' work.

NOTE Students practice solving story problems about combining two quantities.
MWI An Addition Story Problem about Stickers

UNIT 1 | 73 | SESSION 4.2   © Pearson Education 2

STUDENT ACTIVITY BOOK, P. 74

HOMEWORK

NAME   DATE

Birds in the Tree

Solve the problem. Show your work.
Write an equation.

There are 7 birds in the tree.
13 more birds fly to the tree.
How many birds are there in all?

20 birds; Review students' work.

NOTE Students solve a story problem about combining two quantities.
MWI An Addition Story Problem about Stickers

UNIT 1 | 74 | SESSION 4.2   © Pearson Education 2

PROFESSIONAL DEVELOPMENT

PD TEACHER NOTE 14: Using Notation to Record Strategies

MATH WORDS AND IDEAS

MWI A Subtraction Story Problem: Giving Away Baseball Cards

Strategies for Solving an Addition Story Problem

MATH FOCUS POINTS

○ Visualizing, representing, and solving put together/take apart story problems with the total unknown, and add to and take from story problems with the result unknown

○ Using standard notation (+ and =) to represent addition situations

○ Using numbers, symbols, pictures, and/or words to represent a solution to a problem

○ Sharing strategies for solving a put together/take apart story problem with total unknown

TODAY'S PLAN	MATERIALS
(10) Class **CLASSROOM ROUTINES: REVIEW AND PRACTICE** *What Time Is It?*	Teacher Presentation (or use the demonstration clock) Materials from Session 2.1
(10) Class **1 ACTIVITY** **Story Problems Aloud**	
(10) Class **2 ACTIVITY** **Introducing How Many Rocks?**	Student Activity Book, p. 75
(20) Individuals **3 ACTIVITY** **How Many Rocks and Marbles?**	Student Activity Book, pp. 75–76 Number line 100 chart Connecting cubes (as needed)
(20) Class **4 DISCUSSION** **Strategies for Combining**	Student Activity Book, p. 75 (completed; from Activity 3) Number line 100 chart Connecting cubes (as needed) Chart: "Strategies for Solving 16 + 24"*
SESSION FOLLOW-UP: REVIEW AND PRACTICE **Daily Practice**	Student Activity Book, p. 77

* See *Materials to Prepare* in the Investigation 4 Planner.

Common Core State Standards	**Classroom Routines:** Supports 2.MD.C.7 **Session:** 2.OA.A.1, 2.NBT.B.9, 2.MD.B.6	**Daily Practice:** 2.OA.A.1

CLASSROOM ROUTINES: REVIEW AND PRACTICE

What Time Is It?

MATH FOCUS POINTS

 Naming, notating, and telling time to the half hour using analog and digital formats

Suggest several half-hour times—some verbally (e.g., four-thirty, half past five) and some in digital format (e.g., 7:30, 1:30)—and ask pairs to set their clocks to that time. Students can also pair up and take turns suggesting and setting the time.

Display the Teacher Presentation (or use the demonstration clock). End by setting the demonstration clock to several half-hour times, and asking students to record the times in digital format.

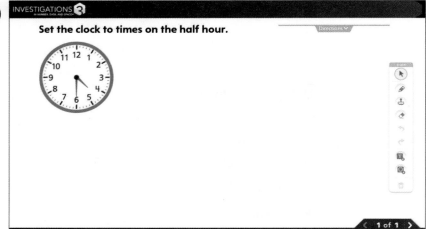

---

1 ACTIVITY

Story Problems Aloud

Again, begin the session by telling two stories, asking students to imagine them in their minds as you tell them. For each, have students retell the story and discuss it with a partner; then retell it in the whole group and discuss whether there will be more or fewer items at the end of the story; solve the problem with a partner; and finally, discuss strategies in the whole group.

Jake has 13 blueberries. He ate 6 blueberries. How many blueberries are left?

Sally has 8 flowers. Kira gives her 5 more flowers. How many flowers does Sally have in all?

2 ACTIVITY

Introducing How Many Rocks?

Display Problem 1 from *Student Activity Book* page 75. Follow the same steps as in Activity 1: read the story aloud, encouraging students to visualize what is happening in the problem and then to retell it.

What is happening in this problem? Don't solve it yet. Just explain what you see in your mind.

After a couple of volunteers have shared their thinking, ask these questions:

○ **In this problem, what are we trying to find?** (how many rocks the children collected)

○ **What information do we already know?** (Jake found 16 rocks and Sally found 24 rocks)

○ **Will the answer be more than 16 or less than 16? Why do you think so?**

○ **What equation could we write to represent what is happening in this problem?**

Ask pairs to talk about an equation for this problem, and record their suggestions. **MPN1**

Also use vertical notation to write the equation that represents the problem, emphasizing that the notation used to represent a problem does not necessarily indicate how it should be solved. **MPN2** **TN** **PD**

3 ACTIVITY

How Many Rocks and Marbles?

Distribute *Student Activity Book* pages 75–76.

Now you are going to solve this problem, and some others, on paper. Think about the problem before you solve it. Try to visualize what is happening. Remember to write an equation that represents what is happening in the story problem and to check your answers when you are finished. Be sure to show how you solved the problems on *Student Activity Book* pages 75–76. Someone else should be able to look at your work and understand what you did to solve it.

Remind students of the tools available (connecting cubes, number line, 100 chart). Students should work on their own but feel free to discuss their strategies with others. Explain what students should do if they need help reading Problems 2–4.

MATH PRACTICE NOTES

MPN1 **MP6 Attend to precision.** Through writing equations for story problems, students give meaning to mathematical symbols.

MPN2 **MP6 Attend to precision.** When writing equations to represent story problems, many students may interpret the equal sign (=) to mean "the answer comes next." In later sessions, students will have opportunities to consider such equations as $4 + 4 = 5 + 3$, or $9 = 4 + 5$, coming to recognize "=" as an indication of equivalence—that is, the expressions on either side of the equation are equivalent.

TEACHING NOTE

TN **Vertical Notation** Some students may think that a problem written vertically can be solved using only the U.S. standard algorithm. Students should be familiar with both vertical and horizontal forms of notation and should know that the way a problem is written does not necessarily specify the way it should be solved.

PROFESSIONAL DEVELOPMENT

PD TEACHER NOTE 14: Using Notation to Record Strategies

ONGOING ASSESSMENT   Observing Students at Work

Students solve add to and take from story problems with result unknown, and put together/take apart story problems with the total unknown, and show their work.

○ **Can students retell the stories and explain the situation?** Can they identify what information is known/unknown? Do they know whether there will be more or fewer [rocks, marbles] at the end of the story? Can they write an equation that represents what is happening? 🔍 **MP1**

○ **Can students solve the problems accurately?** What strategies do they use? Do they draw or count all? Count on or back? Do they count by 1s or by groups? Do they reason numerically (e.g., "I took 4 from the 24 and gave it to the 16. Then I had 20 + 20," or "35 − 10 = 25, then minus 2 more is easy.")?

○ **How do students record their strategy?** Do they use equations? Pictures? Words? A combination? Can you follow their thinking by looking at their written work? Does it match their verbal explanation?

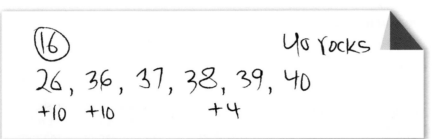

[Problem 1]

[Problem 1]

[Problem 3]

STUDENT ACTIVITY BOOK, P. 75

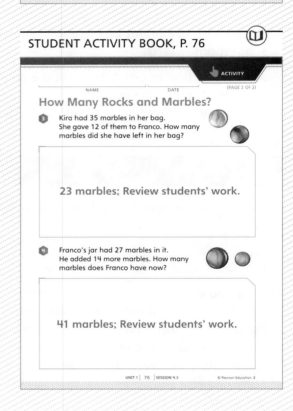

(PAGE 1 OF 2)

NAME   DATE

How Many Rocks and Marbles?

Solve each problem. Show your work.
Write an equation.

1   Jake and Sally were collecting rocks.
    Jake found 16 rocks and Sally found
    24 rocks. How many rocks did the
    children collect?

    40 rocks; Review students' work.

2   Jake and Sally were collecting rocks.
    Jake found 26 rocks and Sally found
    24 rocks. How many rocks did the
    children collect?

    50 rocks; Review students' work.

UNIT 1 | 75 | SESSION 4.3   © Pearson Education 2

STUDENT ACTIVITY BOOK, P. 76

(PAGE 2 OF 2)

NAME   DATE

How Many Rocks and Marbles?

3   Kira had 35 marbles in her bag.
    She gave 12 of them to Franco. How many
    marbles did she have left in her bag?

    23 marbles; Review students' work.

4   Franco's jar had 27 marbles in it.
    He added 14 more marbles. How many
    marbles does Franco have now?

    41 marbles; Review students' work.

UNIT 1 | 76 | SESSION 4.3   © Pearson Education 2

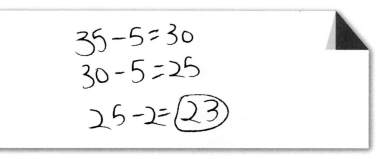

[Problem 3]

$$35 - 5 = 30$$
$$30 - 5 = 25$$
$$25 - 2 = \boxed{23}$$

[Problem 3]

Focus your observations on students' strategies (e.g., count all, count on, break the numbers apart) for Problem 1 to prepare for the end-of-session discussion.

 DIFFERENTIATION Supporting the Range of Learners

INTERVENTION Adapt the Learning Situation Meet in a small group with students who have difficulty getting started. Read each problem together. Ask students to discuss what they think is happening in the problem. Is it about putting groups together or taking a group apart? Then review each part of the problem, one step at a time. Have students use cubes to represent the quantities.

EXTENSION Extend Thinking Challenge students who solve the problems easily and record their work clearly to think about and try to describe the relationship between Problems 1 and 2. They may find ways to double-check their answers, or a second way to solve the problems.

ENGLISH LANGUAGE LEARNERS Repeat and Clarify Work with students to complete *Student Activity Book* pages 75–76. Read each problem with students and have them restate the problem in their own words before they begin to solve it. Ask guiding questions, such as: **What do you know? What do you need to find? Will there be more or fewer rocks at the end? Will you add or subtract? How can you write an equation to show it?** Encourage students to use tools and to draw pictures to solve the problems and to explain their thinking/solutions.

4 DISCUSSION

Strategies for Combining

MATH FOCUS POINTS FOR DISCUSSION

○ Sharing strategies for solving a put together story problem with total unknown

○ Using numbers, symbols, pictures, and/or words to represent a solution to a problem

Gather students to share and record strategies for solving Problem 1. As you discuss and record students' work, label each strategy and help them think about what a complete piece of student work looks like. **MPN** **PD1**

Strategies for Solving 16 + 24	
$16 + 24 = $ _____ $\begin{array}{r} 16 \\ + \underline{24} \end{array}$	
24; 25, 26, 27, …, 40 **Count up**	$16 + 10 = 26$ $26 + 10 = 36$ $36 + 4 = 40$
$10 + 20 = 30$ $\begin{array}{r}16\\ +\underline{24}\\ 30 \ (10+20)\\ +\underline{10} \ (6+4)\\ 40\end{array}$ $6 + 4 = 10$ $30 + 10 = 40$	$24 + 10 = 34$ $34 + 6 = 40$
Adding 10s and 1s	**Add one number in parts**

While most beginning second graders count on or add one number in parts, some add by place for problems about adding 2-digit numbers. (This strategy is a focus in Unit 3.) Use equations to record each step of their strategy. Some students experiment with vertical notation, adding the tens and then the ones (or adding the ones first and then the tens). Consider showing students how to record such a tens and ones strategy vertically, next to the strategy that shows using equations, so that students can make connections between them. If you have students who use or attempt to use the U.S. standard algorithm, explain that you will record that strategy in a way that makes the steps clearer to the class as a whole. **PD2** **TN**

SESSION FOLLOW-UP: REVIEW AND PRACTICE

Daily Practice

 DAILY PRACTICE For reinforcement of this unit's content, students complete *Student Activity Book* page 77.

STUDENT ACTIVITY BOOK, P. 77

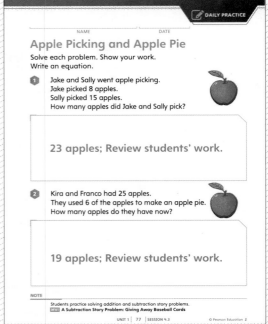

Apple Picking and Apple Pie
Solve each problem. Show your work.
Write an equation.

1   Jake and Sally went apple picking.
Jake picked 8 apples.
Sally picked 15 apples.
How many apples did Jake and Sally pick?

23 apples; Review students' work.

2   Kira and Franco had 25 apples.
They used 6 of the apples to make an apple pie.
How many apples do they have now?

19 apples; Review students' work.

NOTE
Students practice solving addition and subtraction story problems.
A Subtraction Story Problem: Giving Away Baseball Cards
UNIT 1   77   SESSION 4.3   © Pearson Education 2

MATH PRACTICE NOTE

MPN **MP6 Attend to precision.** Working together as a class, students develop an understanding of what must be written down to effectively communicate their thinking, and they also learn how to interpret what their classmates write.

PROFESSIONAL DEVELOPMENT

PD1 DIALOGUE BOX 12: What Does It Mean to Be Finished?

PD2 TEACHER NOTE 14: Using Notation to Record Strategies

TEACHING NOTE

TN **Forms of Notation** When using vertical notation to add, you line up numbers by place, suggesting a calculation strategy that treats each place separately. However, when adding single digits, students often lose sense of the whole number—for example, when adding 24 + 16, the 2 in 24 stands for 20. The conciseness of the notation obscures this information. Horizontal notation provides a more complete picture of the steps needed to solve the problem (4 + 6 = 10, 20 + 10 = 30; 10 + 30 = 40). For this reason, it is important to draw students' attention to the correspondences between the two forms of notation, both of which are based on adding parts by place.

Strategies for Subtracting

MATH FOCUS POINTS

○ Visualizing, representing, and solving put together/take apart story problems with the total unknown, and add to and take from story problems with the result unknown

○ Using standard notation (– and =) to represent subtraction situations

○ Using numbers, symbols, pictures, and/or words to represent a solution to a problem

○ Sharing strategies for solving a take from story problem with result unknown

TODAY'S PLAN	MATERIALS
10 Class — CLASSROOM ROUTINES: REVIEW AND PRACTICE ***Fact Fluency***	Students' envelopes of "Facts I Know" and "Facts I Am Still Working On" (from Sessions 2.5 and 3.2)
10 Class — **1** ACTIVITY **Story Problems Aloud**	
10 Class — **2** ACTIVITY **Introducing How Many Pennies?**	📖 *Student Activity Book*, p. 78
20 Individuals — **3** ACTIVITY **How Many Pennies, Rocks, and Shells?**	📖 *Student Activity Book*, pp. 78–79 Number line 🔧 100 chart 🔧 Connecting cubes (as needed)
20 Class — **4** DISCUSSION **Strategies for Subtracting**	📖 *Student Activity Book*, p. 78 (completed; from Activity 3) Number line 🔧 100 chart 🔧 Connecting cubes (as needed)
SESSION FOLLOW-UP: REVIEW AND PRACTICE **Daily Practice and Homework**	📖 *Student Activity Book*, pp. 80–81

Common Core State Standards	**Classroom Routines:** 2.OA.B.2 **Session:** 2.OA.A.1, 2.NBT.B.9, 2.MD.B.6	**Daily Practice:** Supports 2.MD.C.7

CLASSROOM ROUTINES: REVIEW AND PRACTICE

Fact Fluency

MATH FOCUS POINT

○ Developing fluency with addition and subtraction within 20

Explain that practicing addition and subtraction facts will be another Classroom Routine that students will encounter regularly during the year. In this first instance, the Classroom Routine will mirror what students have done previously in Math Workshop. Students review and practice the facts in their "Facts I Am Still Working On" envelope. Partners can also work together, quizzing each other, and sharing strategies for finding and remembering the sums and differences. **TN1**

1 ACTIVITY

Story Problems Aloud

Again, begin the session by telling several stories, asking students to imagine them in their minds as you tell them. For each, have students retell the story to and discuss it with a partner; then retell it in the whole group and discuss whether there will be more or fewer items at the end of the story; solve the problem with a partner; and finally, discuss strategies in the whole group. **TN2**

Sally has 9 red marbles and 6 blue marbles. How many marbles does she have in all?

Jake has 7 books. Kira gives him 4 more books. How many books does he have in all?

2 ACTIVITY

Introducing How Many Pennies?

Display Problem 1 from *Student Activity Book* page 78. Follow the same process as in Activity 1: read the story aloud, encouraging students to visualize what is happening in the problem and then to retell it.

What is happening in this problem? Don't solve it yet. Just explain what you see in your mind.

> **TEACHING NOTE**
>
> **TN1 Fact Fluency** Students continue to practice the facts in their "working on" envelope in the Classroom Routine: Fact Fluency. Other variations will provide practice in different contexts (e.g., games or short activities). Subsequent units include homework assignments or Math Workshop activities focused on developing fluency with the facts students are still working on, and on additional sets still to be introduced.
>
> **TN2 Solving Story Problems** The series of steps presented in Sessions 4.1–4.4 are intended to establish a routine that students can use whenever they solve story problems. Visualizing what is happening in a situation, asking what is known and unknown, and thinking about reasonable solutions are helpful habits in many problem situations and give students strategies to call on when they feel stuck or are unsure of how to proceed.

After a couple of volunteers have shared their thinking, ask these questions:

○ **In this problem, what are we trying to find out?** (how many pennies Kira has left)

○ **What information do we already know?** (how many pennies Kira had, how many pennies Kira spent)

○ **Will the answer be more than 30 or less than 30? Why do you think so?**

○ **What equation could we write to represent what is happening in this problem?**

Ask pairs to talk about an equation that represents this problem. Record their suggestions, using both horizontal and vertical notations, emphasizing that they mean the same thing and do not necessarily indicate how the problem should be solved.

3 ACTIVITY

How Many Pennies, Rocks, and Shells?

Distribute *Student Activity Book* pages 78–79.

Now you are going to solve this problem, and some others, on paper. Remember to write an equation and to check your answers. Be sure to show how you solved the problems on *Student Activity Book* pages 78–79. Someone else should be able to look at your work and understand what you did to solve it.

Remind students of the tools available (connecting cubes, number line, 100 chart), and what they should do if they need help reading a problem.

ONGOING ASSESSMENT Observing Students at Work

Students solve take from and add to story problems with result unknown, and put together/take apart story problems with the total unknown, and show their work.

○ **Can students retell the stories and explain the situation?** Can they identify what information is known/unknown? Do they know whether there will be more or fewer [pennies, rocks, shells] at the end of the story? Can they write an equation that represents what is happening? 🔍 **MP1**

○ **Can students solve the problems correctly?** What strategies do they use? Do they draw or count all? Count on or back? Do they count by 1s or by groups? Do they reason numerically (e.g., "$30 - 20 = 10$, but it's minus 19, so I have subtracted 1 too many," or "$12 + 20 = 32$, and then I have to add 4 more")?

○ **How do students record their strategy?** Do they use equations? Pictures? Words? A combination? Can you follow their thinking by looking at their written work? Does it match their oral explanation?

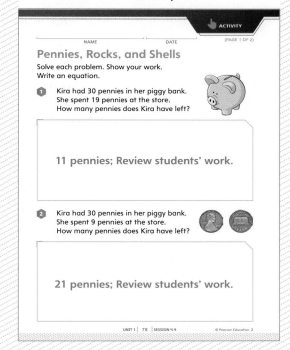

STUDENT ACTIVITY BOOK, P. 78

Pennies, Rocks, and Shells
Solve each problem. Show your work.
Write an equation.

1 Kira had 30 pennies in her piggy bank.
She spent 19 pennies at the store.
How many pennies does Kira have left?

11 pennies; Review students' work.

2 Kira had 30 pennies in her piggy bank.
She spent 9 pennies at the store.
How many pennies does Kira have left?

21 pennies; Review students' work.

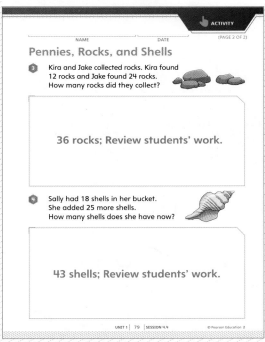

STUDENT ACTIVITY BOOK, P. 79

Pennies, Rocks, and Shells

3 Kira and Jake collected rocks. Kira found
12 rocks and Jake found 24 rocks.
How many rocks did they collect?

36 rocks; Review students' work.

4 Sally had 18 shells in her bucket.
She added 25 more shells.
How many shells does she have now?

43 shells; Review students' work.

$30 - 10 = 20$

$20 - 5 = 15$

$15 - 4 = 11$ pennies

[Problem 1]

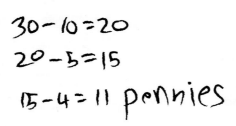

11 pennies

[Problem 1]

$12 + 24 = 36$

1 2 3 4 5 6 7 8 9 10 11 12
○ ○ ○ ○ ○ ○ ○ ○ ○ ○ ○ ○

13 14 15 16 17 18 19 20 21 22 23 24 25 26 27 28 29 30 31 32 33 34 35 36
○ ○

[Problem 3]

$24 + 12 -$

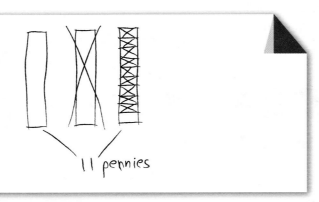

$24 +$ 🗸🗸🗸🗸🗸🗸🗸🗸🗸🗸 🗸🗸
       25 26 27 28 29
     30 31 32 33 34

$34 + 2 = 36$
rocks

[Problem 3]

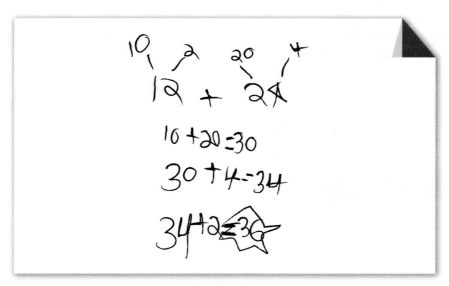

[Problem 3]

[Problem 3]

As you observe, make note of which strategies students use to solve Problem 1 (e.g., count all, count back, add on, use something you know) to inform the discussion at the end of this session.

DIFFERENTIATION Supporting the Range of Learners

INTERVENTION Clarify the Problem If students are having difficulty getting started, see whether they can retell the story. Do they understand that they are trying to determine the number of pennies Kira has left? Suggest that they model the problem with cubes.

INTERVENTION Scaffold a Solution If students are having difficulty recording their strategy, ask them to explain how they solved the problem. Then repeat or rephrase their process and help them record their steps. **You started with 30, and then you counted back. The first thing you said was 30. Can you write that on your paper? Now, how can you show that you counted back from 30? What numbers did you say? How many did you count back?**

⎡ For a more comprehensive intervention activity to be done outside of class,
  see *Visualizing Story Problems* at the end of this investigation. ⎦

EXTENSION **Extend Thinking** Challenge students who solve the problems easily and record their work clearly to think about and try to describe the relationship between Problems 1 and 2. They may find ways to double-check their answers, or a second way to solve the problems.

> For a more comprehensive extension activity to be done outside of class, see *Story Problems with Multiple Parts* at the end of this investigation.

4 DISCUSSION

Strategies for Subtracting

MATH FOCUS POINT FOR DISCUSSION

○ Using equations, pictures, and/or words to represent a solution to a problem

Gather students to share and record strategies for solving Problem 1.

Kira had 30 pennies in her piggy bank. She spent 19 pennies at the store. How many pennies does Kira have left?

Model, or ask volunteers to model, students' strategies with cubes and on the number line or class 100 chart.

A few students may count all (e.g., draw 30, cross out 19, count what is left).

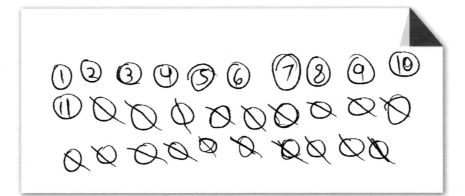

Some students may count back by 1s (on fingers, 100 chart, number line).

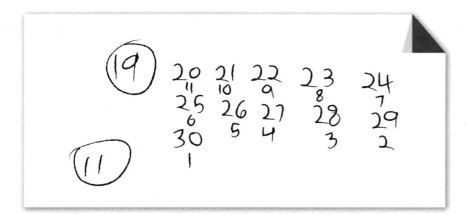

Others may count back, or subtract, in larger groups (e.g., $30 - 10 = 20$ and $20 - 9 = 11$).

$$30 - 19 = 11$$

$$30 - 10 = 20$$
$$20 - 9 = \boxed{11}$$

Some students may turn this problem into one about finding a missing addend. A few may count up by 1s, but more common is adding up in larger groups (e.g., $19 + \underline{1} = 20$, $20 + \underline{10} = 30$, $1 + 10 = 11$).

$$30 - 19 = \underline{}$$

$$19 + 1 = 20$$
$$20 + 10 = 30$$
$$\pm\boxed{11}$$

Some students may use a known combination and then adjust (e.g., "30 − 20 = 10, but I took away 1 too many, so I need to add 1 on, and that's 11").

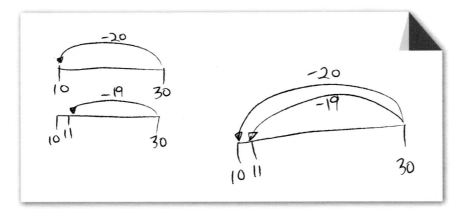

SESSION FOLLOW-UP: REVIEW AND PRACTICE

Daily Practice and Homework

DAILY PRACTICE For reinforcement of this unit's content, students complete *Student Activity Book* page 80.

HOMEWORK On *Student Activity Book* page 81, students solve a story problem that involves combining two quantities.

STUDENT ACTIVITY BOOK, P. 80

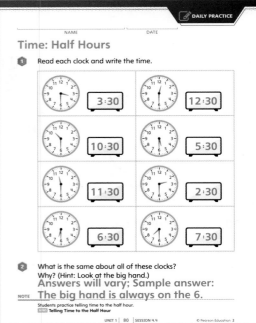

STUDENT ACTIVITY BOOK, P. 81

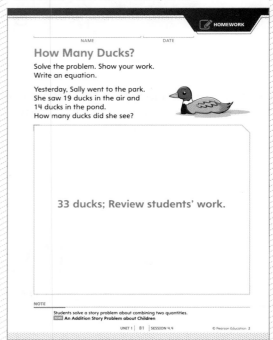

Solving Story Problems

MATH FOCUS POINTS

○ Visualizing, representing, and solving put together/take apart story problems with the total unknown, and add to and take from story problems with the result unknown

○ Using standard notation (+, −, =) to represent addition and subtraction situations

○ Using numbers, symbols, pictures, and/or words to represent a solution to a problem

TODAY'S PLAN	MATERIALS
(10) Class — CLASSROOM ROUTINES: REVIEW AND PRACTICE ***Today's Number: 18***	Teacher Presentation (or use a number line) *Student Activity Book*, p. 83
(60) Individuals — **1** ASSESSMENT ACTIVITY **Solving Story Problems**	A8–A10* Connecting cubes 100 chart Number line (as needed)
SESSION FOLLOW-UP: REVIEW AND PRACTICE **Daily Practice**	*Student Activity Book*, p. 84

* See *Materials to Prepare* in the Investigation 4 Planner.

Common Core State Standards	**Classroom Routines:** 2.OA.B.2, 2.MD.B.6 **Session:** 2.OA.A.1, 2.NBT.B.9, 2.MD.B.6	**Daily Practice:** 2.OA.A.1

CLASSROOM ROUTINES: REVIEW AND PRACTICE

Today's Number: 18

MATH FOCUS POINTS

○ Generating equivalent expressions for a number

○ Using standard notation (+, −, =) to record expressions or equations

Display the Teacher Presentation (or use a number line).

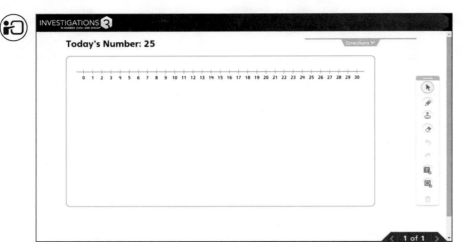

Explain that Today's Number is 18, and ask students to help you find it on the number line and write the number word (i.e., eighteen). Students individually generate addition and/or subtraction expressions for the number 18 and record them on *Student Activity Book* page 83. This set of work, the series of *Today's Number* samples that students will compile over the course of the year, will provide information about how well students can compose and decompose numbers.

---

1 ASSESSMENT ACTIVITY

Solving Story Problems

Students solve three story problems. For each, they write an equation that shows what the problem is asking, solve the problem, and show their work. **TN1** **TN2**

BENCHMARK	QUESTIONS
4: Solve put together/take apart story problems with the total unknown, and add to and take from story problems with the result unknown	1–3

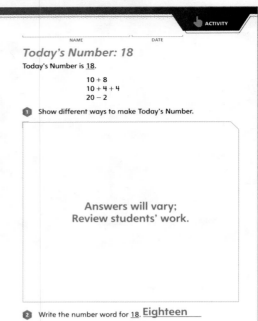

Today's Number: 18

Today's Number is <u>18</u>.

$$10 + 8$$
$$10 + 4 + 4$$
$$20 - 2$$

1 Show different ways to make Today's Number.

Answers will vary;
Review students' work.

2 Write the number word for <u>18</u>. <u>Eighteen</u>

UNIT 1 | 83 | SESSION 4.5   © Pearson Education 2

TEACHING NOTES

TN1 **Assessing Students' Use of the Number Line** These problems also provide an opportunity to see whether and how students are making use of the number line as a tool for representing, solving, and/or recording strategies for solving problems involving addition and subtraction.

TN2 **Assessing Students' Ability to Explain Their Strategy** These problems also provide the opportunity to observe students' growing ability to explain their strategies for solving addition and subtraction problems. Note whether students' strategies rely on place value and/or properties of operations (e.g., thinking $29 + 29 = 20 + 20 + 9 + 9$, or $25 - 14 = 25 - 10 - 4$, or $25 + 18 = 25 + 20 - 2$). Students will grow in their ability to explain their strategies and to use their developing knowledge of place value and operations to add and subtract throughout Grade 2.

Explain that students will work individually, so that you can get a sense of how they have grown in their ability to solve such problems and show their work. Remind them that for each problem, they should also include an equation that represents what is happening in the problem.

Distribute and read aloud the story problems on A8–A10 (or the Online Assessment). Explain the materials that are available (connecting cubes, 100 charts, the number line), and that you will reread the problems for students, as needed, as they work.

Problem 1: There were 29 students on a bus, waiting to go on a field trip. Then, 29 more students got on the bus. How many students are on the bus?

Problem 2: A teacher has 25 new pencils. She gives out 14 pencils. How many pencils does she have left?

Problem 3: On Monday, there was a bicycle race in the park. There were 25 children and 18 adults in the race. How many people were in the race?

ONGOING ASSESSMENT Observing Students at Work

Students solve an add to story problem and a take from story problem with result unknown, and a put together/take apart story problem with total unknown, and record their work. **PD**

○ **Can students make sense of the situations?** Can they write an equation that represents what is happening?

○ **Can students solve the problems correctly?** What strategies do they use? Do they draw or count all? Count on or back? Count by 1s or in chunks? Do they work numerically, breaking numbers into useful chunks and using facts and relationships they know?

○ **What tools, if any, do students use?** Do they use connecting cubes? A number line? A 100 chart?

○ **How do students record their strategies?** Do they use equations? Pictures? Words? A combination? Can you follow their thinking by looking at their written work? Does it match their verbal explanation?

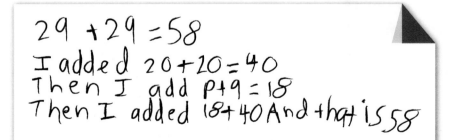

[Problem 1]

ONLINE ASSESSMENT

INVESTIGATIONS

◀ Solving Story Problems
For the problem, write an equation. Solve the problem. Use the DrawPad to show your work.

◀ 1. There were 29 students on a bus, waiting to go on a field trip. Then, 29 more students got on the bus. How many students are on the bus?

1 of 3

RESOURCE MASTERS, A8

ASSESSMENT

NAME   DATE   (PAGE 1 OF 1)

Solving Story Problems

For each problem, write an equation. Solve the problem. Show your work.

1 There were 29 students on a bus, waiting to go on a field trip. Then, 29 more students got on the bus. How many students are on the bus?

58 students; Review students' work.

UNIT 1 | A8 | SESSION 4.5   © Pearson Education 2

PROFESSIONAL DEVELOPMENT

PD TEACHER NOTE 15: Assessment: Solving Story Problems

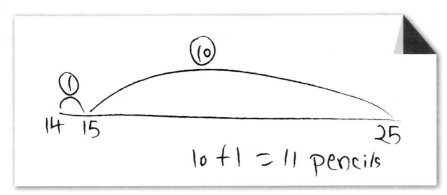

[Problem 2]

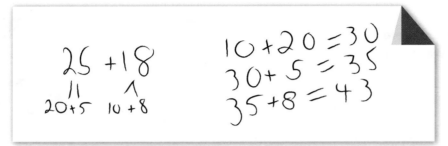

[Problem 3]

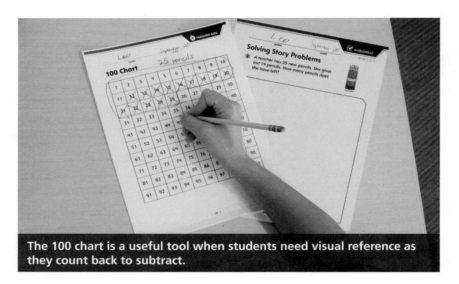

The 100 chart is a useful tool when students need visual reference as they count back to subtract.

When students have finished working, have them read their explanations to you. Do not tell them whether they are correct or incorrect, but point out parts that are unclear or where information seems to be missing and have them revise their work.

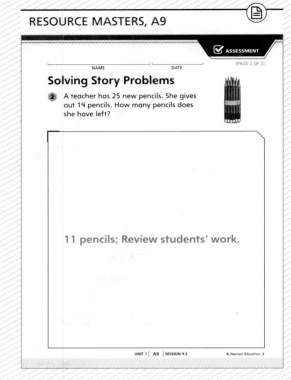

RESOURCE MASTERS, A9

(PAGE 2 OF 3)

Solving Story Problems

2 A teacher has 25 new pencils. She gives out 14 pencils. How many pencils does she have left?

11 pencils; Review students' work.

UNIT 1 | A9 | SESSION 4.5   © Pearson Education 2

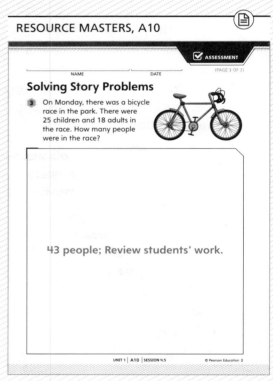

RESOURCE MASTERS, A10

(PAGE 3 OF 3)

Solving Story Problems

3 On Monday, there was a bicycle race in the park. There were 25 children and 18 adults in the race. How many people were in the race?

43 people; Review students' work.

UNIT 1 | A10 | SESSION 4.5   © Pearson Education 2

DIFFERENTIATION Supporting the Range of Learners

For a more comprehensive practice activity to be done outside of class, see *Solving Story Problems* at the end of this investigation.

ENGLISH LANGUAGE LEARNERS **Allow Varied Responses** When asked to verbally explain their solutions, some students may respond by using their first language, by pointing, or by using gestures. Allow this, and ask questions to discern students' mathematical knowledge from their understanding of English. Restate students' responses in English, and have them repeat after you.

SESSION FOLLOW-UP: REVIEW AND PRACTICE

Daily Practice

 DAILY PRACTICE For reinforcement of this unit's content, students complete *Student Activity Book* page 84.

STUDENT ACTIVITY BOOK, P. 84

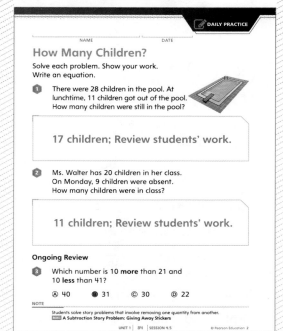

DAILY PRACTICE

NAME   DATE

How Many Children?

Solve each problem. Show your work.
Write an equation.

1 There were 28 children in the pool. At lunchtime, 11 children got out of the pool. How many children were still in the pool?

> 17 children; Review students' work.

2 Ms. Walter has 20 children in her class. On Monday, 9 children were absent. How many children were in class?

> 11 children; Review students' work.

Ongoing Review

3 Which number is 10 **more** than 21 and 10 **less** than 41?

Ⓐ 40   ● 31   Ⓒ 30   Ⓓ 22

NOTE

Students solve story problems that involve removing one quantity from another.
A Subtraction Story Problem: Giving Away Stickers

UNIT 1 | 84 | SESSION 4.5   © Pearson Education 2

Visualizing Story Problems

MATH FOCUS POINTS

○ Visualizing, representing, and solving add to/take from story problems with the total/result unknown

○ Using numbers, symbols, pictures, and/or words to represent a solution to a problem

VOCABULARY: plus sign, equal sign, minus sign

MATERIALS: connecting cubes (as needed), blank paper

I'm going to read a story problem. Listen carefully. Close your eyes and try to picture what is happening. Think about the information given in the story.

Display and read the following problem.

> **Jake and Kira brought juice boxes for the class party. Jake brought 15 juice boxes and Kira gave him 12 more juice boxes. How many juice boxes do they have for the party?**

Read the problem twice and then discuss the action in the problem and what is known and unknown. **How does the story begin? What happens in the story? What is the problem asking you to find? Will there be more or fewer juice boxes in the end? Why?**

Record the known information:

> **Jake: 15 juice boxes**
>
> **Kira: 12 juice boxes**

Provide students with a sheet of blank paper (folded in half) and access to connecting cubes. Direct them to use the left half of their papers to record the known information.

Discuss students' ideas for solving the problem and then have them solve it. They should record their solutions on the right half of their papers.

Before students share their solution strategies, ask them to help you write an equation for the problem. Connect the numbers and symbols (+ and =) to each part of the story. **What does the 15 stand for? The 12? The plus sign shows that the two groups of juice boxes are being combined into one group.** Point to the numbers on either side of the equal sign. **The equal sign shows that two things are the same or equal.**

Discuss and model how to record each strategy. **[Leo] drew each juice box and then counted them all, and [Anita] showed the two groups of juice boxes using a set of 15 cubes and a group of 12 cubes.**

Display and read the following problem and repeat the process.

> **There are 28 apples in the basket. Six students eat one apple each. How many apples are left in the basket?**

Students discuss, solve and record, and then share strategies. When writing the equation for the subtraction problem, connect the numbers and symbols back to the problem and explain that the minus sign in this problem shows that some of the apples (6) are being taken from the original number of apples in the basket (28).

DIFFERENTIATION

ENGLISH LANGUAGE LEARNERS **Repeat and Clarify** Help students understand the story problems. For example, explain to students that *brought* is the past tense of *bring*. Provide sample sentences to show the words in context: **Today, I** *bring* **my books to class. Yesterday, I** *brought* **my books to class.** Have students repeat the sentences. If necessary, restate each problem in the present tense to help students understand it. For example: **Jake** *brings* **15 juice boxes. Kira** *brings* **12 more juice boxes. How many juice boxes in all?**

ADDITIONAL RESOURCE

Math Words and Ideas An Addition Story Problem; Solving an Addition Story Problem; A Subtraction Story Problem

Solving Story Problems

MATH FOCUS POINTS

○ Visualizing, representing, and solving add to/take from story problems with the total/result unknown

○ Using numbers, symbols, pictures, and/or words to represent a solution to a problem

MATERIALS: connecting cubes (as needed), S20

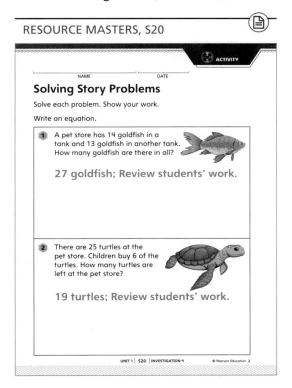

RESOURCE MASTERS, S20

ACTIVITY

NAME   DATE

Solving Story Problems

Solve each problem. Show your work.

Write an equation.

1 A pet store has 14 goldfish in a tank and 13 goldfish in another tank. How many goldfish are there in all?

27 goldfish; Review students' work.

2 There are 25 turtles at the pet store. Children buy 6 of the turtles. How many turtles are left at the pet store?

19 turtles; Review students' work.

UNIT 1 | S20 | INVESTIGATION 4   © Pearson Education 2

Display and read the following problem aloud.

> **Jake had 28 seashells. He gave 13 of them to Sally. How many seashells did Jake have left?**

Ask students to retell the problem to a partner and then discuss the information that is known. **At the beginning, how many seashells did Jake have? What is the action in this story problem? Will Jake have more than or less than 28 seashells? How do you know?**

Discuss strategies for solving the problem. **How would you solve the problem? What tools would you use to model the problem? Does anyone have a different way?**

" STUDENTS MIGHT SAY "

"Show 28 cubes. Take away 13 of them. Count how many are left."

"Show 28 minus 13 on a number line."

After students solve the problem, write an equation together. **What number is first? How do you know? What symbol shows that some were given away? Where does the equal sign go?**

Then have students share their ways of recording their solution strategies. [Luis] made dots to stand for the seashells, and then [he] crossed some out. **What part of [Luis]'s solution shows the answer? [Carla] only put the important numbers from the problem on the number line. [She] didn't have to write them all. Why did [she] write a 28? What part shows the 13 shells that Jake gave away? What is the answer? How do you know?**

Display and read the following problem aloud. **Kira had 17 seashells. Franco gave her 15 more seashells. How many seashells did Kira have then?**

Discuss the information given in the problem. Have students solve the problem, record their strategies, and write an equation. Then discuss their solutions and strategies as a group.

Distribute copies of Solving Story Problems (S20).

DIFFERENTIATION

ENGLISH LANGUAGE LEARNERS **Partner Talk** Pair students to solve the last problem. Ask them the following questions to help them get started: **How many seashells did Kira have at first? How many did Franco give her? Then how many did she have?** Encourage pairs to discuss their solution and strategy in preparation for the group discussion.

ADDITIONAL RESOURCE

Math Words and Ideas An Addition Story Problem about Children; A Subtraction Story Problem: Giving Away Baseball Cards   (MWI)

Story Problems with Multiple Parts

MATH FOCUS POINTS

○ Visualizing, representing, and solving add to story problems with multiple addends and the total unknown

○ Using numbers, symbols, pictures, and/or words to represent a solution to a problem

MATERIALS: connecting cubes (as needed), paper, S21

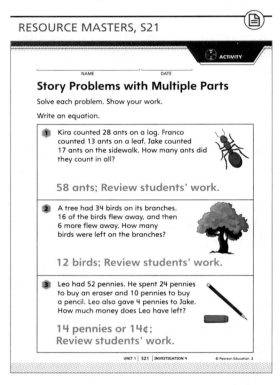

RESOURCE MASTERS, S21

NAME   DATE

Story Problems with Multiple Parts

Solve each problem. Show your work.

Write an equation.

1   Kira counted 28 ants on a log. Franco counted 13 ants on a leaf. Jake counted 17 ants on the sidewalk. How many ants did they count in all?

58 ants; Review students' work.

2   A tree had 34 birds on its branches. 16 of the birds flew away, and then 6 more flew away. How many birds were left on the branches?

12 birds; Review students' work.

3   Leo had 52 pennies. He spent 24 pennies to buy an eraser and 10 pennies to buy a pencil. Leo also gave 4 pennies to Jake. How much money does Leo have left?

14 pennies or 14¢; Review students' work.

UNIT 1 | S21 | INVESTIGATION 4   © Pearson Education 2

Display and read the following story problem:

> **Franco has 26 marbles. Sally has 18 marbles. Kira has 7 marbles. They decided to combine their marbles. How many marbles do Franco, Sally, and Kira have in all?**

What are we asked to find in this problem? Is this a problem about combining groups or separating groups? How do you know? In this problem, what are the parts? What is the whole?

Students solve the problem individually on paper. They should write an equation that represents the problem and record their work so that someone else can follow their solution strategy.

When students have finished, bring the group back together to discuss their work. **What equation did you write to go with this problem? Can you explain each part? Next ask students to share their strategies. How did you solve the problem?**

❝ STUDENTS MIGHT SAY ❞

"I added 10 and 20 together for 30. I put the 8 and 6 together for 14. That's 30 plus 14, or 44 in all. Then I added on the 7 and got 51."

"I added 18 and 7 and got 25. Then I added 26 on the 100 chart. I started at 25 and went 35, 45, 50, 51."

Record students' strategies. **Did anyone solve the problem in a different way? Did anyone get a different answer?** Guide students who got incorrect answers in retracing their steps and finding their mistakes.

Distribute copies of Story Problems with Multiple Parts (S21).

DIFFERENTIATION

ENGLISH LANGUAGE LEARNERS **Provide a Sequence** Provide a sequence to help students explain their solutions. *First, I _____. Next, I _____. Then, I _____.* If students need additional support, model using the sequence. For example, ask students to show you how they solved the problem. Then have them describe what they did for each step. Then ask them to demonstrate each step again as you narrate what they are doing. After each step, ask the student to describe what they did. First, you [wrote 26 + 18 + 7 = ?] because [you knew you needed to add to combine the groups of marbles]. Next, you [added 18 + 7 and got 25]. Then, you [added 26 + 25 and got 51]. You found that there are 51 marbles in all.

ADDITIONAL RESOURCE

Math Words and Ideas Story Problem Routine

COINS, NUMBER STRINGS, AND STORY PROBLEMS

TEACHER NOTES

DIALOGUE BOXES

INDEX

Algebra Connections in This Unit

In this unit, your students will have opportunities to engage with ideas that lay a foundation for algebra. Seven- and eight-year-olds can and do think algebraically. Part of the work of Grade 2 is helping students learn to verbalize those thoughts and begin considering such questions as: Is this statement always true? Does it work for all numbers? How can we know? Such skills will provide the basis for making sense of algebraic notation and proof when it is introduced years from now.

A teacher asks students to explain how they figured out 5 + 9. Consider the following vignette.

Amaya:	I made a train with 5 cubes and another train with 9 cubes. Then I counted all the cubes and got 14.
Luis:	I know it is 14 because I counted on. I knew I had 5, and then I used my fingers—6, 7, 8, 9, 10, 11, 12, 13, 14.
Malcolm:	I did it sort of like Luis, but I started with 9, and then I said 10, 11, 12, 13, 14. When I got to my fifth finger, it was 14.
Melissa:	I know 5 + 10 is 15. Since 9 is one less than 10, the answer has to be 14 because it's 1 less than 15.
Monisha:	I took 1 from the 5 and gave it to the 9. That changed 5 + 9 into 4 + 10, and that's 14.

Each student has found a different way to solve this particular problem, 5 + 9. Amaya and Luis have modeled the problem directly (counting all and counting on), whereas Malcolm, Melissa, and Monisha have changed the problem in some way to make the problem easier to solve. At this stage of second grade, it is important to appreciate the thinking of Amaya and Luis, but it is also important to recognize the different *kind* of thinking Malcolm, Melissa, and Monisha are engaged in. Implicit in the solution methods of these three children are generalizations that involve an understanding of whether and how changes in an addition expression change the sum.

Switching the Order of Addends

5 + 9 = 9 + 5 Malcolm uses the idea that you can change the order of addends and get the same sum. Since 9 + 5 gives the same result as 5 + 9, he knows he can count on from 9 instead of counting on from 5, as Luis did. This idea often arises in other contexts in Grade 2. For example, when students are listing all the combinations of 10, they may notice that both 6 + 4 and 4 + 6 are on the list, as are 2 + 8 and 8 + 2. Once they notice this regularity, they might check it with other numbers: 3 + 7 and 7 + 3 are also listed.

Second graders often make up their own terms for this rule: "opposites," "turn arounds," "switch arounds," "reversibles." Whatever term your students use, have them describe it. It is this activity that is meant by MP8, Look for and express regularity in repeated reasoning.

Ask students to think about the idea behind switching the order of addends. How sure are they that changing the order of the addends does not change the result? Do they believe this to be true for any pair of numbers? Students may use cubes to demonstrate, holding up a stack of cubes in each hand, and then switching hands to show the total is unchanged. They may say, "You're just switching them around and putting them in different spots. You're not adding some or taking any away." Although their cubes represent particular numbers, students may use a stack to stand for "any number."

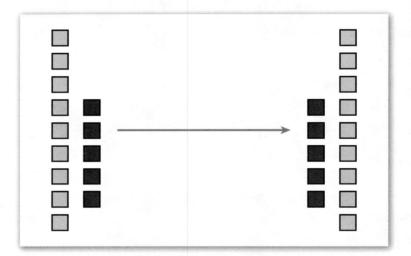

The generalization these students are acting on is the commutative property of addition: Two numbers added in either order yield the same sum. Written algebraically, the commutative property of addition is expressed as $a + b = b + a$. See **Teacher Note 6:** Does the Order Matter? and **Dialogue Box 3:** Combinations of 10.

There are other opportunities to *notice regularity* in this unit, as illustrated by the strategies offered by Melissa and Monisha.

Adding 1 to an Addend and Subtracting 1 from the Total

5 + 9 = 5 + 10 − 1 Melissa's method is based on the idea that if 1 is added to an addend, the sum increases by 1, and if 1 is subtracted from an addend, the sum decreases by 1.

Since 9 is one less than 10, 5 + 9 must be one less than 5 + 10. Applying this reasoning, students can use known combinations to solve problems they do not know. For instance, once students learn their "make 10" facts, they can use this idea to find 3 + 8 (3 + 7 + 1) or 7 + 2 (7 + 3 − 1). Or if students know their doubles, they can use them to solve 6 + 5 (5 + 5 + 1) or 8 + 9 (9 + 9 − 1).

Katrina is using the same idea.

[Katrina's Work]

When you notice students using such reasoning, ask them to explain. How do they verbalize the idea? Can they show their reasoning with cubes?

When you ask your students to explain, it might at first be difficult for them to articulate their thinking. However, by hearing similar kinds of questions repeatedly, some of your students will start to anticipate them and will begin to have ideas to offer. As the year continues, you will find that more students learn to articulate their thinking and, with these ideas in the air, more students will begin to use them. You might hear such language as, "I know that 4 + 4 = 8. So 5 + 4 = 9. You're just adding one more and putting it on the 4 so it can turn to a 5. Then the 8 changes to a 9." At a more general level, a student might say, "If you're adding two numbers and add 1 to one number, your answer goes to the next number."

When these young children become older, they will learn how to express these ideas using variables. They might say, "If $a + b = c$, then $(a + 1) + b = c + 1$ and $a + (b + 1) = c + 1$." Or they might write it more compactly: "If I add two numbers, $a + b$, and then I add 1 to one of the addends, $(a + 1) + b$ or $a + (b + 1)$, then I increase the total by 1, $(a + b) + 1$." That is, $(a + 1) + b = a + (b + 1) = (a + b) + 1$.

Taking 1 from an Addend and Adding 1 to the Other

5 + 9 = 4 + 10 When asked to solve 5 + 9, Monisha explains, "I took 1 from the 5 and gave it to the 9. That changed 5 + 9 into 4 + 10, and that's 14." The more general idea implied by her move is that if 1 is subtracted from one of the addends and 1 is added to the other addend, then the total remains unchanged. This is true for any two numbers that are added. Since 34 + 56 = 90, then 33 + 57 = 90, 32 + 58 = 90, and so forth.

In your classroom, you are likely to see this idea arise in a variety of situations, including *Today's Number*. For example, Juan started with 1 + 9 = 10 to generate other combinations of 10.

[Juan's Work]

As students begin to use this idea, ask them to verbalize what they are doing. Have them act out their idea with cubes to illustrate how they know it works. Students may explain that this works by showing two stacks of cubes. If they take a cube off of one stack and attach it to the other, the total number of cubes remains unchanged.

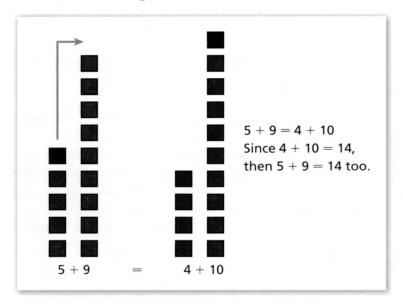

$$5 + 9 = 4 + 10$$
Since $4 + 10 = 14$,
then $5 + 9 = 14$ too.

$$5 + 9 \qquad = \qquad 4 + 10$$

You might hear language like Monisha's: "I took 1 from the 5 and gave it to the 9. That changed $5 + 9$ into $4 + 10$, and that's 14." Or, more generally, "When I add two numbers, I can take 1 from one number and give it to the other, and the answer stays the same." When they are older, children will learn how to express these ideas using words and variables: "When I add two numbers, a and b, the answer to $a + b$ is the same as if I take 1 away from the a (e.g., $a - 1$) and give it to the b (e.g., $b + 1$) and add those together: $(a - 1) + (b + 1)$." Written as an equation, it looks like $a + b = (a - 1) + (b + 1)$. Or, even more generally, $a + b = (a - c) + (b + c)$.

For most adults, such notation (the use of variables, operations, and equal signs) is the chief identifying feature of algebra. Underlying this notation, however, are ways of reasoning about how the operations work. This *reasoning*—about how numbers can be put together and taken apart under different operations—*not* the notation, is the work of elementary students in algebra. In fact, the examples shown above illustrate the kind of "early algebraic reasoning" that is fully accessible to elementary-aged students. *Investigations* students are encouraged to verbalize the generalizations they see about numbers and operations and to explain and justify them using materials and tools, such as cubes. These discussions are not so much about finding an answer to a particular problem, but about describing a way to find answers to a *whole class* of problems. They are not exclusively about, say, how $5 + 9$ is equivalent to $4 + 10$, but how any addition expression can be transformed into a different, but equivalent, expression.

Students from *Investigations* classrooms in Grade 1 may have already begun participating in discussions of the generalizations they notice, and you may find some of your students are already thinking about regularities in the number system like these. Other students may begin to think in these ways toward the end of this unit; others still later in the year. In this unit, you will see students begin to use early algebraic reasoning to remember their addition facts. As the year continues, you will find that they apply the same principles in a variety of contexts. In particular, look for the same ideas as students begin to solve 2-digit addition problems.

The Number Line and the 100 Chart: Two Models of Our Number System

The number line and the 100 chart are used throughout the *Investigations* curriculum as two models of our number system. These tools help students understand how our number system is structured. Understanding this structure supports the development of greater facility in adding and subtracting numbers. Students use these as tools for computation and for representing strategies.

The Number Line

The number line is a linear model of our number system. It represents the unending nature of the counting numbers—it can extend endlessly in either direction. Students often think about jumps as they relate to 10, an important landmark in our number system. For example, students see that it takes 10 jumps of 10 to get to 100, that 40 to 50 is 10, and that 45 to 55 is 10 because they can see the two groups of 5 on either side of the landmark 50. In fact, any jump of 10 (1 to 11, 2 to 12, etc.) represents the same distance on the number line.

This idea of quantity as distance is an important contribution the number line can make as students tackle addition and subtraction situations. For example, when adding two numbers, students can visualize the second addend as one (or several) jump(s) on the number line. Students can also visualize any subtraction problem as finding the distance between the two numbers, or as a jump back on the number line. Over time, students need fewer numbers labeled and eventually use an unmarked number line to show only the part needed for a particular problem. In later grades, students use the number line to help make sense of numbers less than zero, as well as fractions and decimal numbers.

The 100 Chart

The 100 chart is a 2-dimensional model of the numbers from 1 to 100, organized in a 10-by-10 array. Because of this organization, students can see all of the numbers from 1 to 100 and their relationship to one another. Students can see, for example, that 47 is composed of 4 rows of 10 plus 7 more, that it is 3 away from 50, that it is 10 more than 37 and 10 less than 57, and that it is almost halfway between 1 and 100. All of these are useful pieces of information when thinking about numbers and number relationships. Later in Grade 2, students build on their understanding of the structure of the 100 chart as they read and write numbers to 1,000, attending not only to the patterns of the written numbers but also thinking about where numbers are in relation to other numbers. In later grades, students use 100 charts to construct 2-dimensional models of 1,000 and 10,000. Once again they are able to think about the composition of numbers (1,000 is 10 groups of 100) and where numbers are in relationship to each other.

The Relationship Between the Number Line and the 100 Chart

Another important aspect of students' work is to consider the similarities and differences between the number line and the 100 chart. Students will recognize that both tools are organizations of the counting numbers from 1 to 100, but the number line is a linear representation and the 100 chart is organized into 10 rows of 10.

Consider this conversation that a teacher had with students in Session 1.4.

Teacher: What do you notice when you compare the number line to the 100 chart?

Rochelle: They both go up to 100.

Amaya: That (100 chart) is going down and that (the number line) goes across.

Simon: Yeah, the 100 chart is square, and the number line is long.

Monisha: The 100 chart doesn't start on 0, but the number line starts on 0.

Esteban: The 100 chart is going in rows, but the number line doesn't have any rows.

Teacher: How many rows does the 100 chart have?

Esteban: 10.

Juan: If you put the number line in rows it would be like a 100 chart.

Juan has seen how one representation can be transformed into the other. Having such a good sense of both tools and how they are similar and different can help students think about which tool would be most useful for a particular problem situation.

Using the Number Line and 100 Chart to Solve Addition and Subtraction Problems

As students become familiar with the structure and organization of the 100 chart and the number line, they can begin to use them as tools for adding and subtracting. For example, consider the problem "How far is it from 29 to 53?" Some second graders count on by 1s from 29 to 53, while others use groups of 10. Some may use a combination of the two strategies. What is important is that students understand the problem and recognize that they are finding the difference between the two numbers. Both tools offer students a model of the relationship between these numbers.

100 Chart

1	2	3	4	5	6	7	8	9	10
11	12	13	14	15	16	17	18	19	20
21	22	23	24	25	26	27	28	29	30
31	32	33	34	35	36	37	38	39	40
41	42	43	44	45	46	47	48	49	50
51	52	53	54	55	56	57	58	59	60
61	62	63	64	65	66	67	68	69	70
71	72	73	74	75	76	77	78	79	80
81	82	83	84	85	86	87	88	89	90
91	92	93	94	95	96	97	98	99	100

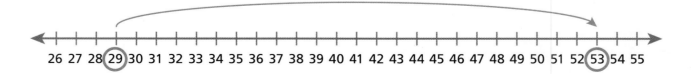

26 27 28 29 30 31 32 33 34 35 36 37 38 39 40 41 42 43 44 45 46 47 48 49 50 51 52 53 54 55

Counting by Groups

Counting is the basis for understanding our number system and for much of the number work in the primary grades. It involves knowing the number names, their sequence, and how to read and write each number. It also involves organizing and counting a set of objects in order to quantify and answer "How many?" or producing a set when asked to show a specific amount. While it may seem simple, counting is actually quite complex and involves the interplay between a number of skills and concepts.

In order to count accurately and efficiently, students must know the counting sequence, assign one number to one object, organize and keep track of what has been counted and what remains to be counted, and understand that each time they say the next number, the quantity increases by one, and the final number in the sequence describes the quantity of the objects in the set. Successful counters also know that a quantity remains constant no matter how it is arranged or grouped.

Learning to count happens over time. While students may have accurate and efficient strategies for counting smaller sets, these strategies may not be as effective with larger quantities. Students are likely to revisit many aspects of counting as they work with larger sets and use greater numbers.

When dealing with large quantities, counting by groups is more efficient and makes students less prone to errors than counting by ones. Students, however, need to be consistent with all aspects of counting by ones if they are to fully understand and apply counting by groups in meaningful ways.

Counting a set of objects by equal groups such as 2s, 5s, or 10s requires that each of the steps mentioned above happen again, at a different level, and requires students to make an important shift in thinking—that a collection of single objects can also be described as one group.

In order to successfully count a set of objects by groups, students need to know:

○ the rote sequence [10, 20, 30, 40 . . .]

○ that each time they say a number they are adding another group of [ten]

○ how to keep track of what has been counted and what remains to be counted

○ that the last number tells you how many in the set/the total number of objects

They also must recognize that in some situations, for example when there are equal groups and a number of leftovers, it is necessary to shift from counting by groups (5, 10, 15, 20) to counting the remaining items by ones (21, 22, 23).

Counting—by ones and by groups—underlies all of the work students do in number and operations. It is this fluency that leads to an understanding that *10 ones* is equivalent to *one group* of ten or *a ten*, which is the basis for students' work with place value and the base-10 number system. See **Teacher Note 11:** Place Value in Second Grade. Similarly, counting by groups is a main math idea for the foundations of multiplication work that students do later in Grade 2 (Unit 7) and in Grade 3 and beyond.

This first unit in Grade 2 offers an opportunity to assess and reinforce students' counting skills to ensure that students who are not fluently and accurately counting by 1s receive immediate support in order to reinforce and solidify these essential skills.

Money as a Mathematical Tool

Money can be a powerful mathematical tool. Coins and bills are engaging real-world objects that many students are familiar with. Students encounter, or see adults encounter, mathematical situations based on money almost every day. In addition, coins provide a concrete model for counting by 5s, 10s, and 25s, and for adding and subtracting numbers that are multiples of 5.

Coin Values and Equivalencies

Your students will probably vary widely in their understanding of coin values and equivalencies. Some of the things that students will struggle with have to do with social conventions such as what names and values go with which coins. For example, the dime is the smallest coin, but does not represent the smallest amount. Similarly, the nickel is bigger than the dime, but worth less. Knowledge of coin names and values develops as students gain experience with them through Classroom Routines (i.e., *Quick Images*: Coins), games (i.e., *Do We Have 100?*), and discussions.

The same ideas that make coins a powerful mathematical tool can also make them difficult for students to understand and use meaningfully. Students who are still thinking primarily in 1s may have a hard time thinking of *one* nickel as the same as *five* pennies. While some students may readily trade coins and understand equivalencies, others will not initially be ready to make trades and will work with just pennies. As they play games such as *Collect 50¢* repeatedly, they will begin to make simple trades, such as five pennies for a nickel, and then more complicated trades, such as five pennies and a nickel for a dime.

Some students may find it hard to keep coin values and relationships in mind while also concentrating on counting and keeping track of a growing collection. For example, some students may accurately count a small set of coins, such as a nickel and two pennies ("5 and 2, that's 7 cents"), but with a larger set, such as five nickels and 15 pennies, they may mistakenly count some of the nickels as "ones." Some may comfortably trade a set of five pennies for a nickel, but have difficulty trading a set of 20 pennies for nickels. And some students may tell you that they know a nickel is worth five pennies and a dime is worth ten pennies, but nonetheless count each coin as "one" to figure out how many cents there are. These students will need more experiences, both with coins and with counting objects, before they are able to count a larger set of coins accurately.

Students will have many opportunities to continue developing their understanding of coins and coin equivalencies throughout the Grade 2 *Investigations* curriculum. Over time, as they work with coins in many different ways, they will gain a deeper understanding of coin equivalencies and will become comfortable with making up amounts of money in different ways.

Understanding and Learning to Tell Time

The number system used most widely in the world today is the base-10 system. However, the ancient civilizations that first measured parts of a day used other systems. Ancient Egyptian astronomers, who used a base-12 system, divided daylight into 12 parts and dark into 12 parts. Eventually, those parts were standardized into 24 equal hours per day. The number of minutes in an hour and the number of seconds in a minute come from the Babylonians, who made astronomical calculations in a base-60 system. Our way of telling time today is derived from the work of these ancient astronomers.

For students who are learning to tell time, there are several conceptual challenges. One is thinking of time as something that can be measured. Another is the challenge of coordinating multiple units. For example, not only must students recognize that 2:30 refers to two different units—2 hours and 30 minutes—but they must also recognize how those units are related—60 minutes make up 1 hour; 30 minutes is $\frac{1}{2}$ hour.

This challenge is related to a conceptual hurdle in understanding the base-10 system. Students come to recognize that in the number 45, for example, each digit refers to a different unit (4 tens and 5 ones), and those units are related (10 ones make up 1 ten). Coming to this understanding about the base-10 system is hard work for many students. Shifting to another set of units— hours and minutes—increases the challenge.

On the clock, when the small hand progresses from one number to the next, one hour has elapsed. But when the large hand progresses from one number to the next, five minutes have elapsed. That means that when the large hand points to the 9, it is 45 minutes after the hour. Even more confusing, when the large hand points to the 12, it is 0 minutes after the hour!

Furthermore, some of the associations students make in the base-10 system no longer apply. Dealing with money, students may become fluent with fractions of a dollar: $\frac{1}{4}$ dollar is 25 cents; $\frac{1}{2}$ dollar is 50 cents; $\frac{3}{4}$ dollar is 75 cents. However, dealing with time, $\frac{1}{4}$ hour is 15 minutes; $\frac{1}{2}$ hour is 30 minutes; $\frac{3}{4}$ hour is 45 minutes. The difference is the relationship between the different units: 100 cents make a dollar, whereas there are 60 minutes in an hour.

Learning to read an analog clock face is one aspect of what it means to "learn how to tell time." Understanding how time is represented on the clock and bringing meaning to that representation involves coordinating several different challenging conceptual ideas. This understanding develops for students over time.

In Grade 1, students focus on the parts of the clock, and on the visual appearance of clocks to read and write familiar times (to the hour and half hour). In Grade 2, students deepen their understanding of time and elapsed time as they count by 5 minute intervals, work with fractional parts of a whole (60 minutes), and understand why a single time can be named in different ways (e.g., 2:45, 45 minutes past two, quarter to 3).

Does the Order Matter?

In Grade 2, the question of order in addition can come up in a variety of contexts:

○ As students work together to list all of the two-addend combinations of 10, the question often arises: is 6 + 4 the same as 4 + 6?

○ A student solves the problem 1 + 8 by saying, "8 and 1 more is 9." The teacher asks, "The problem said 1 + 8, but Esteban solved it by doing 8 and 1 more. Can Esteban do that?"

○ As students add more than two numbers, for example, 4 + 3 + 6, they might say, "4 + 3 is 7, and 6 more is 13," or they might say, "4 and 6 is 10, and 3 more is 13."

Many students realize that, in an addition problem, when the order of addends changes, the total does not. They may explain that this happens because you are just changing the placement of the amounts, but the amounts stay the same. "You're not adding in any more, and you're not taking any away," so the total stays constant. See **Dialogue Box 3:** Combinations of 10.

Using the Commutative Property of Addition

From a formal mathematical perspective, the ideas these students are working on involve two basic properties. The first is the commutative property of addition, which says that two numbers added in either order yield the same sum. Some students call these opposites; others dub them reversibles or turnarounds. The very fact that students have given names to this phenomenon indicates that they have formulated a generalization—if the two numbers to be added are switched around, the sum will be the same. Written in general and formal algebraic terms, the commutative property of addition is expressed as $a + b = b + a$.

Using the Associative Property of Addition

The associative property of addition says that when three numbers are added together, they can be regrouped without changing the order and yield the same sum. For example, $(4 + 3) + 6 = 4 + (3 + 6)$. In the expression to the left, first add 4 + 3 to get 7, and then add 7 + 6. In the expression to the right, first add 3 + 6 to get 9, and then add 4 + 9. Written in general and formal algebraic terms, the associative property of addition is expressed as $(a + b) + c = a + (b + c)$.

When performing addition with two numbers, the commutative property applies. When adding three or more numbers, the reordering might involve the commutative property, the associative property, or both.

These two properties—commutativity and associativity of addition—are at the basis of strategies for adding multidigit numbers. That is, although the strategies vary according to how the numbers are broken apart, every strategy puts the parts in a different order or grouping to more easily find the total. For example, when adding 48 + 25, one might think of 48 as 40 + 8 and 25 as 20 + 5. So (40 + 8) + (20 + 5) becomes (40 + 20) + (8 + 5), which equals 60 + 13 = 73. Another strategy might be to think of 25 as 2 + 23. In this case, 48 + (2 + 23) becomes (48 + 2) + 23 = 50 + 23 = 73.

As students continue to learn about operations and calculations, questions about order will repeatedly arise: Does order matter when you subtract? When you multiply? When you divide? (They will find that it does matter when subtracting or dividing, but not when adding or multiplying.) Does it matter when you add fractions or integers (which include numbers below zero)? Students will work to answer these questions in months and years to come.

Strategies for Addition and Subtraction

Primary students typically progress through the following strategies for solving addition and subtraction problems:

25 marbles, plus 11 more
$$25 + 11 =$$

25 birds, 11 flew away
$$25 - 11 =$$

COUNTING ALL In order to visualize and describe a problem situation, some students need to directly model it with a physical model or drawing. For example, to solve a problem about combining marbles (25 + 11) they count out groups of 25 and 11 counters, and then count them all from one; to solve a problem about birds flying away (25 − 11) they draw 25 birds (or tallies), cross out 11 of them, and count the number left. These students are treating all of the quantities in the problem as a collection of ones and using counting as their primary strategy. The goal is for students to develop mental representations that allow them to think and work with groups.

COUNTING ON OR BACK BY 1s Students who can visualize the problem mentally can use strategies that involve counting on to add a quantity or counting back to remove a quantity. For example, for the marble problem (25 + 11) a student might think: "There were 25 marbles, so I counted 11 more: 26, 27, 28, . . . 35, 36." This student feels confident enough about visualizing the actions in the problem that she is able to hold the 25 in her head and add 11 to it, rather than count out each quantity separately. Counting on, or counting back for subtraction, involves double-counting. The student must simultaneously keep track of the numbers she is counting (26, 27, 28, . . . 35, 36) and how many numbers she has counted (1, 2, 3, . . . 10, 11). This double-counting becomes even more complex when the student is counting back to subtract one quantity from a total amount. If a student counts back to solve the bird problem (25 − 11), she must count down from 25 (24, 23, 22, . . . 15, 14), while at the same time counting up to keep track of how many numbers she has counted (1, 2, 3, . . . 10, 11).

COUNTING DOWN TO (SUBTRACTION ONLY) While less common, some students count from the known amount (the 25 birds), down to the other given amount (the 11 that flew away) and keep track of the number counted. For example, some count back by ones: "25; 24, 23, 22...11; that's 14 jumps" and others count down by groups: "25 − 10 gets me to 15, minus 4 more gets me to 11; that's 14 jumps." The number line is a particularly good tool for seeing the difference between counting back and counting down to:

$$25 - 11 = \_\_\_\_\_$$

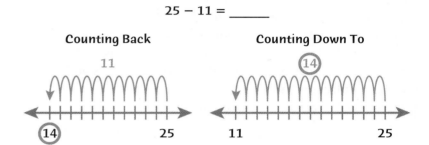

Counting Back   Counting Down To

ADDING OR SUBTRACTING ONE NUMBER IN PARTS
Strategies that involve counting on or back evolve into more efficient strategies as students begin to add or subtract groups, instead of ones. For example, some students break apart a number into 10s and 1s and add on (e.g., 25 + 10 = 35; 35 + 1 = 36) or they use a fact they know (e.g., 25 + 5 = 30; 30 + 6 = 36). In both of these strategies the student kept one number whole (25) and added on the other (11) in parts. This strategy is also effective in subtraction. A typical solution for 25 − 11 is to keep the total amount (25) intact and subtract the 11 in parts, using either tens and ones (e.g., 25 − 10 = 15, 15 − 1 = 14) or a known fact (e.g., 25 − 5 = 20; 20 − 6 = 14).

ADDING/SUBTRACTING BY PLACE As students gain more understanding of the 10s and 1s structure of our number system, they apply this knowledge as they add and subtract numbers. For example, in the marble problem (25 + 11), many second graders break apart both numbers into 10s and 1s (20 + 5 + 10 + 1), combine like parts (20 + 10 = 30; 5 + 1 = 6), and then combine those amounts (30 + 6 = 36). This place-value strategy is often done mentally as students become fluent with number combinations. This strategy is also reliable regardless of the size of numbers or if the number of ones (or any place) exceeds 10.

Because many students use the strategy of adding by place successfully and efficiently, some assume that this strategy will work as efficiently with subtraction. While breaking apart both numbers of a subtraction problem into their place value is possible, the depth of understanding required is quite complex. For example, in the bird problem ($25 - 11$), students might reason that "$20 - 10 = 10$; $5 - 1 = 4$; $10 + 4 = 14$." Students must understand and keep track of what represents the total and what represents the part being removed. In a situation in which there are more ones in the quantity being subtracted than in the original quantity (e.g., $35 - 17$), coordinating all parts of the problem can be complicated. Students may reason "$30 - 10 = 20$; $20 - 7 = 13$; $13 + 5 = 18$." The decision to add (or subtract) the five is directly related to a student's ability to visualize subtraction and understand which parts are part of the total and which are being removed.

Subtraction strategies that involve keeping one number whole and subtracting the other number in parts tend to be more reliable and understandable strategies for second graders.

ADDING UP (SUBTRACTION ONLY) Some students use the relationship between addition and subtraction to make sense of subtraction problems (e.g., $25 - 11 = \underline{}$) by thinking about them as problems about finding a missing addend (e.g., $11 + ? = 25$). These students might count by 1s, or add on in parts (e.g., "$11 + \underline{9} = 20$, $20 + \underline{5} = 25$, I added on 14.").

CHANGING AND ADJUSTING Some students look at a problem and see ways to turn it into a problem that is easier to solve, often adjusting the numbers so that one is a multiple of 10. For example: to solve $25 + 11$, they think "take 1 from the 11, give it to the 25 and you've got $26 + 10$." With different numbers, different strategies arise. For example, to solve $24 + 29$ a student might instead solve $24 + 30$, and then subtract 1 from the total. Others may change both numbers in a problem, (e.g., $25 + 30$) and know then to adjust the total by subtracting the amount that was added. The same is true with subtraction. Given a problem like $52 - 29$, some students subtract 30 instead, and then figure out how to compensate. Another common strategy for subtraction is to add (or subtract) 1 (or any amount) from both of the numbers in the problem, thus maintaining a constant difference, and making an equivalent problem that is easier to solve. So, $25 - 11$ becomes $24 - 10$. These strategies are all grounded in students' understanding of the operations and the relationship between addition and subtraction.

A Note about the U.S. Standard Algorithms

The U.S. Standard Algorithm for addition (i.e., the "carrying" algorithm), which some second graders are familiar with, is an example of the adding by place strategy. Rather than beginning with the largest place, as students often do naturally (which yields a more accurate estimate of the answer), this algorithm begins with the smallest place. It includes a shorthand way of notating the value of numbers as the digits in each place are added, and when the value requires regrouping a ten or hundred. For many 7- and 8-year olds, the compressed notation of this algorithm can obscure both the place value of the numbers and the meaning of each step of the procedure. If and when this strategy arises, encourage students to think about it as adding ones and tens, and to compare it to adding tens and ones. Similarly, model the notation, but compare and contrast it with more transparent ways of notating.

$\overset{1}{5}3$ $+17$ $\overline{70}$	53 $+17$ $\overline{10}$ $(3 + 7)$ 60 $(50 + 10)$ $\overline{70}$	$53 + 17 =$ $50 + 10 = 60$ $7 + 3 = 10$ $60 + 10 = 70$

Students will also likely experiment with the U.S. Standard Algorithm for subtraction (i.e., the "borrowing" algorithm). Unlike the addition algorithm, which is closely related to adding tens and ones, the subtraction algorithm does not closely resemble typical second-grade strategies for subtracting. Although a few students may be able to use it with understanding, many see and use it as a series of memorized steps, especially when regrouping a ten or hundred is required, rather than relying on that they know about the numbers in the problem and the operation of subtraction. Students who misapply standard algorithms should focus on more accessible strategies for solving problems and notating their work. Throughout second grade, students are expected to understand the strategies they use, and to have more than one strategy, thereby demonstrating flexibility—one aspect of fluency with addition and subtraction. Students will have an opportunity to study the U.S. Standard Algorithms for addition and subtraction in Grade 4.

Learning Addition and Subtraction Facts in Second Grade

Efficient computation strategies are based, in part, on developing fluency with addition and subtraction facts. Fluency means that facts are quickly accessible mentally, either because they are immediately known or because the calculation that is used is so effortless as to be essentially automatic (in the way that some adults quickly derive one combination from another—for example, thinking $8 + 9 = 8 + 8 + 1$). In *Investigations*, the development of fluency begins in Kindergarten where students are expected to fluently add and subtract within 5. Fluency within 10 is expected in Grade 1 and within 20 by the end of Grade 2.

More Than Just "Facts"

Addition combinations and their subtraction counterparts are traditionally referred to as "the facts," and that terminology is used in this curriculum. However, "fact" often implies something that can only be memorized (such as the first president of the United States, or the capital of Nebraska) and not something that can be learned through reasoning. In *Investigations*, students learn addition and subtraction facts by using what they already know about numbers and number relationships, about the properties of addition and subtraction, and about the relationship between these two operations. Relying on memory alone is not sufficient. If students forget answers, they are left with no way to think about the problem. If, however, their learning of the facts is based on reasoning, they have a way to determine the answer.

For example, the sum of $7 + 8$ can be determined in many ways. If we forget that $7 + 8 = 15$, but understand what addition is, and know some related combinations, we can reason to find the sum. For example, if we know that $7 + 7 = 14$, we can add 1 more to get 15. If we know that $8 + 8 = 16$, we can take 1 away and get 15. If we know that $7 + 3 = 10$, we can add the 5 that's left to get 15 ($7 + 8 = 7 + 3 + 5 = 15$). In K–2, students use the facts repeatedly, in a variety of contexts, while also building an understanding of the properties of the operations, specifically the commutative and associative properties, and the relationship between addition and subtraction.

Practicing the Facts

As in K–1, students encounter many activities, games, and story problems that involve adding and subtracting within 20. In Grade 2, designated time to review and practice the facts is built into the curriculum, in sessions and as a recurring Classroom Routine, *Fact Fluency.*

Fact Cards are also introduced as a tool to support fluency as well as independent responsibility for keeping track of "Facts I Know" and "Facts I Am Still Working On." Fact Cards for addition present two related problems—except for the Doubles, which have one—building on and strengthening students' understanding of the commutative property of addition. Subtraction Cards present only one problem. While Grade 2 students come to see that $10 - 4$ and $10 - 6$ are related not only to each other but also to their addition counterparts (i.e., $4 + 6$ and $6 + 4$), they develop this understanding of the relationship between the operations of addition and subtraction over time. Because students often view these as unrelated problems early in the year, when students first get the cards, they are purposely presented on two different Fact Cards.

$$1 + 2$$
$$2 + 1$$

Clue: _____

$$2 - 1$$

Clue: _____

Over the course of the year, students receive sets of Fact Cards that represent various groups of addition and subtraction facts and sort them into two envelopes: "Facts I Know" and "Facts I Am Still Working On". In this way, students determine which facts they know and which they need to practice. After opportunities to practice, the clue line provides scaffolding for challenging facts that remain hard to remember.

In Unit 1, the fact work focuses on reviewing addition and subtraction within 10, a Grade 1 benchmark, plus a few additional facts, and on thinking about categories of facts. The focus on groups of related facts helps students learn effective strategies for finding solutions.

Fact Cards: Set 1*	Fact Cards: Set 2
Doubles	Minus Half
Plus 1	Minus 1
Plus 2	Minus 2
Make 10	10 Minus
Other 3 + 4 and 4 + 3 3 + 5 and 5 + 3 3 + 6 and 6 + 3 4 + 5 and 5 + 4	Other 4 − 3 5 − 3, 5 − 4 6 − 4, 6 − 5 7 − 3, 7 − 4, 7 − 5, 7 − 6 8 − 3, 8 − 5, 8 − 6, 8 − 7 9 − 3, 9 − 4, 9 − 5, 9 − 6, 9 − 7, 9 − 8

* Some combinations fall into more than one category.
For example, 1 + 9 and 9 + 1 is a Make 10 and a Plus 1 Fact.

Later units provide practice with these facts, and introduce and practice the remaining facts.

Fact Cards: Set 3*	Fact Cards: Set 4
Near Doubles	Plus 10
	Minus 10

Fact Cards: Set 5	Fact Cards: Set 6
Plus 9	Remaining Facts
Minus 9	

* Some combinations fall into more than one category.
For example, 9+8 and 8+9 is a Near Double and a Plus 9 Fact.

Every unit in the Grade 2 sequence includes practice of the facts so that, by the end of the year, students have no (or very few) cards left in their "Facts I Am Still Working On" envelopes. The ongoing nature of this work provides teachers many opportunities to assess students' fluency with these problems. If, over time, there are students who are not moving many cards from their "Facts I Am Still Working On" to their "Facts I Know" envelopes, that is important information, and an opportunity to provide focused support and practice.

In *Investigations*, developing fluency with the addition and subtraction facts is based on work that is focused and deep. Learning a set of facts is not distinct from developing an understanding about quantities and operations and the relationship between them. In fact, even when students are engaged in an activity that might seem like pure number practice, for example solving Number Strings, they are working to make sense of and understand the task. This flexibility and sense making results in fluency with the addition and subtraction facts that contributes to the development of computational fluency in the primary grades and beyond.

Assessment: Number Strings

PROBLEMS 1–4

Benchmark Addressed:

Benchmark 2: Use known combinations to add several numbers in any order.

In order to meet the benchmark, students' work should show that they can:

○ Accurately combine more than two numbers in efficient and sensible ways (i.e., using known combinations and not working only in order);

○ Explain how they solved the problem.

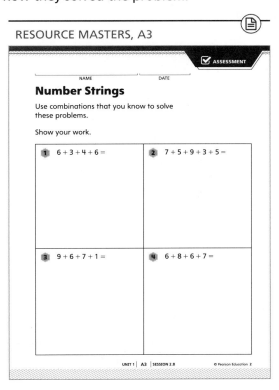

Meeting the Benchmark

The following examples of student work provide a range of typical responses. All of these students meet the benchmark— they were able to interpret the problem and solve it accurately. They also used combinations they knew and did not work exclusively in order.

Problem 1: 6 + 3 + 4 + 6

Most students add 6 + 4 and 6 + 3 and then combine 10 and 9 to get 19. Others, like Katrina, add 6 + 4 and then add the two remaining numbers on, one at a time.

6 + 3 + 4 + 6 = 19

6 + 4 = 10
10 + 3 = 13
13 + 6 = 19

[Katrina's Work]

Some students add 6 + 6 and 3 + 4, and then combine 12 and 7 to get 19. Monisha used this strategy and also showed how she added 12 and 7 by thinking about 12 as 10 and 2. Other students add the two remaining addends on, one at a time (e.g., 12 + 3 = 15, and 15 + 4 = 19).

6 + 3 + 4 + 6 = 19

6 + 6 = 12
3 + 4 = 7
10 + 7 = 17
17 + 2 = 19

[Monisha's Work]

Problem 2: 7 + 5 + 9 + 3 + 5

Most students, like Luis, see and use the two combinations of 10: 7 + 3 and 5 + 5. Then, they add 10 + 10 + 9.

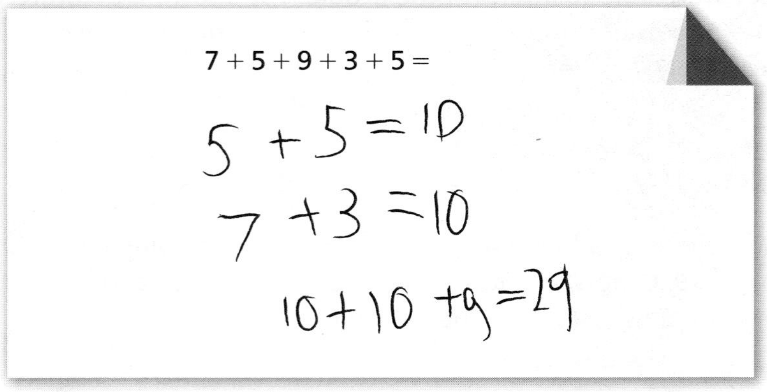

$$7 + 5 + 9 + 3 + 5 =$$
$$5 + 5 = 10$$
$$7 + 3 = 10$$
$$10 + 10 + 9 = 29$$

[Luis's Work]

Some, like Anita, start with one of the combinations of 10 and proceed from there.

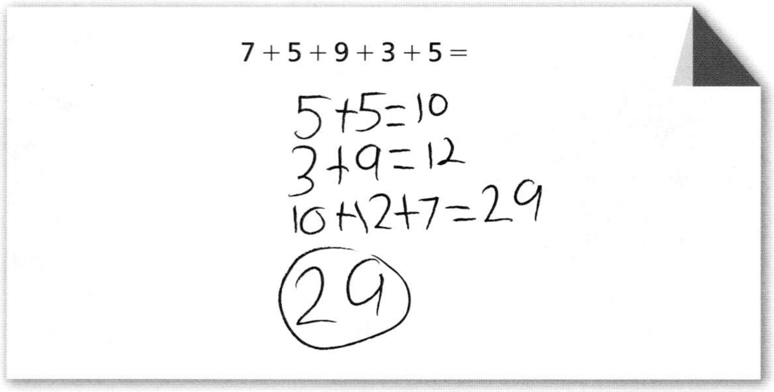

$$7 + 5 + 9 + 3 + 5 =$$
$$5 + 5 = 10$$
$$3 + 9 = 12$$
$$10 + 12 + 7 = 29$$
$$\boxed{29}$$

[Anita's Work]

Problem 3: 9 + 6 + 7 + 1

Most students add 9 + 1, then add 6 + 7, and then combine 10 + 13. Some, like Nadia, think about 6 + 7 as 6 + 6 + 1, or 12 + 1. She adds 9 + 1 and then adds the two remaining addends on, one at a time.

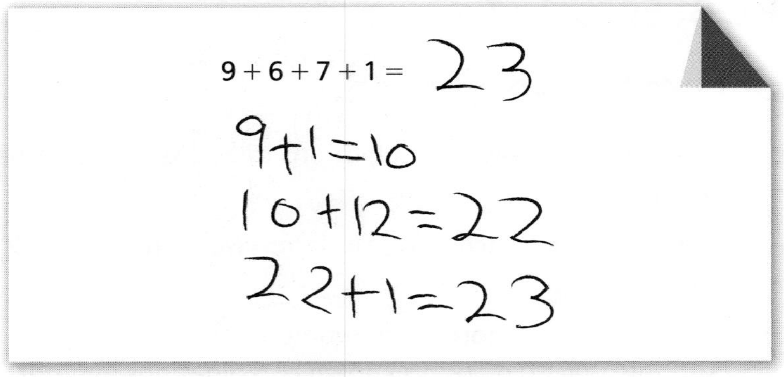

$$9 + 6 + 7 + 1 = 23$$
$$9 + 1 = 10$$
$$10 + 12 = 22$$
$$22 + 1 = 23$$

[Nadia's Work]

Some students, like Amaya, see that if they add 6 + 1 they will have a double, 7 + 7, and then 14 + 9 = 23.

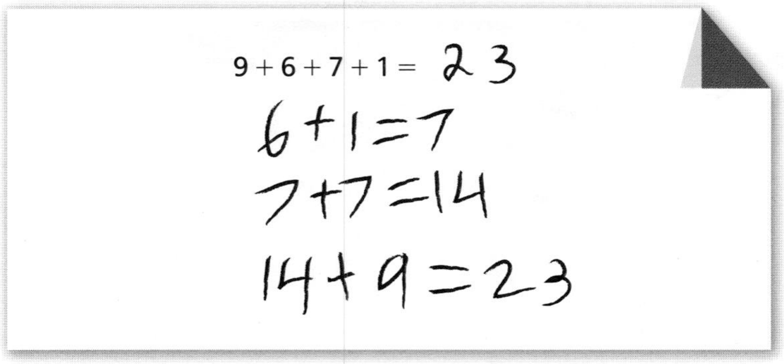

$$9 + 6 + 7 + 1 = 23$$
$$6 + 1 = 7$$
$$7 + 7 = 14$$
$$14 + 9 = 23$$

[Amaya's Work]

Problem 4: 6 + 8 + 6 + 7

Most students add 6 + 6 and 8 + 7 and then combine 12 and 15. Some, like Chen, show how they used 8 + 8 to solve 8 + 7. Others add 6 + 6 and then add on the remaining two numbers, one at a time; for example, 6 + 6 = 12, 12 + 8 = 20, and 20 + 7 = 27.

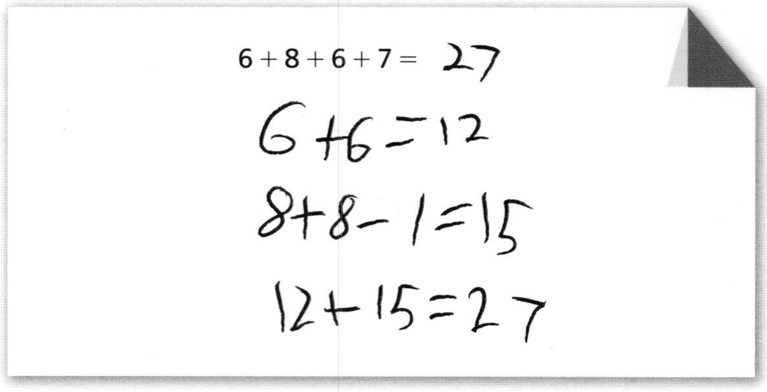

$$6 + 8 + 6 + 7 = 27$$
$$6 + 6 = 12$$
$$8 + 8 - 1 = 15$$
$$12 + 15 = 27$$

[Chen's Work]

Some students add 6 + 8 and 6 + 7 and then combine 14 and 13, or they combine two of the numbers (e.g., 8 + 6 = 14) and then add the others on, one at a time (14 + 6 = 20 and 20 + 7 = 27).

Partially Meeting the Benchmark

Some students understand the structure of the problem—that it is about combining several addends—and get the right answer, but they add the numbers almost exclusively in the order given in the problem. Check in with these students. Are they not convinced that they can add in any order? Do they not recognize familiar combinations within a larger number string?

Others may get the right answer but may have trouble showing their work. For example, some students show only some of their steps, like Melissa. Others, like Leo and Henry, struggle to use standard notation to show their steps or seem unable to use standard notation to show correctly their process for adding. (This teacher met with Melissa and Leo after checking their work and added steps to the recording sheet with their help.)

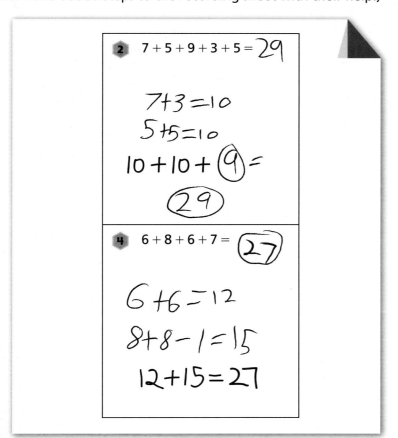

[Melissa's Work]

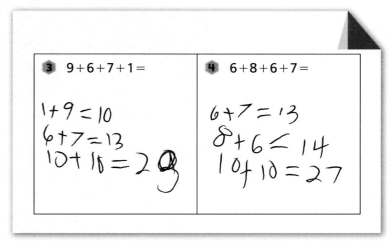

[Leo's Work]

[Henry's Work]

Others understand the structure of the problem but make mistakes as they count or combine the quantities in the problem. After you review their assessments, ask these students to double-check their work. For example, "Your paper says that 8 plus 7 is 16. How could you double-check that?" See whether they can find and correct such errors on their own. Encourage these students to take their time and work carefully to avoid such errors in the future. In addition, note whether these kinds of errors are consistent across problems or a one-time occurrence.

Not Meeting the Benchmark

Some students struggle to keep track of more than two addends. Some do not add all of the numbers, and others add some numbers more than once. Help these students develop a method for keeping track of what has been (and what remains to be) added.

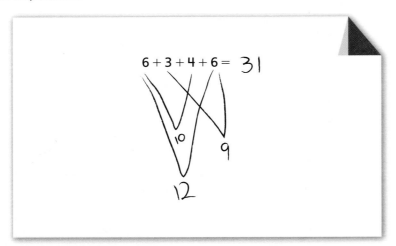

Yama understands some important aspects about these kinds of problems. She knows some combinations and starts with those—a great first step. However, she struggles to combine those subtotals accurately and is not yet fluent with the use of standard notation. It is not clear what her answers are or how she got them. In order to learn more and to plan appropriate next steps, meet and talk with students who turn in such work to find out more about what they were thinking, what they understand, and what ideas they are still working on.

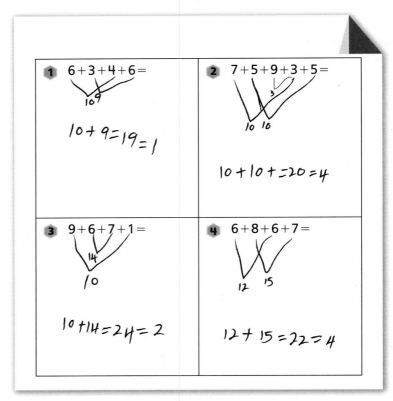

[Yama's Work]

Types of Story Problems

Students encounter a variety of addition and subtraction problem types in the early grades. The context of some problems involves actions like combining, removing, or comparing; others involve a static situation of two parts and a whole. Problems can also vary in terms of what information is known and unknown.

ADD TO/TAKE FROM: PROBLEMS ABOUT COMBINING AND REMOVING These problems involve an action. In their most familiar form, they ask students to combine two amounts (Add To) or to remove one amount from another (Take From), and determine how many there are at the end of the story (Result Unknown). In other words, students need to find the sum or the difference. In other variations, the unknown is the amount added or removed (Unknown Change), or the amount at the beginning of the story (Unknown Start).

PUT TOGETHER/TAKE APART: PROBLEMS ABOUT PARTS AND WHOLES These stories do not involve actions like combining or removing; nothing is joined or amassed, given away or used up. Rather, students are asked to consider two parts (e.g., the number of red flowers in a vase and the number of blue flowers in a vase) that make up one whole (e.g., the number of flowers in a vase). Students can be asked to determine the whole when the two parts are known (Total Unknown); one of the parts when the other part and the whole are known (Addend Unknown, also commonly known as Finding a Missing Part); or how a given whole could be broken into two parts (Both Addends Unknown).

	RESULT UNKNOWN	CHANGE UNKNOWN	START UNKNOWN
Add To	Two bunnies sat on the grass. Three more bunnies hopped there. How many bunnies are on the grass now? $2 + 3 = ?$ (GK) (G1) (G2)	Two bunnies were sitting on the grass. Some more bunnies hopped there. Then there were five bunnies. How many bunnies hopped over to the first two? $2 + ? = 5$ (G1) (G2)	Some bunnies were sitting on the grass. Three more bunnies hopped there. Then there were five bunnies. How many bunnies were on the grass before? $? + 3 = 5$ (G1) (G2)
Take From	Five apples were on the table. I ate two apples. How many apples are on the table now? $5 - 2 = ?$ (GK) (G1) (G2)	Five apples were on the table. I ate some apples. Then there were three apples. How many apples did I eat? $5 - ? = 3$ (G1) (G2)	Some apples were on the table. I ate two apples. Then there were three apples. How many apples were on the table before? $? - 2 = 3$ (G1) (G2)

Adapted from © Copyright 2010. National Governors Association for Best Practices and Council of Chief State School Officers. All rights reserved.

Note: Each skill is assessed at the grade levels in purple and is not assessed at the grade levels in black.

	TOTAL UNKNOWN	ADDEND UNKNOWN	BOTH ADDENDS UNKNOWN
Put Together/ Take Apart	Three red apples and two green apples are on the table. How many apples are on the table? $3 + 2 = ?$ (GK) (G1) (G2)	Five apples are on the table. Three are red and the rest are green. How many apples are green? $3 + ? = 5, 5 - 3 = ?$ (G1) (G2)	Grandma has five flowers. How many can she put in her red vase and how many in her blue vase? $5 = 0 + 5, 5 = 5 + 0$ $5 = 1 + 4, 5 = 4 + 1$ $5 = 2 + 3, 5 = 3 + 2$ (GK) (G1) (G2)

Adapted from © Copyright 2010. National Governors Association for Best Practices and Council of Chief State School Officers. All rights reserved.

Note: Each skill is assessed at the grade levels in purple.

COMPARE: PROBLEMS ABOUT COMPARISON These problems ask students to compare two quantities, to determine how many more (or fewer) one has than the other (Difference Unknown). Other variations give one quantity, and a difference, and ask students to find the other quantity (Bigger Unknown, Smaller Unknown).

	DIFFERENCE UNKNOWN	BIGGER UNKNOWN	SMALLER UNKNOWN
Compare version with more	Lucy has two apples. Julie has five apples. How many more apples does Julie have than Lucy? 2 + ? = 5, 5 − 2 = ? (G1) (G2)	Julie has three more apples than Lucy. Lucy has two apples. How many apples does Julie have? 2 + 3 = ?, 3 + 2 = ? (G1) (G2)	Julie has three more apples than Lucy. Julie has five apples. How many apples does Lucy have? 5 − 3 = ?, ? + 3 = 5 (G1) (G2)
Compare version with fewer	Lucy has two apples. Julie has five apples. How many fewer apples does Lucy have than Julie? 2 + ? = 5, 5 − 2 = ? (G1) (G2)	Lucy has 3 fewer apples than Julie. Lucy has two apples. How many apples does Julie have? 2 + 3 = ?, 3 + 2 = ? (G1) (G2)	Lucy has 3 fewer apples than Julie. Julie has five apples. How many apples does Lucy have? 5 − 3 = ?, ? + 3 = 5 (G1) (G2)

Note: Each skill is assessed at the grade levels in purple and is not assessed at the grade levels in black.

Note that the information above is intended to describe the problem types and to help teachers distinguish among them; students should not be expected to name these categories or say to which category a problem belongs. What is important is that they can visualize the relationship among the quantities in all types of situations, regardless of which quantities are given and which must be determined. From that ability to visualize, students can then apply the operations of addition and subtraction appropriately.

It is also important to note that, if teachers choose to personalize the text of story problems (e.g., using names of students in the class or situations or topics that are more relevant to your particular group of students), it is important to retain the structure of the original problem.

Place Value in Second Grade

Understanding the place-value structure of our base-10 number system and how it applies to, and supports, number composition and computation is a central piece of work in the number and operations strand of the *Investigations* curriculum. The base-10 number system is a "place value" system. That is, any numeral, say 2, can represent different values, depending on where it appears in a written number: it can represent 2 ones, 2 tens, 2 hundreds, 2 thousands, and so forth. Understanding our place-value system requires coordinating the way we write numbers —e.g., 217—and the way we name numbers in words—two hundred seventeen—with how the value of each place represents quantities.

In order to successfully work with place value, students need to know that 1 ten is equal to 10 ones, and be able to coordinate groups of tens and ones. Consider, for example, the number 32: one aspect of understanding the value of each place in this number is knowing that the 3 represents 3 groups of ten, the 2 represents 2 ones, and this can be expressed as $30 + 2$. It is also important for students to understand 32 as 2 groups of ten and 12 ones ($20 + 12$). Similarly, as students work with greater numbers such as 132, they must recognize the number of hundreds, tens, and ones ($100 + 30 + 2$) but also know that 132 can also be thought of as 13 groups of ten and 2 ones. The compactness of the base-10 system is what makes it powerful, but that very compactness means it is dense with ideas, which young students must put together.

Foundational Ideas of Place Value

In Kindergarten, students develop fluency with ones as they master the counting sequence and count quantities. They use Ten Frames to reinforce the foundational idea that 10 ones can also be thought of as a *group* of 10 ones, and explore the two-addend combinations of 10. These are precursors to work with place value. Similarly, representing teen numbers on Ten Frames, seeing them as 10 ones and some leftover number of ones, and using equations (e.g., $15 = 10 + 5$) to represent this information helps students notice important regularities in these numbers and the way we write them (i.e., the 1 in 15 refers to the group of ten and the 5 refers to the number of leftover ones).

In Grade 1, students make a critical shift from thinking and working primarily in ones to thinking and working with *groups* of tens and ones. They strengthen their understanding of this critical 10:1 relationship as they work with contexts and models (e.g., fingers, Ten Frame cards, connecting cubes organized into towers of ten) that represent groups of tens and ones.

With these models in mind, Grade 1 students represent 2-digit quantities and discuss how 15 and 51 are different as they build the understanding that numbers have different values depending on their place, and that the way we write, read, and say 2-digit numbers is connected to the number of tens and ones. Grade 1 students also use these place-value models to represent addition and subtraction of 2-digit numbers. In doing so, they connect a model to notation and use the model to explain their thinking.

While much of the foundation for work with place value is laid in Kindergarten and Grade 1, coming to *understand* and *know* that 10 ones is equivalent to 1 ten, *applying* this 10:1 relationship to larger quantities and multidigit numbers (e.g., 10 tens is 1 hundred and 10 hundreds is 1 thousand), *coordinating* these multiple units (i.e., groups of tens and groups of ones), and *using* these ideas to develop and refine strategies for addition and subtraction is the focus of the place-value work in Grade 2.

Grade 2 and the Base-10 Number System

In Grade 2, students continue to work with models that represent the place-value structure of our base-10 number system. In Unit 1, students are introduced to coins and coin values, and also to a "sticker" context, where stickers come in singles, strips of ten, and sheets of 100. In Unit 3, they use both contexts to think about the composition of 2-digit and 3-digit numbers (to 500 in Unit 3 and 1,000 in Unit 5). Numbers are composed as they focus on making different combinations of stickers or coins to equal a given quantity. For example, 87 (or 87¢) can be composed of 8 strips of 10 and 7 individual stickers, (or 8 dimes and 7 pennies) but it can also be composed of 7 strips of 10 and 17 individual stickers (or 7 dimes and 17 pennies). Students also work with other models including connecting cubes organized into towers of 10, the 100 chart, and a shorthand notation for the sticker context. The purpose of these models is to help students build mental images that they can then use in visualizing and solving problems. While no single model is a perfect match for every idea, the purpose of these contexts and models is to give students different examples to use and compare. With these models in mind, students can more easily discuss how 15, 51 and 510 are different as well as learn to read and write numbers to 1,000. For example, in Units 3 and 5, students "fill in" targeted numbers on a series of 100 charts, each representing numbers in the 100s, 200s 300s etc. as they play a game that involves adding or subtracting 10 (and eventually 100) to, or from, a number they have assembled with digit cards. With the goal of covering three numbers in a row, students must first decide whether starting on 258 or 285 is more advantageous, and then determine whether adding or subtracting 10 to this number will land them closer to their goal of three-in-a row. This game not only provides students with an engaging way to practice reading and writing numbers, it also provides a context for discussing what happens to a 2- or 3-digit number when 10 or 100 is added or subtracted, looking at both how the digit in the tens or hundreds place changes (increases/decreases by 1), and how the value of the number changes (increases/decreases by 10 or 100). Throughout Grade 2, students engage in a variety of activities and games that develop and reinforce the hundreds, tens, and ones structure of the base-10 number system.

Place Value and Computational Fluency in Grade 2

A thorough understanding of the base-10 number system is one of the critical building blocks for developing computational fluency. The composition of numbers from multiples of 1, 10, 100, 1,000, and so forth, is the basis of most of the strategies students use for computation with whole numbers. In all units of Grade 2, students refine strategies for addition, (e.g., adding by place and adding on one number in parts) and for subtraction (e.g., keeping one number whole and subtracting the other in parts) and develop fluency for adding and subtracting 2-digit numbers. Students apply these same strategies as they work with 3-digit numbers, using familiar models and contexts to represent and explain their strategies for addition and subtraction of greater numbers as they solve story problems of all types with unknowns in all positions. In Grade 2, story problem contexts, introduced in Units 1 and 3, such as Enough for the Class? and How Many Stickers? evolve in Units 5 and 8 into Enough for the Grade? and How Many to 1,000?, providing students with opportunities to solve addition and subtraction problems with greater numbers, using familiar contexts. Supporting the development of fluency with addition and subtraction is an array of games, such as *Close to 100* (adding 2-digit numbers that total close to 100) and *Capture 5* (adding and subtracting 10 and multiples of 10 to/from 2 and 3-digit numbers) which offer repeated practice adding and subtracting 100s, 10s, and 1s.

For many reasons, Grade 2 is somewhat of a turning point for the work students are on the brink of doing with understanding number and operations. In Kindergarten and first grade, students developed many of the foundational pieces necessary to shift their thinking primarily from working with single units (ones) to thinking and working with groups. In Grade 2, students deepen this work with 2-digit numbers and extend the work to 3-digit numbers. They need the time and opportunity to solidify these ideas and relationships as they represent numbers in a variety of ways using hundreds, tens, and ones and as they think flexibly about how numbers can be combined and separated. Building a solid understanding of 2-digit numbers and having fluent and accurate strategies for adding and subtracting them is the basis for developing fluency with 3-digit numbers in Grade 3 and beyond.

Assessment: Enough for the Class?

Benchmark Addressed:

Benchmark 3: Solve a comparison story problem with the difference unknown.

In order to meet the benchmark, students' work should show that they can:

○ Solve the problem accurately;

○ Show how they solved the problem.

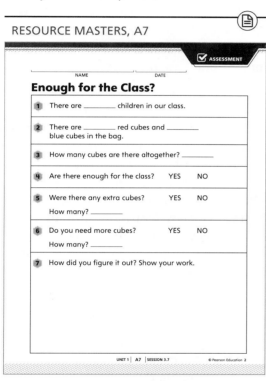

RESOURCE MASTERS, A7

Some students count and directly model the situation to solve the problem; others count up (or back) from one amount to the other or reason about the quantities in the problem in various ways.

Meeting the Benchmark

The following examples of student work provide a range of typical responses. All of these students meet the benchmark— they were able to interpret the problem and solve it accurately. Note that students who are counting on or back (Jacy) or who are reasoning about the quantities in the problem (Tia and Simon) are working more efficiently than those who need to directly model the situation in a one-to-one fashion (Lonzell and Carla).

Lonzell and Carla both match a cube to each person in their class. They then count the leftover cubes and know there are enough for the class, with three left over. Both students have a workable strategy for solving this comparison problem. They are clear about the two groups being compared and what the extra cubes represent.

[Lonzell's Work]

[Carla's Work]

Many students use a similar strategy at this point in the year. They make a train of 29 (16 blue and 13 red) cubes, break off 26 for the students in the class, and count the leftovers.

Tia and Jacy use similar strategies to determine whether there are enough for the class.

Tia: I know that there are 16 blue cubes, and 16 is 10 less than 26. There are 13 red cubes, and 10 plus 3 is 13, so I can use 10 of the reds for the class. There are 3 leftover reds in the bag.

Jacy: I just thought there are 16 blue so 17, 18, 19, 20, 21, 22, 23, 24, 25, 26 (she uses her fingers to keep track). I need 10 more cubes and there are 13 reds, so there is enough for the class.

Both students start with the group of 16 blue cubes and then figure out the difference between 16 and 26. They compare this difference, 10, to the group of 13 red cubes and easily see that they do have enough for the class.

Simon uses the total number of cubes to help him solve the problem. He adds 16 and 13 and then compares the total, 29, to the number of students in the class.

Simon breaks the numbers into familiar parts and then recombines the parts in order to get the total. He indicates that "29 was three more than 26" and he "counted up" from 26 (27, 28, 29) as a way of finding the difference between 26 and 29.

1. There are __26__ children in our class.

2. There are __13__ red cubes and __16__ blue cubes in the bag.

3. How many cubes are there altogether? __29__

4. Are there enough for the class? (YES) NO

5. Were there any extra cubes? (YES) NO
   How many? __3__

6. Do you need more cubes? YES (NO)
   How many? __0__

7. How did you figure it out? Show your work.

   There are 29 in the bags
   Blue 16   10+10 = 20
   Red 13   6+3 = 9
                 20 +9 = 29
   There are 3 extra because
   29 is 3 more than 26
   I know because I conted
   up from 26.

[Simon's Work]

Partially Meeting the Benchmark

Some students understand the structure of the problem—that it is about finding the difference between the number of cubes and the number of students—but make mistakes as they count or combine the quantities in the problem. After you review their assessment, ask these students to double-check their work. For example, "Your paper says that 16 plus 13 is 28. How could you double-check that?" See whether they can find and correct such errors on their own. Encourage these students to take their time and work carefully to avoid such errors in the future. In addition, note whether these kinds of errors are consistent across problems or one-time occurrences.

Some students understand the structure of the problem but struggle with knowing where to start and stop when counting on (or back). These students may be losing the connection between the numbers and the situation and may benefit from seeing how the process of counting on (or back) connects to a concrete model of the situation. See **Dialogue Box 7:** Are There Enough for the Class?, for more on how one teacher did this while leading a whole-class discussion. Note that students who are using this strategy with little meaning (perhaps trying to mimic a method they have seen their classmates use) might fall into the category below.

Not Meeting the Benchmark

Other students may not yet understand the structure of the problem. They may combine the two amounts, or decide that the answer is either the number of cubes in the bag (29) or the number of students in the class (26). These students need more support to make sense of what the problem is asking. Focus on smaller amounts and modeling the situation with cubes until students understand the structure of the problem. Then they can revisit and practice problems that are based on the size of your class. *Student Activity Book* page 51 provides an Are There Enough? problem, which can serve as a model for making more for students who need more practice.

Story Problems in Second Grade

As students develop strategies for solving addition and subtraction problems, they are involved in three major tasks: understanding the structure of the problem, developing strategies for solving the problem, and communicating their solutions and strategies orally and in writing.

Understanding the Structure of the Problem

To understand the structure of a problem, students need to form a mental image or build a concrete model of what is happening. They need to be able to visualize the situation and understand what is being asked. Therefore, students are asked to picture story problems in their minds, to retell them in their own words, and to model them. Because the focus is on making sense of the situation, avoid labeling problems as addition or subtraction. A critical skill in solving problems is deciding what operation is needed. Further, many problems can be solved in a variety of ways, and students need to choose a solution strategy that makes sense to them based on their understanding of the situation.

ADAPTING THE CONTEXT Many teachers adapt the story problems provided in order to use names and/or contexts that reflect their own class. This is expected and encouraged; however, it is important to think carefully when changing a problem in order to avoid altering its underlying structure, or its relationship to the other problem in a related set. See **Teacher Note 10:** Types of Story Problems.

RELATED PROBLEMS Periodically, students solve related story problems. That is, the numbers in the problems are related in such a way that some students might use their solution to the first problem to help them solve the second. Presenting two problems, and asking if the first could help with the second, encourages students to look for and notice relationships between problems and to think about and use what they know when they solve a new problem. This helps students begin to notice that the same reasoning works across problems and contexts, and they eventually begin to formulate generalizations about the behavior of the operations (e.g., in addition, if you add one to one of the addends, the sum will be one more).

Developing Strategies for Solving the Problem

Students typically progress through a set of strategies for solving addition and subtraction problems: from counting all, to counting on/back, to breaking up the numbers so they can add or subtract bigger chunks. See **Teacher Note 7:** Strategies for Addition and Subtraction.

Focus your support on helping students make sense of the situation, rereading the story, and asking them to tell the story in their own words and to model it with cubes or other materials (e.g., coins, stickers).

"KEY WORDS" It can be tempting to suggest that students look for "key words" (e.g., *altogether* or *more* for addition, and *left* or *fewer* for subtraction) that signal which operation to choose to solve the problem. This suggestion however, often prevents students from fully engaging in making sense of a problem as a whole and can be misleading. The flaw in this approach is that these words may be used in many ways and may be part of a problem that requires a different operation. For example: *There are 28 students in our class altogether. There are 13 boys. How many girls are there?* If we trust in key words, then *altogether* in this problem should signal addition of the numbers in the problem: 28 + 13. In fact, the problem calls for finding the *difference* between 28 and 13. If students are able to visualize or build a model of what is happening in a problem, they are more likely to make sense of what is being asked and apply a sensible strategy for solving it.

ADAPTING THE PROBLEM At times it may be appropriate to adapt the numbers in a given story problem to meet the needs of the range of learners in your classroom. Before adjusting the numbers, first ask students to solve the problem provided. In this way, both you and students have some immediate information about the level of difficulty of the problem. Then, once you see how students solve the problem, you will be better able to provide an appropriate follow-up problem. For example, students who are primarily using counting by ones strategies are probably not ready for problems with larger numbers. Giving these students smaller numbers to work with may allow them to hold onto the smaller quantity in their head and then count on/back the other amount. Similarly, students who are consistently counting on or back may be able to apply a numerical strategy if the numbers are adjusted so that they relate to a known fact or a number that lends itself to being decomposed into 10s and 1s.

When adapting the size of numbers, be sure to consider what strategy, or piece of mathematics, the numbers provided are pushing students toward. For example, in the following problem the numbers were chosen because of the combination of 10 in the ones place. *Franco had 24 baseball cards in his collection. Jake gave him 16 more. How many cards does Franco have now?* Note whether students use the same strategy for both problems; if students revert to a less sophisticated strategy, the size of the numbers is probably too large.

Note that there are other ways to adapt problems besides changing the size of the numbers. Challenge students who solve problems efficiently and accurately, and who show their strategy clearly, to solve the problem in another way and ask them to compare their two strategies. Encourage them to think about how the strategies are alike and ask them to explain which one is more efficient and why. Students can also work on a related problem, and try to identify and describe the relationship between problems, or try to write a problem that is related to one they just solved on a *Student Activity Book* page. Or, give these students an equation and challenge them to write a story problem that reflects the equation.

Communicating Strategies

Learning how to communicate their thinking, both orally and in writing, is another important piece of students' work with addition and subtraction in the primary grades. As students communicate their ideas individually to a teacher, with a partner, or during whole-class discussions, they have the opportunity to articulate and clarify their thinking as they talk through their solution. In doing this, students often uncover and correct mistakes that they might not have otherwise noticed. They also encounter others' strategies and have the opportunity to compare different ways of solving the problem or representing a strategy on paper. The text often suggests strategies to focus on and ways to model and notate them.

Notating strategies is an important and natural extension of oral explanations. One thing to watch for is students whose written work does not match their oral explanation. Teachers say it is common for students to record a strategy that is easy to show on paper rather than the strategy they actually used. For more information on how to record students' strategies, model notation, and help students record their work, see **Teacher Note 14:** Using Notation to Record Strategies.

Using Notation to Record Strategies

Making sense of a problem situation, and representing it with numbers and symbols (or vice versa), is an important part of elementary school students' work with whole-number operations. Developing clear and efficient methods to notate their strategies for solving such problems is another. Students come to understand and use notation over time, as they see it modeled and have many opportunities to see, talk about, and use such symbols and language themselves.

Writing an Equation that Shows What the Problem Is Asking

Most second graders are familiar with addition and subtraction notation (+, −, =), and had experience with it in previous grades. In Unit 1, students review the language for and meaning of the symbols as they work together to write equations that show what a problem is asking, before solving it.

Kira has 12 marbles and Franco gave her 10 more. How many marbles does Kira have?

$$12 + 10 = \underline{\qquad}$$

Recording Students' Strategies

As students are making sense of addition and subtraction situations and developing strategies to solve these problems, it is important that they see a variety of ways to use pictures, numbers, symbols, and equations to record their work. As you model ways to notate students' ideas, the focus should be on making connections between the language that students use and the symbols and numbers that represent this language.

Use horizontal and vertical notation interchangeably when notating student's strategies. It is important that students see both ways of recording, understand that they represent the same problem situation, and realize that the way a problem is written does not indicate how it should be solved. Linking horizontal and vertical notation for addition and subtraction is addressed in Units 3, 5, and 7.

Throughout such discussions, the focus should be on the connection between the numbers and symbols and the story.

However, you can also begin to draw students' attention to how different representations can be used to represent the same strategy.

Strategies that involve counting all or counting on/back by 1s typically do not lend themselves to being notated in equation format. Rather, they are more effectively recorded with sketches or on the number line. (Perhaps after modeling them with cubes/on the 100 chart.) For example, consider the following for the above problem:

If a student counted 12 cubes, then 10 cubes, then counted them all, sketch the strategy:

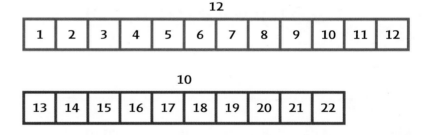

If a student counted on by 1s from 12:

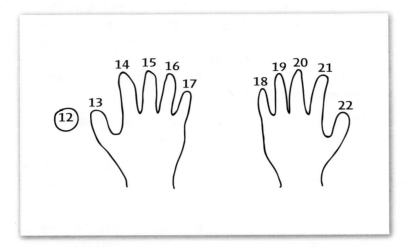

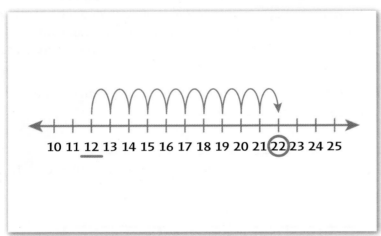

When students use other strategies, use equations to capture each step of the student's thinking as accurately as possible.

Student says	You record
"I know that 12 is 10 and 2. Then, 10 + 10 is 20. And 2 more is 22."	12 = 10 + 2 10 + 10 = 20 20 + 2 = 22

As a summary, you can also record 12 + 10 = 10 + 2 + 10 *or* 10 + 10 + 2 = 20 + 2.

Note that some students may be surprised by equations where the equal sign follows (rather than precedes) the answer and/or where there are two or more addends on both sides of the equal sign. Because they most often see equations like 10 + 2 = 12, students can come to see the equal sign as meaning "now write the answer" rather than as a symbol of equivalency. Experience with a wide array of formats will broaden their understanding of this symbol.

As students deepen their understanding of how numbers are composed and as they refine their understanding of the operations of addition and subtraction, this is reflected in their problem-solving strategies. Consider the work for the following problem:

Kira and Jake collected rocks. Kira found 12 rocks and Jake found 24. How many rocks did they collect?

While the above described strategies still apply, most Grade 2 students are transitioning from counting on by 1s to counting on in larger groups (i.e., keeping one number whole and adding the other on in parts).

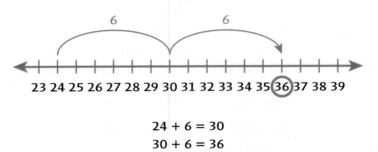

$$24 + 6 = 30$$
$$30 + 6 = 36$$

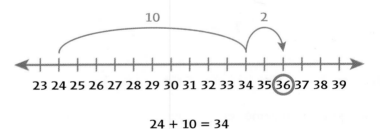

$$24 + 10 = 34$$
$$34 + 2 = 36$$

Other students are applying their growing understanding of place value and breaking apart numbers by place and combining the tens and the ones. Such strategies can be recorded as follows:

Student says	You record
"I knew that 24 is 20 and 4. And 12 is 10 plus 2. Then, 20 and 10 is 30. And 4 plus 2 is 6. So, 30 plus 6 is 36."	24 = 20 + 4 12 = 10 + 2 20 + 10 = 30 4 + 2 = 6 30 + 6 = 36

The student thought of this problem as $24 + 12 = 20 + 4 + 10 + 2$. This strategy can also be recorded by using vertical notation.

$$
\begin{array}{r}
24 \\
+\ 12 \\
\hline
30 \\
+\ 6 \\
\hline
36
\end{array}
$$

"20 and 10 is 30"

"And 4 plus 2 is 6"

"So, 30 plus 6 is 36"

In this notation, the fact that the 24 and 12 have been broken into tens and ones is implicit. In fact, the vertical notation can become a shorthand for the equations written horizontally above. As you do with other representations, draw students' attention to the similarities between the horizontal and vertical notations.

It can be tempting to jump directly to this shorthand notation because it takes less time and writing and because it closely resembles the U.S. standard algorithm for addition. However, it is important for students to see how their oral descriptions of their strategies can be represented with numbers, symbols, and equations. The focus throughout should be on how a given representation shows the mathematical thinking of the person who solved the problem and then on how different ways of notating strategies are related.

When Students Notate Their Strategies

Modeling a variety of ways to show how students solved a problem (e.g., pictures, numbers, symbols, equations, number lines, and the 100 chart) supports students as they begin to record their own mathematical strategies. As you model the correct use of symbols and standard notation and discuss the connection between it and the strategy it represents, students see equations used correctly and begin to incorporate them in their work. There is often, however, a gap between what a student observes and can discuss in regards to using notation and how they use notation to record their strategies. Consider some typical issues that arise as students record their work on story problems.

PICTURES AND NOTATION As a first step toward successfully writing equations, some students show each quantity in a problem via pictures, and then add symbols to their drawings.

[Holly's Work]

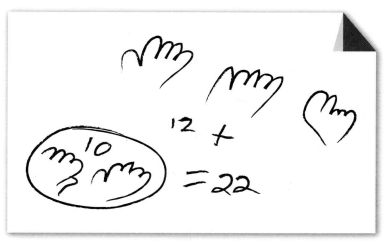

[Chen's Work]

RUN-ON EQUATIONS Another common mistake is using a string of equal signs to indicate the sequence of operations being performed. While these may convey a student's thinking, $10 + 10$ is not equivalent to $20 + 1 + 1$ or $20 + 2$, or 22.

$$10 + 10 = 20 + 1 + 1 = 22$$

[Amaya's Work]

$$10 + 10 = 20 + 2 = 22$$

[Luis's Work]

HORIZONTAL AND VERTICAL NOTATION In trying to use vertical notation, some students use aspects of both vertical and horizontal notation.

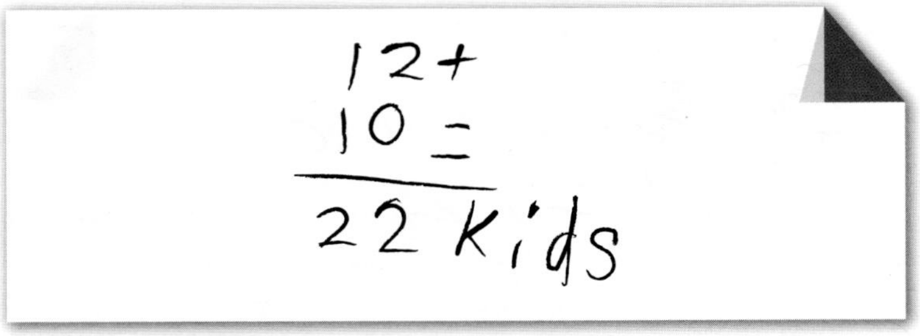

$$12+$$
$$10=$$
$$\overline{}$$
$$22\ Kids$$

[Simon's Work]

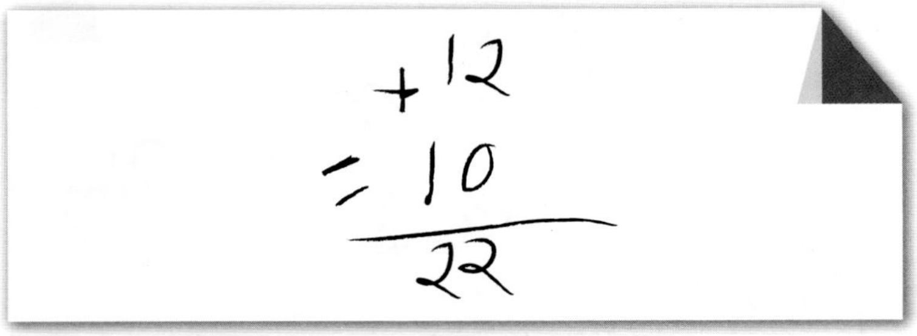

$$+12$$
$$=10$$
$$\overline{22}$$

[Carla's Work]

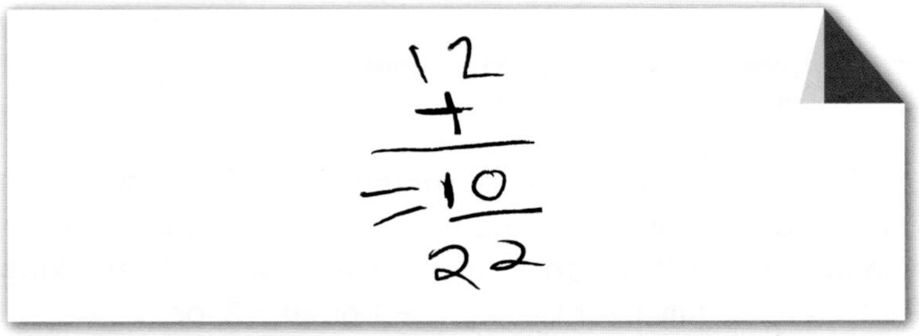

$$12$$
$$+$$
$$\overline{=10}$$
$$22$$

[Tia's Work]

The focus of modeling standard notation is to help students develop language and form images of the actions that these symbols represent. Students' understanding and use of notation will develop over time, through plenty of experience seeing, talking about, and using such symbols and language throughout the primary grades.

In Grades 3, 4, and 5, *Investigations* students continue to work with both horizontal and vertical notation for addition and subtraction. In this work, they compare several strategies, including the U.S. standard algorithms for addition and subtraction, with a focus on achieving computational fluency.

Assessment: Solving Story Problems

PROBLEMS 1–3

Benchmark Addressed:

Benchmark 4: Solve put together/take apart story problems with the total unknown, and add to and take from story problems with the result unknown.

In order to meet the benchmark, students' work should show that they can:

○ Solve the problem accurately;

○ Show how they solved the problem.

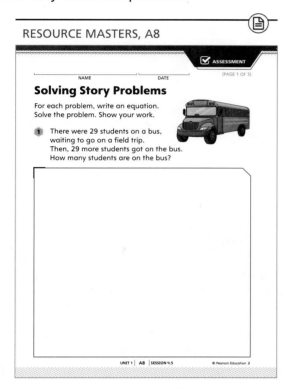

RESOURCE MASTERS, A8

PROBLEM 1

Meeting the Benchmark

The following examples provide a range of responses that meet the benchmark; all of these students are able to interpret the problem and solve it accurately. However, the students who add 29 + 29 (or 30 + 30), or count on, are demonstrating a deeper understanding of the operation of addition and of the quantities in the problem than those who are counting all.

Nate draws a picture to solve the problem. He represents each person in each group with a stick figure, drawing two rows of 29. Nate also represents the problem numerically as a problem involving two equal groups, writing the expression 29 + 29. In observing Nate's work, his teacher notes, "Nate counted his pictures by 1s, beginning at 1."

[Nate's Work]

Many early second graders use a strategy similar to Nate's, although some use cubes instead of drawings. Some represent both groups of 29 but count on from 29 rather than beginning at 1. Others use a number to stand for the first group of 29, and count on from there.

Chen adds 29 + 29, breaking apart the numbers and then recombining the parts in order to get the total. He also provides a detailed explanation.

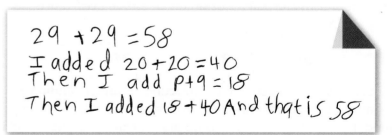

[Chen's Work]

Juan realizes that 29 + 29 is very close to 30 + 30. He uses something he knows, 3 + 3 = 6, to solve the larger problem, 30 + 30 = 60. Then, he accounts for the extra person he added to each group.

I added 30 + 30 and I know 3 + 3 was 6 so 30 + 30 is 60. Take away the 2 extra people and its 58.

[Juan's Work]

Partially Meeting the Benchmark

Some students understand the structure of the problem—that it is about combining two groups and finding the total—but make errors as they try to count and keep track of the quantities. After you review their work, ask these students to see whether they can find and correct such errors on their own. Encourage them to take their time and work carefully to avoid such errors in the future. In addition, note whether these kinds of errors are consistent across problems or simply one-time occurrences.

Not Meeting the Benchmark

A few students may still be constructing an understanding of what it means to combine two groups. They may benefit from modeling the action of such problems directly with cubes and by working on problems with lesser numbers.

PROBLEM 2

RESOURCE MASTERS, A9

ASSESSMENT

(PAGE 2 OF 3)

NAME   DATE

Solving Story Problems

2 A teacher has 25 new pencils. She gives out 14 pencils. How many pencils does she have left?

UNIT 1 | A9 | SESSION 4.5   © Pearson Education 2

Meeting the Benchmark

The following examples of student work provide a range of typical responses. All of these students meet the benchmark—they are able to interpret the problem and solve it accurately.

Some students show all and remove some, directly modeling the situation to solve the problems. Others count up (or back) from one number to the other. Still others break one or both numbers apart in order to subtract or use the answer to a problem they know to find the answer to this one. Students who are counting on or back or who are breaking apart the numbers are working more efficiently than those who need to model the situation directly in a one-to-one fashion.

SHOW ALL AND REMOVE SOME These students count out or draw 25, remove or cross out 14, and then count or label the number remaining. Some, like Rochelle, use groups to help them keep track of their count.

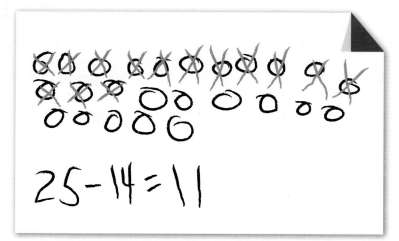

[Malcolm's Work]

[Simon's Work]

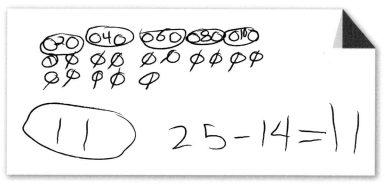

[Rochelle's Work]

COUNT BACK OR UP These students remove the 14 from 25 by counting back from 25 to 14, keeping track of how many numbers they count until they reach 14. A few students, like Paige, think about the problem as "How many do I have to add to 14 to get to 25?" and count up from 14 to 25.

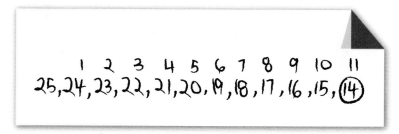

[Juan's Work]

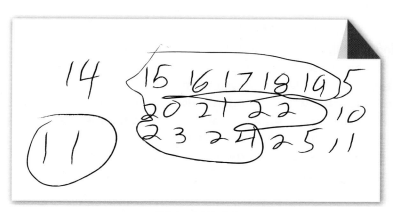

[Paige's Work]

KEEP ONE NUMBER WHOLE AND SUBTRACT IN PARTS These students break the 14 into 10 and 4 and then subtract each part from 25.

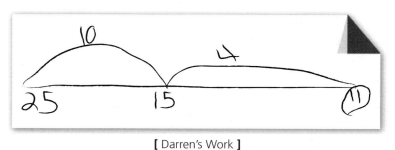

[Darren's Work]

[Tia's Work]

FIND THE DIFFERENCE These students find the difference between the two numbers in the problem. In other words, they figure out the distance from 14 to 25 or vice versa. The number line is often a useful way to represent this strategy.

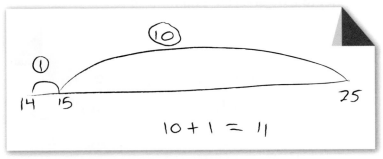

[Alberto's Work]

USE A KNOWN COMBINATION These students look at 25 − 14 and see other familiar problems to which they know the answer. For example, some students think, "25 − 15 is 10, so 25 − 14 . . . I take away one less so I have one more left." Others, like Holly, reason similarly. These students also understand that in subtraction, if the total increases by 1 then the result also increases by that same amount (Holly) or, similarly, if one more is subtracted from the total (i.e., 25 − 15) then the result increases by 1.

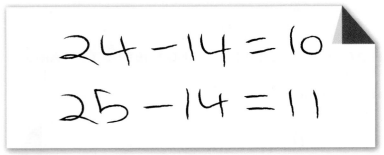

[Holly's Work]

Partially Meeting the Benchmark

Some students understand the structure of the problem—that it is about removing one quantity from another and then finding out how many are left—but make small computational mistakes or errors in keeping track. For example, it is easy to miscount if you are counting all or to stumble over where to start and stop when counting up or back.

Not Meeting the Benchmark

Some students may have difficulty interpreting and modeling a story that is not about combining or adding. They may just see the numbers in the problem and add them or show both groups, but then not know how to proceed. These students need more practice retelling and modeling stories that are about removing one amount from another. How Many Children? on *Student Activity Book* page 84 provides subtraction story problems that students can solve in class and for homework. Students will also continue to have many opportunities to solve subtraction problems in upcoming units.

PROBLEM 3

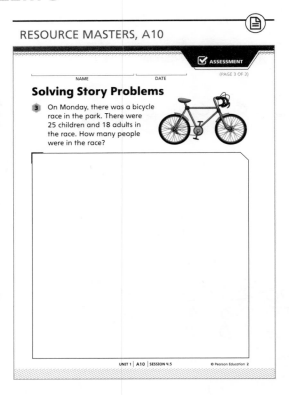

Meeting the Benchmark

The following examples of student work provide a range of typical responses. All of these students meet the benchmark— they were able to interpret the problem and solve it accurately using one of the specified strategies. Some students count on to solve the problem, and others break apart the numbers in various ways and add the parts.

COUNTING ON BY ONES Some students count on from 25 to solve the problem.

$$25 + 18 = 43$$

[Amaya's Work]

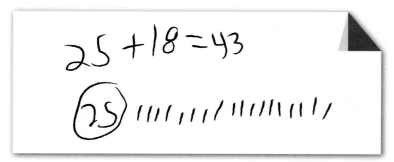

[Malcolm's Work]

ADDING ON IN PARTS Some students keep one number whole and add on the other in useful parts. Most common are students who break 18 into 10 and 8 and then add both numbers on to 25.

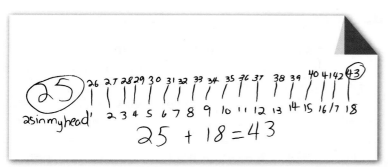

[Alberto's Work]

[Roshaun's Work]

whole

$$25 + 18 =$$

$$25 + 10 = 35$$

$$35 + 8 = 43$$

$$25 + 18 = 43$$

My anwser is 43.

[Katrina's Work]

ADDING BY PLACE Similar to students who add one of the numbers on by place (i.e., 10s and 1s), some students break apart both numbers into tens and ones and then combine the like parts. They break 25 into 20 + 5 (or 10 + 10 + 5) and 18 into 10 + 8, and then combine 20 + 10 (or 10 + 10 + 10). Most students then combine 8 + 5 and add on 13, either in one step (Nadia's work) or in parts (Juan's work). Other students, like Paige, proceed by solving 30 + 5 and then 35 + 8 (or 30 + 8 and then 38 + 5).

$$25 + 18$$
$$20+5 \quad 10+8$$
$$10 + 20 = 30$$
$$30 + 5 = 35$$
$$35 + 8 = 43$$

[Paige's Work]

$$25 + 18$$
$$20 \;\; 5 \;\; 10 \;\; 8$$

$$20 + 10 = 30 ✓$$
$$5 + 8 = 13 ✓$$
$$30 + 13 = 43$$

My answer is 43 people.

$$25 + 18 = 43$$

[Nadia's Work]

Partially Meeting the Benchmark

Some students understand the structure of the problem—that it is about combining two groups and finding the total—but make errors as they try to count and keep track of the quantities in the problem. After you have reviewed their work, ask these students to see whether they can find and correct such errors on their own. Encourage them to take their time and work carefully to avoid such errors in the future. In addition, note whether these kinds of errors are consistent across problems or one-time occurrences.

$$25 + 18$$
$$10 + 5 \quad 10 + 8$$
$$10$$

$$10 + 10 + 10 = 30$$

$$5 + 8 = 13$$
$$10 \quad 3$$

$$10 + 30 = 40 \text{ so the } 40 + 3 = 43$$

My anser is 43 kids and adults

[Juan's Work]

$$25 + 18 = 46$$
$$10 + 20 = 30$$
$$30 + 8 = 38$$
$$38 + 5 = 46$$

[Nate's Work]

Other students understand the structure of the problem and how to solve it but struggle with how to adequately show their work. To probe their understanding of the problem, ask these students to tell you how they solved it. Then, encourage them to add to their written explanation when appropriate. Note that these students need more support in showing their work.

I think the answer is 43
I did it on ~~an~~ a number chart

[Rochelle's Work]

25 1 2 3 4 5 6 7 8 9 10 11 12 13 14 15 16 17 18
my answer is 43.

[Henry's Work]

Not Meeting the Benchmark

A few students may still be constructing an understanding of what it means to combine two groups. They may benefit from modeling the action of such problems directly with cubes and by working on problems with lesser numbers.

Guess My Number

Students are introduced to *Guess My Number* in Session 1.1.

Teacher:	We are going to play a game called *Guess My Number*. I'm thinking of a number between 0 and 25. (The teacher puts a clothespin on 0 and another on 25 on the class number line.) You are going to ask a question and try to guess my number in as few turns as possible.
Alberto:	Is it 18?
Teacher:	No, it isn't 18. My number is *less than* 18. (He records < 18 on the board.) What do we know now?
Carla:	The number is lower than 18; it's smaller.
Teacher:	So how should I move the clips?
Carla:	Move that one from 25 down to 18.
Darren:	Is it 8?
Teacher:	It isn't 8. My number is *greater than* 8. (He records this on the board.) What do we know now?
Yama:	It's bigger than 8. You can move the clip to the 8.

There's some discussion about *which* clip, and whether it matters. Yama moves the clip from 0 to 8.

Teacher:	So how many numbers do we have to choose from?
Rochelle:	9 and 10.
Juan:	No, it's up to 18. So 10. One for 9, 2 for 10, 11 that's 3, 12 is 4, and you just keep counting to 18.
Anita:	Is your number 10?
Teacher:	The answer is yes!

When students revisit *Guess My Number* in Session 2.1, the teacher plays several rounds before using the game to establish that Today's Number is 7. In this round, he encourages his class to start thinking about the efficiency of their guesses.

Teacher:	I am thinking of a number between 0 and 50, and I want you to make guesses about what you think it is. I will give you clues by telling you whether my number is greater or less than your guess, and by moving the clips.

Amaya:	Is it 24?
Teacher:	It's greater than 24. (He moves the clip from 0 to 24.)
Jeffrey:	Is it 40?
Teacher:	It's less than 40. (He moves the clip from 50 to 40.)
Holly:	27?
Teacher:	It's more than 27. (He moves the clip from 24 to 27.) But I want to stop here and have someone tell me what they know about my number.
Katrina:	It's somewhere from 28 to 39.
Teacher:	Would 28 be a good guess for our next number?
Tia:	It probably won't make it better, because we just guessed 27.
Simon:	Because there's a whole bunch of other numbers in a row.
Teacher:	What happened when we guessed numbers? Our range was 0 to 50.
Katrina:	It got smaller and smaller.
Teacher:	So what would be a good guess?
Nadia:	34.
Teacher:	Why?
Nadia:	Because it's in the middle of 27 to 40.

Notice how this teacher pauses and asks a student to review what is known so far, and how he encourages students to think about the efficiency of their guesses by asking, "Would 28 be a good guess?" after 27 is guessed.

What Comes After 109?

As they work on counting strips in Sessions 1.4–1.5, students are discussing how they read and write numbers and how they use patterns in the sequence of numbers to think about what comes next.

Amaya has successfully written the numbers up to 59. After a long pause she says, "OK, this time it's a 6." She writes 60, and continues.

Leigh is writing numbers down her counting strip: 1, 2, 3, . . . 18. After writing 19 she writes a one, takes time to think, and then erases the one and writes 20. She continues writing: 21, 22, 23, 24, 25, 26, 27, 29, 30, 31, 32, 33, 34, 35, 36, 37, 39, 40. At this point she pauses, and goes back to recheck her work. On her own, she notices the mistakes and squeezes in 28 and 38.

Holly wonders aloud, "Does it matter which way you make a 10?" Her partner, Nadia, responds, "Yes, it doesn't matter how you make a 0 or 1, but a 10 backward is really one."

The teacher noticed few errors below 100. Most students who made errors, such as Leigh, found and corrected them on their own or in response to a question from her. The most common issues, she noted, were the transitions between decades and students who reversed numbers, writing 05 for 50. Although a few students struggled with certain aspects of writing the numbers below 100, most could accurately write the numbers up to 100. Then interesting mistakes began to crop up. Two students stumbled after writing 100.

One wrote 100, 110, 120, 130, and so on. The other wrote 100, 1001, 1002, 1003. Five students struggled with what to write after 109. Two followed 109 with 200; two wrote "109, 1010," and one wrote "109, 1000."

Having seen a few students struggling with this issue, she decides to bring it up in the discussion in Session 1.6. She posts a counting strip that ends at 109. After discussing it, she focuses on the question about how to write the number that comes after 109.

Teacher: What number comes after 109? (Students call out 110.) Everyone seems pretty sure of the name of the number. The question is how do you write 110?

The teacher gathers students' ideas, including 101, 110, 200, 1010, 10010, and 1000.

Teacher: Are there any that you think could *not* be the way to write 110? Can you explain why it couldn't be the way to write 110?

Leo: Well I know that the last number is one thousand. It's just a number I know.

Other students agree, acknowledging 1000 as a number they are familiar with.

Jacy: I don't think it can be 200 because at first I thought it should be 200. Because, before when it was a nine, the number changed, and it's 109. But when I said the numbers out loud, it didn't sound right. You don't say 109, 200. You say 109, 110.

Teacher: Can you say more about what you mean about the numbers changing after a nine?

Jacy: Well, like it goes 0, 1, 2, 3, 4, 5, 6, 7, 8, 9. And all of those numbers would have the same number in the front. Like here (she shows her counting strip, pointing out the numbers from 20–29; the teacher records these numbers on the board) it's a 2.

Teacher: Jacy is saying that the numbers in the ones place (pointing) go from 0 through 9, and the number in the tens place (pointing) is the same for all those numbers. Does everybody see that? What Jacy is saying is that after the number with a nine in the ones place, the number in the tens place changes. What number comes after 29? (30) Can someone find another example of a place on their counting strip where the numbers change after a 9?

Several examples are shared, then she asks students to consider the remaining potential answers: 101, 110, 1010, and 10010.

Teacher: What about the possibilities we have left—they all have ones and zeros. . . . Are there any we can eliminate?

Malcolm: This one (points to 10010) looks funny to me, but we're trying to write one hundred and ten. If you say 100 and 10, you have to write 100 and the 10.

Melissa: No, you don't need to write all 100. One hundred and one is (writes 101), not (writes 1001) and one hundred and two is (writes 102), not (writes 1002). So one hundred and ten should be (writes 110), not (writes 10010).

Teacher: Melissa used a great strategy. She went back and looked at the numbers that she already wrote before 110 to see whether they could help her. (The teacher writes the numbers from 99 to 109 in a column on the board.) Malcolm, what do you think of Melissa's idea? Did your numbers from 101 to 109 look like Melissa's?

Malcolm: Yeah, they do. They all have three numbers in them. I guess that's why 10010 looked funny.

Teacher: How many digits are in all your numbers in the hundreds so far?

Malcolm: Three. (Others agree.)

Melissa: So if 101 and 102 have three numbers, then 110 has to have three numbers.

Juan: Yes, we don't need to write the entire 100. The one tells you that it is 100, and then you write the 10.

Students at this age are learning the oral counting sequence, the written counting sequence, and how these written and spoken symbols represent quantities. The process is a complex one, particularly once the boundary of 100 is crossed. This teacher knows from past experience that learning to correctly write the numbers in sequence takes time and plans to provide further opportunities for students to bump up against the challenge of how to write larger numbers.

Combinations of 10

During the Classroom Routine in Session 2.2, students are challenged to make *Today's Number*, which is 10, with two addends. After giving students time to work, the teacher asks about the combinations they've found.

Alberto: There's 10 + 0 and 9 + 1 and 7 + 3.

Holly: There's 3 + 7, too.

Tia: Isn't that a repeat? 7 + 3 and 3 + 7 are reversibles.

Alberto: Well, yes and no, I think. I think you should write it next to 7 + 3.

Teacher: We talked about similar combinations the other day when we were finding ways to make 8. Some students thought they were the same, and others thought they were different. Alberto, your idea of writing them next to each other is a good one. OK, are there any others?

Simon: 6 + 4 makes 10, and so does 4 + 6.

Katrina: You can also add 0 + 10.

Tia: We already have that one, too.

Teacher: Someone raised that question about 3 + 7 and 7 + 3. Tia called them reversibles. What do you think about that?

Nate: 1 + 9 is the same as 9 + 1. It's just turned around.

Nadia: It's the same amount in each pile, it's just that you put one number first. If you add 3 to 7, it's the same as adding 7 to 3. Look, I'll show you with the cubes. (Nadia puts a tower of 7 cubes and a tower of 3 cubes on the rug.) See? This is 7 + 3. And this (she moves the tower of 7 on the other side of the tower of 3) is 3 + 7. It's the same amount. So they are the same thing.

Simon: Every one of these combinations of ten is part of a pair: 3 + 7 and 7 + 3, 2 + 8 and 8 + 2.

Alberto: I say that they are different. See, you could have 3 red cubes and 7 blue cubes and that would be different from having 7 red cubes and 3 blue cubes.

Leo: Well, the colors are different, but the total amount of cubes you end up with is still the same. 10 is 10. I think they are reversibles because you could just flip them around and they would be the same. Or if you read it in reverse, 3 + 7 would be 7 + 3.

Teacher: You've all brought up some interesting ideas. Tia's idea of calling these addition combinations reversibles and Simon's observation that each combination is part of a pair are things for us to think about. I have another question for you. How did you figure out 10 using two numbers?

Carolina: I said 9 + 1 and then just kept going lower and lower, like, 8 + 2, 7 + 3, 6 + 4, and when I couldn't go any lower that was all of them.

Rochelle: I used cubes, and I tried all the different ways to break them up and put them in two groups.

Teacher: Did you have any way of keeping track?

Rochelle: No.

Leo: Our group did. We wrote 0 through 5 going down the paper and then I put plus signs in the middle and wrote 5 through 10 going up. Then we went back and checked. It's like a pattern, as one number goes down the other number goes up.

The teacher records Leo's method on the board to confirm his description.

$$0 + 10$$
$$1 + 9$$
$$2 + 8$$
$$3 + 7$$
$$4 + 6$$
$$5 + 5$$

Katrina: Yeah. The numbers on one side go down and on the other side go up. See, it's like if you had some cubes (she takes 10 cubes from the bin). Here's 10 and 0. Then make two groups. Like 9 over here and then 1. Then if you make a group of 8, this one is less, but this group is more because it goes from 1 to 2. (She takes 1 cube from the 9 and connects it to the single cube, making a tower of 8 and 2.)

The teacher asks if someone else can turn the towers of 8 and 2 into the next problem on their list. Several students take turns transforming one problem into the next until they get to 5 + 5.

Chen: And the 5 + 5 is sort of where the pattern turns and goes the other way. So I think we have them all.

Paige: If you include all the pairs then I think there's only 11 ways to make 10 with two numbers. You would take all the ways that Leo just said and double that because of the pairs. That would give you 12 ways but 5 + 5 doesn't really have a pair so subtract 1 from 12 and that's 11.

Teacher: So are you certain that you have all the ways to make 10?

Anita: Well, I got 12 ways counting the pairs, but I'm not absolutely certain that's all of them.

Katrina: I'm certain because if you look at the pattern of going one down and one up then there aren't any numbers in between.

Amaya: And besides, I can't think of any more combinations.

Teacher: So some of you are seeing a pattern with these combinations of 10. How many people think that we have found them all? How many aren't sure? I'm going to leave this chart here for a couple of days, and I'd like you to keep thinking about the pattern that Katrina and Chen noticed. If you discover another combination of 10 using two numbers, let us know and we will add it to the list.

$$10 + 0$$
$$9 + 1$$
$$8 + 2$$
$$7 + 3$$
$$6 + 4$$
$$5 + 5$$

By engaging her class in a discussion about similar combinations, which the class terms "reversibles", the teacher lays the foundation for later discussions about whether order matters in addition.

As students share combinations, the teacher encourages them to consider the patterns they notice, and to use those patterns to reason about whether or not they have found all of the 2-addend combinations that make 10. By leaving the chart with the combinations displayed, she invites her students to ponder this further and creates opportunities to revisit this discussion at a later time.

Does the Order Matter?

Students have been solving problems about combining three groups on *Student Activity Book* pages 31–32. At the end of Session 2.3, the teacher calls them together to share their work. She uses three cube towers (six green, three blue, and four yellow cubes) to discuss whether order matters with addition.

Anita: I did 6 + 4; that's 10. Then 3 more make 13.

Teacher: Anita saw a combination of 10, so she solved 6 + 4 + 3.

The teacher orders the cube towers 6, 4, 3 and records the following on chart paper:

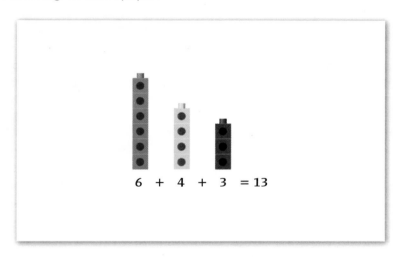

6 + 4 + 3 = 13

Teacher: Did someone work in a different order?

Henry: I did 6 + 3 + 4. I got 13 too because 6 and 3 is 9, and then 10, 11, 12, 13.

The teacher reorders the cube towers and records:

$$6 + 3 + 4 = 13$$

Teacher: So you added the numbers in the order they were given.

Malcolm: I did 4 + 6 is 10, and then 3 more is 13.

Again, the teacher reorders the cube towers and records:

$$4 + 6 + 3 = 13$$

Teacher: Malcolm looked for a 10 just like Anita. They both started with the 6 and the 4.

Darren: I did 6 + 3 + 4.

Leigh: That's the same as Henry.

Darren: I mean 3 + 6 + 4 = 13. I counted the cubes and got the same answer every time.

The teacher asks Darren to demonstrate with the towers. He lines them up as stated and counts each cube. Then he changes the order of the towers and counts each cube again.

Darren: It's 13 however you count.

Teacher: Why is that? Some of you started with the 6, Malcolm started with the 4, and Darren started with the 3, but you all got the same answer. I'm wondering why that is. When we switched them all around, why did we get the same answer?

Paige: It's like Darren said. Because if you . . . (arranges the cube towers into 6, 3, 4) you have 6; 7, 8, 9; 10, 11, 12, 13. And when you put it this way (rearranges the cube towers), it's still the same because it's 1, 2, 3 . . . 13.

Katrina: They have the same numbers so they are going to make 13. If they have the same numbers, they are going to make the same number. One couldn't be 13 and one 14.

Simon: No matter which way you add it, it's still the same numbers. You can just bounce them around.

Teacher: Why doesn't it matter?

Holly: It doesn't matter because you're not adding anything or taking anything away.

Lonzell: I think they're like turnarounds.

As they explored *Today's Number* in Investigation 1 and discussed strategies for adding two numbers in Session 2.2, this class invented the term *turnarounds* for problems with two addends in reverse order, such as 5 + 3 and 3 + 5. Lonzell is extending that idea to problems with more than two addends.

Teacher: So you mean that turnarounds don't have to be just two numbers? Lonzell thinks you can use three numbers.

Carolina: Any way you switch it, it would just be the same thing. You can probably do it with any numbers.

Teacher: Are you saying that you can do this with any numbers and switching the order won't change it?

Students respond enthusiastically, calling out that it would work for 3, 7, 8, and even a "billion" numbers.

Teacher: So you think this will work with any numbers that I pick? So what if I picked 9 and 10 and 2? If I switch those numbers, would I get the same answer?

Yama: I don't agree that if you use a 10 or a 9 or a 2 . . . you wouldn't get 13.

The teacher agrees with Yama and then clarifies, explaining that she is wondering whether 9 + 10 + 2 would give the same answer as 2 + 10 + 9 or 10 + 9 + 2.

Monisha: You're not adding anything or taking anything away. You're just putting them in a different order.

Teacher: You are saying that this will work for any three numbers. I'm wondering whether you really believe it. What if we use numbers like 100, 200, and 300? Would it always equal the same number?

Satisfied that many students seem to be coming to an understanding that order does not matter in addition, this teacher asks them to consider the same generalization with much larger numbers. Although some students are convinced, many are unsure. The teacher knows that students will need to revisit this idea in different contexts over the course of the year.

Introducing the Facts

During Session 2.5, students are introduced to "math facts." They discuss what they are, what it means to know them, and terminology for related sets of addition facts. They get the first of several sets of Fact Cards that will help them develop fluency with addition and subtraction within 20 by the end of the year.

Teacher: Sometimes when people think about Grade 2 math they talk about learning their facts. Sometimes people call them basic facts or math facts, or addition and subtraction facts. Has anyone heard them before?

Simon: I heard it on a television show about math.

Henry: From my brother.

Holly: $2 + 2 = 4$ is a fact.

Katrina: A fact is something you know.

Amaya: I have a book of facts about animals. Did you know that green sea turtles could live for 100 years?

Teacher: There are all kinds of facts. Facts are things that we know are true, but when people talk about math facts, that's a little different. We are going to be studying the addition and subtraction facts this year—when you add two single-digit numbers together, as Holly mentioned before with $2 + 2 = 4$, or subtract them like maybe $5 - 1 = 4$.

Students offer a few other problems, and then the teacher asks what they think it means to know a fact.

Jacy: It's something you already know, like you know $4 + 4$; you just already know it.

Simon: I forget what $8 + 8$ is.

Teacher: So is that one you know or is that something you need to work on?

Simon: Work on.

The teacher thanks Simon for sharing an example of a fact that is hard for him to remember and reminisces about one that was hard for him when he was in school. Then, to think about what it means to know a fact, he writes $2 + 2$ on the board. The students immediately know that the answer is 4. Then he writes $11 + 13$, which students need a minute or two to solve. He contrasts their responses to help them think about what it means to know a fact.

The teacher then distributes a deck of Fact Cards: Set 1 to each student. He gives them time to look through the cards and talk to a neighbor about what they notice. Most notice that some cards have one problem on them instead of two, and are familiar with those facts, the doubles. Other students comment on there being a lot of cards that are "plussing one." He shows the Fact Card for $1 + 7$ and $7 + 1$.

Teacher: Talk for a minute with a neighbor about what you know and how you know it.

Anita: They both equal 8.

Nadia: I know it because I'm 8 and last year I was 7 and one more year is 8!

After a few more Plus 1 examples, the teacher asks if these are easy. Students respond "Yes!" The teacher wonders why.

Gregory: They're only 1-digit numbers.

Katrina: We've been working on them since kindergarten.

Anita: They're only adding 1.

Jeffrey: We're adding 1 to 7, even if it's $1 + 7$.

Teacher: Are you saying that if you know $8 + 1$, then you know $1 + 8$? (Students respond "Yes!") Why?

Esteban: Because they're the same thing, just switched around.

After finding and setting aside all of the Doubles and Plus 1 Facts, the teacher explains that there are two categories left in the cards they still have and challenges students to figure out what the others are. He gives students some time to look at and sort the cards.

Holly:	All the ones that equal 10 are in here.
Katrina:	The other counts by 2s!
Esteban:	They're all 2 + something.
Carolina:	Or something + 2!
Tia:	How about calling them 2 + something?
Teacher:	That's a good idea. We could also call them Plus 2 Facts, since we named the first set Plus 1 Facts. What about the ones Holly was talking about?

Students suggest Combinations of 10. The teacher then hands out envelopes and explains that students will sort the Fact Cards into envelopes of "Facts I Know" and "Facts I Am Still Working On."

Teacher:	Now that you've looked at the cards a bit, do you have more thoughts about what it means to just know something? What does that mean?
Simon:	Right, when you look at it you just know it.
Teacher:	What if you have to continue to work on that fact? How did that work for you, Darren?
Darren:	When I first looked at 2 + 9, I thought that it was 10, then I realized that it was 11.
Teacher:	That's a good example. If there's one that you need to pause in order to figure it out, it's better to put that card in the envelope of facts you're working on. Then you'll get more practice with it and you will get to know it better.

Students get to work sorting their Fact Cards into two envelopes. The teacher occasionally selects cards out of students' "Facts I Know" envelopes and chats with them about how well they know the problems. There is some time left when all of the students have finished sorting their cards.

Teacher:	We have a few minutes of math class left to practice these facts. Work with a partner. Go through the cards in both envelopes, and help each other make smart choices and be honest with yourselves about which facts you need to work on. See whether you know it as well as you knew 2 + 2, just like that (he snaps his fingers). There is nothing wrong with not knowing all of your facts right now, but we're going to work hard on learning them.

Today's Number: 14

In Session 2.6, students do *Today's Number,* generating expressions that equal 14. Students in this class use addition combinations they know, think about ways to break apart 14, and extend patterns they discover (10 + 4, 11 + 3, and so on) to generate expressions.

Jeffrey: 10 + 4.

Teacher: There's an old friend. Why am I saying that?

Monisha: Because you know you have 10 and then count up 4 to get 14.

Teacher: That's right, in the teens you can pull out the 10 and see what's left over.

Katrina: 5 + 5 + 4.

Teacher: What did you do to the 10?

Katrina: Cut it in half.

Nadia: 11 + 3.

Teacher: Can you tell me what you're thinking there?

Nadia: It's kind of like 10 + 4, but I took away 1 from 4 and added it to 10.

Roshaun: 12 + 2. Nadia did 11 + 3 so I put one more adding up.

Teacher: So one more up to make 12 . . .

Roshaun: And one more out of three to get 12 + 2.

Alberto: 14 + 0.

Teacher: What do you know about zero?

Alberto: You can always make the same number when you use it.

Teacher: Right, if you add a number to zero you won't have any more or any . . .? (Students: Less.) Less.

Esteban: 8 + 6.

Teacher: How did you think of that one?

Esteban: I had 8, and then I counted up 6.

Teacher: Esteban, did you go 9, 10 . . .? (Yes.) So you counted by 1s to get to 14. Any other ways?

Monisha: I looked at 5 + 5 + 4 and I did 2 + 3 + 2 + 3 + 2 + 2.

The teacher records 2 + 3 = 5, 2 + 3 = 5, and 2 + 2 = 4 to show how this relates to the earlier equation.

Travis: 3 + 2 + 3 + 2 + 1 + 1 + 1 + 1.

Teacher: What did Travis change?

Simon: He changed the four into four 1s.

Travis: I also changed 2 + 3 to 3 + 2.

Holly: 10 + 2 + 2.

Nate: We have that; we have 10 + 4.

Teacher: It's similar. Holly broke the 4 into 2 + 2.

The teacher records the two equations to show the connection.

Jacy: 7 + 7.

Teacher: There's another familiar friend. Why do I say that? What's that called?

Jacy: Doubles.

Luis: 20 take away... six? Five?

Teacher: What can you use to help you check your answer?

Luis looks up at the 100 chart, and counts backwards from 20 to 14, then says, "Six."

Gregory: 1 + 1 + 1 + 1 + 1 . . .

Teacher: Gregory, how many 1s do you want me to write?

The kids giggle. Gregory says 14, and the teacher records his idea. Then, Carla builds on it.

Carla: 2 + 2 + 2 + 2 . . .

Teacher: How many 2s?

Carla: I don't know.

The class starts to call out answers.

Teacher: I hear some confusion. Let's write it out.

On the board, the teacher writes:

$$2 + 2 + 2 + 2 + 2 + 2 + 2 = 14$$

with the class counting by 2s to keep track until she reaches 14.

Teacher: Does anyone have words to explain this?

Leo: (looking at Gregory's way) You can just smack the 1s together to get 2s.

The teacher records the following:

$$\underset{2}{(1 + 1)} + \underset{2}{(1 + 1)} + \underset{2}{(1 + 1)} + \underset{2}{(1 + 1)} + \underset{2}{(1 + 1)} +$$

$$\underset{2}{(1 + 1)} + \underset{2}{(1 + 1)} = 14$$

Throughout this discussion, the teacher highlights familiar, useful combinations like 10 + 4 and 7 + 7, making strategies such as "pulling out a ten" and "using a double" more explicit and public. Throughout, she encourages students to explain how their expression relates to other combinations and how they used one expression to generate others. She questions students in an effort to understand their thinking and to help them articulate their process.

Are There Enough for the Class?

After working on an Enough for the Class? problem in Session 3.1, students meet to share strategies for finding how many cubes would be left over if each student took 1 cube from a bag with 38 cubes. There are 26 students in the class.

Teacher: Who would like to share the strategy they used to solve this problem? Darren?

Darren: I took 38 cubes. There are 26 kids in our class so I gave each person one. (He counts out 26 cubes by ones, placing them in a circle, like the one they sit in at meeting.) Then I counted the extras, and there are 1, 2, 3, . . . 12.

Teacher: Darren gave one cube to each person and then counted the leftovers. Did anyone else use cubes to solve the problem?

Nate: I made a train of cubes. Then I counted 26 cubes and broke off the rest. I had 10 left, so I think there's 10 left over.

Leo: But 26 and 10 is 36. There's 38 cubes in the bag.

Teacher: So what should Nate do?

Leo: I think he counted out only 36 cubes. He should add on 2 more so that he has 38 in all.

Nate snaps his two trains together and adds 2 more cubes. Then, at the teacher's suggestion, he re-counts. In agreement that he has 38, he then counts and breaks off 26. He smiles as he counts 12 cubes in the leftover train.

Juanita: I did something sort of like Nate, but I made towers. I had 3 towers of 10 and a tower of 8. That made 38. Then there are 26 kids in our class, so I took away 2 towers of 10 for the 20, and then I took away 6 more. 12 were left.

The teacher asks Nate if she can use his cube train to show Juanita's strategy. She breaks the train into 3 towers of 10 and 1 tower of 8.

Teacher: Juanita said that this made 38. How can we check that there are 38 cubes?

Carolina: 10 plus 10 is 20. Plus ten more is 30. Then 31, 32, 33, . . . 38.

The teacher asks students to help her take away 26—one for each student in the class. They remove 2 towers of 10 and then break 6 off of the tower of 8. Together they count the remaining cubes.

Teacher: How about another example? Did anyone use something besides cubes to solve the problem?

Jeffrey: I just made 26 circles, and then underneath those I made more circles until I got up to 38. Then I counted the circles underneath.

Teacher: So Jeffrey drew 26, then he counted up from 26. Did anyone else count up from 26?

Katrina: I started with 26 and then counted until 38.

Teacher: Did you use your fingers to keep track? (Katrina nods shyly.) Don't feel shy about that. Mathematicians use all sorts of tools to get their answers, and your fingers are one tool that you always have with you!

Monisha: I did the same thing as Katrina, but I used the number line.

Teacher: Can you show us how you used the number line?

Monisha shows how she started at 26 and counted on to 38. As she makes each jump of 1 she counts, "1, 2, 3, . . . 12."

Teacher: So there were 26 students in our class. Imagine that each number is one of you or the cube you would get. Monisha counted the extras on the number line.

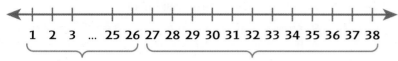

26 kids each get 1 cube   These cubes are leftover

Teacher: When I watched Esteban solve the problem, I noticed that he did something very similar to Monisha. Esteban, what tool did you use to solve the problem?

Esteban: The 100 chart.

Teacher: Can I show what you did?

Esteban nods. The teacher demonstrates how he counted on from 26 to 38 on the 100 chart, just as Monisha did on the number line.

Teacher: OK, any more strategies? Two more? Wow! Paige first, and then Roshaun.

Paige: I counted (points to each number on the line, starting with 38, and holds up one finger for each number) 37, 36, 35, 34, 33, 32, 31, 30, 29, 28, 27, 26. That's 12 numbers, so they are 12 apart, and that means there is 12 left over.

Teacher: How did you know where to stop?

Paige: I stopped at 26 because that's how many kids are in our class.

Teacher: So there were 38 cubes. If you take away 1 cube, that's 37. If you take away another cube, that's 36. . . . She stopped at 26 because that would leave 26 cubes. One for every student in our class.

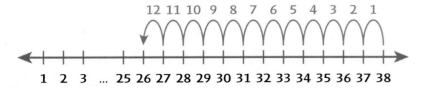

Teacher: OK. Roshaun?

Roshaun: I got 12 because the difference between 30 and 20 is 10, and the difference between 8 and 6 is 2. So add 10 and 2 and that's 12.

$$30 - 20 = 10$$
$$8 - 6 = 2 \qquad 10 + 2 = 12$$

the diverence in between 26 and 38 is 12, I know Because the diverence in between 30 and 20 is 10 and the diverence in between 6 and 8 is 2 and 2 + 10 = 12

[Roshaun's Work]

Notice the variety of tools (cubes, drawings, the number line, the 100 chart, and fingers) that students used to find the difference between the two numbers. Their strategies were diverse as well: represent the situation and count the extras, take the number of students away from the number of cubes, count up from the number of students to the number of cubes, back from the number of cubes to the number of students, and reason numerically about the difference between the numbers.

Order and Subtraction

In Session 3.2, students generated expressions for 7 in *Today's Number,* and considered pairs of expressions such as 2 + 5 and 5 + 2, which they have labeled "turnarounds." The teacher poses a question about whether order matters for subtraction, asking students to investigate 9 − 4 and 4 − 9. After exploring the question in pairs, the class comes back together to share their thoughts.

Teacher: What do you think? What did you find out? Does order matter when you subtract?

Darren: Turnarounds work for subtraction if the answer is zero. 100 − 100 = 0. You turn the numbers around, and you get 100 − 100 = 0.

Luis: But if the answer isn't zero, it doesn't work. 9 − 4 doesn't equal 4 − 9.

Teacher: How did you think about 4 minus 9?

Luis: If you have 9 fingers and you take 4 away, you have 5. If you have 4 fingers and you try to take away 9 fingers, you have none left. So 4 minus 9 is zero.

Teacher: Did anyone think about 4 minus 9 in another way?

Katrina: You can't do 4 take away 9 because after you lose the 4 . . . if you have 4 take away 9 . . . 4 doesn't have 9. 4 is not a 9.

Teacher: Are you saying that 4 isn't enough? That there isn't enough to take away 9? How many could I take away?

Katrina: You could only take away 4 to make zero.

Tia: You can't lose the 4 because after you lose the 4 . . . 3, 2, 1, 0, 0, 0, 0 . . . It's gonna keep on repeating itself until it gets to 9.

Roshaun: I think it wouldn't be zero. It would be negative 5.

Teacher: What do mean by negative 5?

Roshaun: It means you're going lower than zero. Negative 1, negative 2, negative 3, like that.

Nadia: 9 minus 4 equals 5 and 4 minus 9 equals negative 5. If you use the number line . . .

Nadia demonstrates on the class number line how she and her partner counted back nine jumps from 4 and landed on negative 5. Some students are nodding in agreement, but others seem puzzled by this new idea. The teacher decides to revisit the idea of order in subtraction at a later time, using this discussion as just an initial introduction.

As students begin to consider whether order matters in subtraction, they also begin to think about numbers less than zero. Although not all second graders are ready or have an interest in thinking about negative numbers, some are able to use a number line, for example, to model numbers less than zero. Negative numbers or ideas such as "owing" often come up in this discussion, but the focus should stay on whether order matters when subtracting two numbers. Note that the teacher in this class does not resolve what the answer to 4 − 9 is. Her intention was to introduce the idea of order in subtraction, and she plans to revisit this in subsequent discussions.

Our Second Pocket Day

The class is collecting pocket data for the second time. After helping students consider the information needed to develop an informed estimate, the teacher works with the class to find the total number of pockets.

Teacher: Today is the 20th day of school. That means it's Pocket Day. Can someone remind us how Pocket Day works?

Jeffrey: I think I have the same pants on as last time, so I have the same number of pockets!

Carolina: Well, you go to the table with the cubes, you put one cube in each pocket, and then we come back and you call if you have two pockets come up, and then we figure out how many pockets there are in the class by counting the cubes.

Teacher: That's a great explanation. We did one more thing before we went to get cubes. It's a great math word that starts with an e. (Students guess *explain*, *explanation*, and *estimate*.) What does estimate mean?

Malcolm: What you think it might be?

Teacher: Is it a wild, silly guess?

Malcolm: No, it's a good guess.

Teacher: Based on information you know, right? Does anyone remember how many pockets we had last time? (76) Yes, we had 76 cubes and that filled our jar up to here. (She holds up the marked pocket jar.) Do you think the amount will change today? (Students respond "Yes!") We are the same number of students, so why do you think so?

Leigh: People may be wearing different pants, so they might have more pockets.

Jacy: Or less. Because Darren isn't wearing those pants with all the pockets!

Students discuss whether they are wearing more or fewer pockets than last time. The teacher asks for a show of hands from people who are wearing more, and then fewer, pockets than last time. She then collects estimates and lists them on the board in the order they are suggested: 60, 70, 80, 40, 50, 65, 62, 49, and 35. Then she asks students to help her order them from least to most.

Teacher: So our estimates range from 35 to 80. Let's find out. (Students go off to get one cube per pocket.) Last time, I had you come up, just the way Carolina said, but this time we are going to do it a little differently because good mathematicians try different strategies. Today when I call your name, put your cubes in the jar, and then I will write your data in the space next to your name.

The teacher shows students the alphabetical list she made of all their names to record each student's data. About halfway, she pauses. 3, 5, 0, 0, 7, and 4 pockets have been recorded so far.

Teacher: Look at our data so far. Do you think we'll have more or less than last time?

Students call out "Less," and "There's 2 zeros!" The teacher finishes recording the data. The final data are: 3, 5, 0, 0, 7, 4, 8, 2, 2, 5, 5, 5, 5, 5, 5. Students notice that 2 people have no pockets, that no one has 1 pocket, and that the person with the most has 8 pockets. They also comment on the number of people with 5 pockets and suggest counting by 5s.

Teacher: I was going to suggest that we find combinations of 10, but when you looked at our data, you saw all those 5s and suggested counting by 5s, so we'll do that. Then we can see whether there are any combinations of 10 in what's left.

She checks each 5 as the class counts by 5s. The remaining amounts are 3, 7, 4, 8, 2, and 2.

Teacher: Now, let's look at the numbers we have left. Are there any combinations of numbers that make 10?

Gregory: Roshaun and Esteban. (The teacher checks off 7 and 3.)

Alberto: 8 + 2. (The teacher checks off 8 and 2.)

Katrina: And then there's Anita and Leo. That makes . . . (the teacher checks off the 4 and the 2) 6.

Teacher: Now here's a challenge. We have 35, a 10, a 10, and a 6. Does someone have an idea about how we could solve this?

Leo: Start with the 35, take the 10 to make 45 then I think 55, and then 6 more would be 61. (The teacher models Leo's explanation on the 100 chart, which can help students see that 35 + 10 = 45.)

Teacher: How did you count the 6 more?

Leo: I was thinking if it was a 5 it would be a 10, so one more would be 61 because a 5 would give me 60, and 6 is 1 bigger than 5 so I knew it was 61.

Nadia: I did it different. Take the 30 and put it with the 10 and the 10 to make 50.

The teacher realizes that some students are not following and are therefore disengaging. She uses cubes to pull them back into the conversation. She builds 3 towers of 10 and a tower of 5 for 35. Off to the other side there are 2 more towers of 10 and a tower of 6.

Teacher: So Nadia took the 5 off the 35. (She moves the 5 to the other side.) Then what did you do?

Nadia: Take the 30 and put it with the 10 and the 10 to make 50. (The teacher moves the 2 towers of 10 over to join the 30.) Then take the 5 and add it to the 50, that would be 55. And then take 5 from the 6 to make 60. And then there's one left. 61. (The cubes now show 10, 10, 10, 10, 10, 5, 5, 1.)

Luis: If you put those 5s together, that's another 10. Then we could count them by 10s.

The teacher agrees, and the class counts them by 10s aloud, together. They get 61 cubes, although some students count the 61st cube as 70.

Teacher: I noticed that people said two different numbers at the end. I heard 61, and I heard 70. Why would it be 61 and not 70?

Monisha: Because it's (pointing to the single cube) not another of 10, it's only one.

Teacher: OK, one last thing. Let's go back to our estimates. What guesses were closest?

Jeffrey: Whoever thought it was 62 sure was close, they were only 1 ahead of the data.

Juanita: What about 60?

Anita: They're both really close, I don't know.

Teacher: I hear 60 and 62, but which is closer?

Darren: I'm not sure. I think 60 is closer.

Melissa: Both. Because 61 is in between 62 and 60.

Darren: But 60 comes *before* 62.

The teacher models the situation on the number line, locating 60, 61, and 62.

Teacher: We'll think more about this, but they are equally far away. They are both 1 hop away from 61. So both estimates are an equal distance from 61. They are 1 away.

Although the lesson suggested looking for combinations of 10 to find the total number of pockets, this teacher pursues the students' idea to count by 5s since it is based on a good observation about the data collected, which includes a lot of 5s. By using cubes to concretely model the final problem: 35 + 10 + 10 + 6, this teacher helps all of her students access the strategies for combining these numbers that are discussed.

An Addition Story Problem

During Session 4.1, students are discussing how they solved an addition story problem. The teacher is focusing on helping students think about what makes a complete explanation.

Teacher: When I was walking around, I saw a lot of people do something like this. (On chart paper she draws 12 circles and labels them 1–12. Then she draws 10 circles underneath the 12 and labels them with the numbers 1–10. Then she writes 22.) My question is, how did you know that this was 22?

O O O O O O O O O O O O
1 2 3 4 5 6 7 8 9 10 11 12

22

O O O O O O O O O O
1 2 3 4 5 6 7 8 9 10

Rochelle: Because (she comes up to chart paper and counts each circle by ones).

Teacher: Rochelle counted the circles by ones. I saw a bunch of people count out 12, count out 10, and then count them all. Some people drew circles, some people drew people. Some people did it with cubes, and then they drew the cubes. Some people used the 100 chart or the number line.

Henry: I used tally lines. 12 on top and 10 on the bottom. Then I counted up all the rows.

Teacher: I know that Henry's paper looked like this. (On chart paper, she draws a row of 12 marks, followed by a row of 10 marks.)

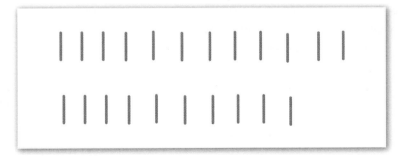

Juan: Don't you need to cross the fives out?

The teacher acknowledges that tally marks make some people think of a particular way of recording. She demonstrates:

Teacher: Why might people make tally marks this way?

Juan: Because then you can count 'em by 5s. 5, 10, 15, 20, 25, 30. No, I mean 21, 22.

Teacher: How about a show of hands. Who showed a group of 12, a group of 10, and then counted all of them? . . . How was your way different, Lonzell?

Lonzell: I used the 100 chart and started at 12. I counted 10 more and got 22.

Teacher: Can you show us how you counted?

Lonzell: Well there were 12 people to start (points to the 12). Then 10 more came. 1, 2, 3, 4, 5, 6, 7, 8, 9, 10. (For each number he says, he moves his finger one number on the 100 chart.) I landed on 22.

Monisha: I did the same thing, but on the number line. (She demonstrates, moving her finger on the number line.)

The teacher draws a number line and Monisha's jumps.

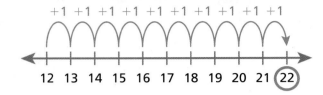

Teacher: Lonzell and Monisha both counted on from one number. They know they had 12, so they just counted the 10. I think Jacy counted on, too. Can you show us?

Jacy: I used my fingers and I kept 12 in my head and then I counted on 10 to 22. (She demonstrates.)

The teacher draws two hands and numbers them on chart paper.

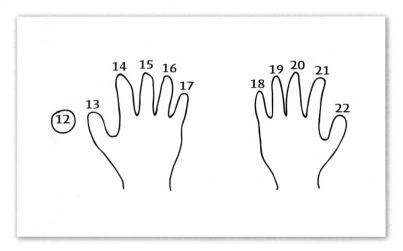

Teacher: Why did you both stop at 22?

Jacy: Because 10 more came.

Teacher: I know that Melissa used a different strategy. She didn't count all or count on. Melissa, will you share what you did?

Melissa: I knew that 10 + 10 = 20, but plus one more equals 21 and one more is 22.

Teacher: Where did you get 10 + 10? In our problem we had 12 and 10.

Roshaun: From 12. Take a 10 from the 12.

Chen: You have to pretend the 12 is a ten. After you take the 2 away, then you think you have 10, and 10 and 10 is 20, and then you put 2 more and that's 22.

The teacher models Chen's explanation with cubes. She builds a tower of 12 and a tower of 10. She shows how these 2 towers can be made into 3 towers—of 10, 10, and 2. One student counts them: 10, 20, 21, 22. The class then counts them together, by ones.

Juan: I did it like that, but without the cubes. 10 and 10 is 20, and 2 more is 22.

The teacher models Juan's explanation on a number line.

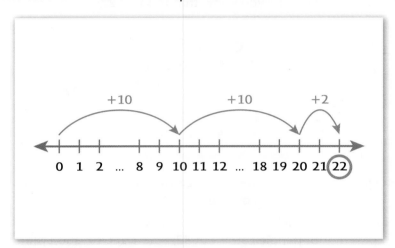

Because this teacher gathered information while observing, she was able to start the discussion in a particular way, sharing an example of how many students were recording. She was also able to record the ways that students solved the problem to be sure that certain strategies were shared.

Note how this teacher labeled students' strategies by the math idea inherent in them (counted all, counted on) and how she made sure that the various strategies were rephrased and modeled with a variety of tools (fingers, cubes, the 100 chart, the number line, and equations). This helps students see a variety of models for making sense of and solving the problem and helps all students have access to the various strategies used.

A Subtraction Story Problem

During Session 4.2, students are discussing their strategies for solving the following story problem:

Kira had 16 baseball cards. She gave 7 of them away. How many baseball cards does Kira have left?

Teacher:	Who wants to start us off?
Yama:	I took 16 cubes.
Teacher:	(She makes a tower of 16 cubes and double-checks her count.) Now what should I do?
Yama:	Take away 7.

The teacher snaps off 7 cubes. There are now 2 towers, one with 9 and one with 7.

Teacher:	Where's my answer? (Henry points to the tower of nine.) How do you know?
Henry:	Because she gave away 7, and that's that tower. So that's how many she has left.
Teacher:	How could we show this strategy on paper? (The teacher draws a cube tower of 16 on the chart paper.) What should I do next?
Carla:	Show the part that you took away. Make an X on the first 7. Then next to the leftover cubes write the numbers.

The teacher does this, and then labels the two parts "the cards Kira still has" and "the cards Kira gave away."

Teacher:	Did anyone have another way?
Simon:	I counted back 7 from 16.
Teacher:	Can you show us what you did?
Simon:	I went 15, 14, 13, 12, 11, 10, 9.
Teacher:	What are you doing with your fingers?
Simon:	Keeping track.
Teacher:	What do you mean?
Simon:	Every time I say a number I put up a finger. My fingers are the cards Kira gave away.

The teacher asks Simon to demonstrate again. As he does, she keeps track on the number line.

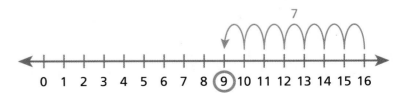

Then, Leigh comments that she did something similar.

Leigh: I took 7; in my mind I had 7. On my fingers I counted on my fingers until I got to 16. I was counting by 1s. I counted on from 7 to 16 and kept track of how many there were. I got 9. [She demonstrates.] I thought it might be harder if you did 16 backwards, like Simon did.

Teacher: Why did you stop with 16?

Leigh: That's the number in the problem.

Teacher: So you did something called counting up. We could show that on the number line, too.

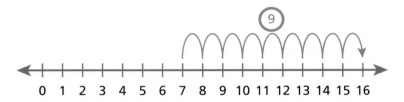

Teacher: I think Monisha thought about adding too. Monisha will you share your strategy?

Monisha: Well, I know that 8 + 8 = 16. I know that if you take 1 away from one of the 8s and give it to the other 8, I knew I'd have 7 + 9 = 16.

Teacher: Monisha, did you think in your head 7 plus what equals 16? (Monisha says, "Yup.") Monisha was thinking "7 plus what equals 16." Then she thought, "I know something that equals 16: 8 + 8!" She thought, "If I take 1 from this 8, and give it to the other 8, I'll have 7 + 9." She used what she knew about 8 + 8 to fill in the blank.

$$7 + \underline{} = 16$$
$$8 + 8 = 16$$
$$7 + \underline{9} = 16$$

$$-1 \overset{8 + 8}{\underset{7 + 9}{\curvearrowright}} + 1$$

The teacher asks a student to demonstrate the connection between 8 + 8 and 7 + 9 with cubes. Then they move on to another strategy.

Juan: If I have 16 and I minus 7, I thought 10 and 6 makes 16, so, 16 minus 6 would be 10. But it's minus 7, so you have to minus 1 more minus the 10, and that's 9.

Teacher: So it sounds like Juan used something he knew, just like Monisha. Juan knew that 10 + 6 = 16. Then he said something interesting. He said if 10 + 6 = 16 then 16 − 6 = 10.

The teacher uses 10 red and 6 blue cubes to model 10 + 6 making 16, and 16 − 6 making 10.

Teacher: Then Juan thought, "If 16 − 6 = 10, then 16 − 7 . . . ?"

Juan: 9. It's minus 1 more.

Chen: Mine's kinda like Juan's, but I didn't really think about it like what he just said. I did, first I took away 6, then I took away 1.

Teacher: Why did you take away 6?

Chen: Because I know 16 − 6 is 10.

The teacher models this on the number line and records the equations on the board.

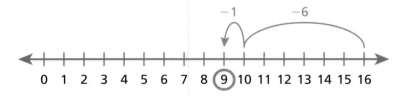

$$16 - 6 = 10$$
$$10 - 1 = 9$$
$$\text{So, } 16 - 7 = 9$$

In this discussion, the teacher highlights a variety of strategies for solving a subtraction problem and demonstrates how to represent each of those strategies on paper. Notice that after providing opportunities for students to share their strategies, the teacher restates what students shared and creates a visual representation. In doing so, she offers students multiple access points to make sense of this problem in new ways, and to make connections between the different strategies students have shared.

What Does It Mean to Be Finished?

In second grade, students are often asked to record their strategies so that someone else can understand clearly how they approached the problem. You will need to help them learn what this means. They may think that what they wrote or drew explains their thinking even when there are gaps in their recordings. Taking the point of view of a reader of their work is a new skill that students will need to practice.

In this discussion, in Session 4.3, the teacher is giving students feedback on the following problem:

Jake and Sally were collecting rocks. Jake found 16 rocks and Sally found 24 rocks. How many rocks did the children collect?

Carla: (reading her explanation to the teacher) 40 rocks. I used cubes and I counted.

Teacher: OK, so that tells me how many rocks they collected and it tells me that you used cubes. How did you use the cubes to help you solve the problem?

Carla: Well, I counted out 16 and then I counted 24 more and altogether that was 40.

Teacher: Do you remember how you counted the cubes to get 40?

Carla: I counted the tower of 16 from 24. Like I went 25, 26, 27, 28, and I ended up with 40.

Teacher: So you counted on by 1s from 24?

Carla: Yes.

Teacher: That sounds like a good strategy. See whether you can go back and add those ideas to your explanation. Think about how you just explained to me what you did and write it down. Jeffrey, you're next.

Jeffrey: (reading his work) They have 40 rocks. I used my brain.

Teacher: That's a good start, Jeffrey. Can you explain more about how you used your brain?

Jeffrey: I just thought 20 + 10 is 30 and 4 + 6 is 10. So 30 and 10 is 40.

Teacher: I've heard you use that strategy before. Remember when we were working on a similar problem yesterday, we wrote down many strategies people used. Sometimes I used words or numbers to explain what people did. And sometimes I used both. How could you record your thinking so that someone reading your paper would know just what you did?

Jeffrey: I'll try numbers.

Carla: (reads her revised work to the teacher) 40 rocks. I used cubes and I counted. I made a tower of 16 cubes and a tower of 24 cubes. Then I counted from 24. 25, 26, 27, 28, 29, 30, 31, 32, 33, 34, 35, 36, 37, 38, 39, 40. (Carla has also added a picture of two towers, one with 16 cubes and one with 24.)

Teacher: That tells me much more information about what you did. I can understand how you solved the problem from this information. Before you write about the next problem, think about what you did. You can even explain it to a friend or to yourself to help you start writing.

When the teacher checks in with Jeffrey, he has added the following to his recording:

24 + 16 = 40
20 + 10 = 30   4 + 6 = 10   30 + 10 = 40
i used my brane

[Jeffrey's Work]

Only by continuing to insist that students record their work fully can the teacher eventually help students visualize their work.

H

Half hour, telling time to, 192, 208, 237

Hexagons, 33

Homework, 15, 37, 88, 111, 159, 176, 206, 220

Horizontal notation, 212, 258

How Many Pockets?. See Games: *How Many Pockets?.*

I

Intervention. *See* Differentiation in Investigations: intervention; Differentiation: Supporting the Range of Learners: intervention.

Investigation Planners. *See* Planners.

Isosceles trapezoid, 33

K

Known facts, 88, 92–93, 111, 114–115, 117–118, 130, 145, 149, 172, 200, 219

L

Less than/greater than, 24–25, 77–78, 266

M

Make 10 facts, 110, 231, 242

Mathematical Practices in This Unit, 8–11

Mathematics in This Unit, 4–7

Math facts

fluency in, 2, 15, 65, 85, 149, 214, 241–242

introducing, 107–110, 147–148, 273–274

known, 88, 92–93, 111, 114–115, 117–118, 125, 130, 145, 149, 172, 200, 219

near-double, 126, 242

place value and, 239–240

practicing, 121–122, 127, 155, 161–163, 176, 180, 241–242

types of, 93, 108–110

Math Focus Points, 4–7. *See also* Today's Plan and Classroom Routines in each session.

for Discussion, 29–30, 37, 43–44, 52, 54–56, 59–61, 63–65, 80–81, 86–88, 98–99, 116–118, 126, 143, 157–159, 163–164, 169–170, 181–182, 196–198, 204–206, 212, 218–219

Math manipulatives. *See* Connecting cubes; Pattern blocks, filling outlines with.

Math Notes

Comparing Math Tools, 48

Comparison Problems, 141

Counting Back, 205

Equations That Show What the Problem Is Asking, 193

Explaining An Answer, 27

Generating Expressions, 81

Groups of 2s, 5s, and 10s, 168

I Don't Know How Many Cubes There Are, 156

The Number Line, 24

Pattern Blocks, 33

The Relationship Between Addition and Subtraction, 201

Size of Numbers, 192

Tallies, 78, 102

Ten Frames, 59

Types of Story Problems, 193

Using Addition or Subtraction, 205

Vertical Counting Strips, 49

Vertical Notation, 198

What Counts as Different?, 33

Writing Numbers in the 100s, 64

Math Practice Notes

Attend to precision, 49, 64, 141, 209, 212

Construct viable arguments and critique the reasoning of others, 30, 60, 65, 78, 95, 99, 143, 196

Look for and express regularity in repeated reasoning, 10–11, 44, 49, 61, 79, 80, 88, 92, 95, 114, 125, 146, 163, 166, 168, 204, 205

Look for and make use of structure, 29, 34, 43, 50, 79, 88, 92, 111, 123, 126, 145, 147, 148, 154

Make sense of problems and persevere in solving them, 8–9, 27, 34, 49, 79, 140, 149, 163, 167, 173, 180, 192, 204

Model with mathematics, 26, 140, 193

Reason abstractly and quantitatively, 32, 91, 92, 103, 151

Use appropriate tools strategically, 24, 123, 145, 202

Use mathematical tools strategically, 54

Math tools. *See* Number lines; 100 chart.

Math Workshop

Adding and Subtracting Single-Digit Numbers, 121–122, 126–127

Adding Two or More Numbers, 93–97, 104–105

Coins, Facts, and Cubes, 153–157, 161–163

Counting and Coins, 49–51, 58–59, 65

Counting and Exploring Coins, 40–42

Counting Cubes and Pattern Blocks, 34–37

Tens and Ones, 174–176, 180

Minus Half facts, 147–148, 242

Minus Ones facts, 147–149, 231, 242

Minus Twos facts, 147–149, 242

Missing addends, 148, 205, 219, 240

Money as mathematical tool, 236. *See also* Coins; Dollars and dollar bills.

Multiple addends, 91–99, 104–105, 122, 126–128, 130–131, 228, 243–246

Multiples

counting by, 57–58, 103, 141, 151, 156, 161, 166–170, 174, 178, 236, 275, 279

hours as, 120, 139

N

Near-double facts, 126, 242

Nickels, 39–41, 43, 46, 52, 54–57, 55–56, 90, 152–153, 155, 158–159, 236

Notation. *See* Standard notation.

Number cubes, 114–116, 127, 130, 151–153

Number lines

addition on, 174, 281–282

for comparison problems, 143, 163–164, 179, 184, 276–278

counting and, 87, 151, 161, 166, 178, 280

equivalent expressions and, 79, 83, 101, 113, 146, 222

as model of number system, 233–234

number sequences on, 24–25, 32, 39, 48, 63, 68, 77–78, 266

Triangles, 33, 60–61

U

U.S. Standard Algorithm, 209, 212, 240, 258

V

Vertical notation for addition/subtraction, 198, 206, 209, 212, 215, 255, 257–258

Vocabulary
add, 26
add one number in parts, 197
add up, 118
addends, 92
addition and subtraction facts, 107
analog clock, 66
big hand, 67
cents, 39
cents sign, 55
combinations that make ten, 93
count all, 87
count back, 117
count on, 87
data, 100
diagonally, 85
digital clock, 66
dime, 39
dollar, 39
dollar sign, 55

double, 43
equals, 26
equal sign, 193
equations, 193
greater than, 24
half, 192
half hour, 192
half-past, 192
hexagon, 33
horizontally, 85
hour, 67
hour hand, 67
less than, 24
Make 10 Facts, 110
minus, 114
Minus Half Facts, 148
Minus Ones, 147
minus sign, 201
Minus Twos, 147
minute hand, 67
money, 39
nickel, 39
number line, 24
o'clock, 67
100 chart, 47
order, 92
penny, 39
plus, 26
Plus 1 Facts, 109

Plus 2, 110
Plus Ones, 110
plus sign, 193
quarter, 39
rhombus, 33
small hand, 67
square, 33
subtracted in parts, 205
subtracting, 78
sum, 84
taking away, 78
tallies, 78
10 Minuses, 148
Ten Frame, 122
trade, 153
trapezoid, 33
triangle, 33
two-thirty, 192
use a known fact, 88
vertically, 85
zero, 101

W

What Time Is It?. *See* Classroom Routines: *What Time Is It?.*

Writing
about data, 104
equations, 26
numbers, 26, 63–65, 78, 267–268